Department of Transport
Scottish Development Department
Welsh Office
Department of the Environment for Northern Ireland

HIGHWAY CONSTRUCTION DETAILS

London
Her Majesty's Stationery Office

DECEMBER 1987

Contents

1 Introduction

This book contains standard detail drawings of roadworks aspects for use in the construction, re-construction and maintenance of the Department of Transport's Trunk Roads.

2 Associated documents

The drawings are compatible with, and should be used in conjunction with the Department's Specification for Highway Works 6th edition, Method of Measurement for Highway Works 3rd edition and Library of Standard Item Descriptions for Highway Works 3rd edition, all published by HMSO.

3 Numbering of drawings

No drawing shall be altered and retain its original drawing number. Changed drawings must adopt a numbering system unique to the Region or Scheme. Appendix 0/4 to the Specification for Highway Works is to list the numbers of all drawings incorporated in the contract including those selected from this book of Highway Construction Details.

4 General notes

The following applies to each drawing unless otherwise stated therein:

i   All dimensions are in millimetres
ii   All references to SHW means a reference to the Department of Transport's Specification for Highway Works published by HMSO. For any Contract the publication dates of the Parts included are to be given in the Preamble to the Specification.
iii   References to the numbered Appendices eg Appendix 1/15 means a reference to those Appendices to the SHW particularly prepared for the Contract and included in the Contract documents and listed in Appendix 0/3 therein.

Series A —
Highway Cross Sections

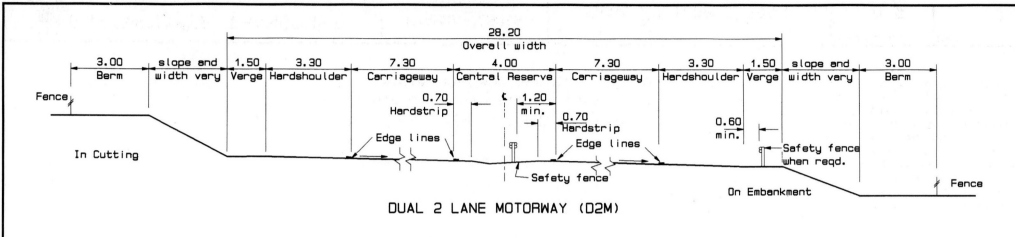

28.20
Overall width

| 3.00 Berm | slope and width vary | 1.50 Verge | 3.30 Hardshoulder | 7.30 Carriageway | 4.00 Central Reserve | 7.30 Carriageway | 3.30 Hardshoulder | 1.50 Verge | slope and width vary | 3.00 Berm |

Fence

0.70 Hardstrip

1.20 min.

0.70 Hardstrip

0.60 min.

In Cutting

Edge lines

Safety fence

Edge lines

Safety fence when reqd.

On Embankment

Fence

DUAL 2 LANE MOTORWAY (D2M)

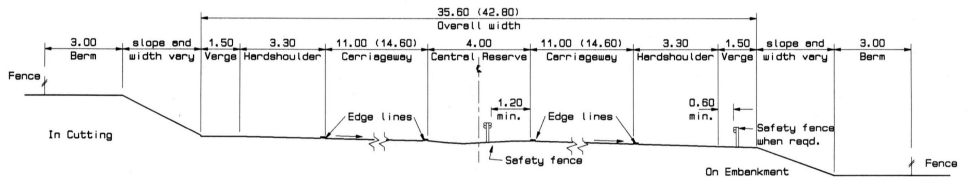

35.60 (42.80)
Overall width

| 3.00 Berm | slope and width vary | 1.50 Verge | 3.30 Hardshoulder | 11.00 (14.60) Carriageway | 4.00 Central Reserve | 11.00 (14.60) Carriageway | 3.30 Hardshoulder | 1.50 Verge | slope and width vary | 3.00 Berm |

Fence

1.20 min.

0.60 min.

In Cutting

Edge lines

Safety fence

Edge lines

Safety fence when reqd.

On Embankment

Fence

DUAL 3 LANE MOTORWAY (D3M)

DUAL 4 LANE MOTORWAY (D4M)
As D3M but with dimensions in brackets
for carriageway and overall width

NOTES
1. ALL DIMENSIONS ARE IN METRES
2. The cross sections shown are typical only.
3. Normal crossfall on balanced carriageways shall be 2.5%
4. Permanent fence lines may vary from the position shown and the Contractor shall erect the fences in the positions indicated in the contract.
5. See Drawing No A11 for edge and lane line details.

| DEPARTMENT OF TRANSPORT HIGHWAY CONSTRUCTION DETAILS | HIGHWAY CROSS SECTIONS | RURAL MOTORWAYS | Drawing No. **A1** | Date |

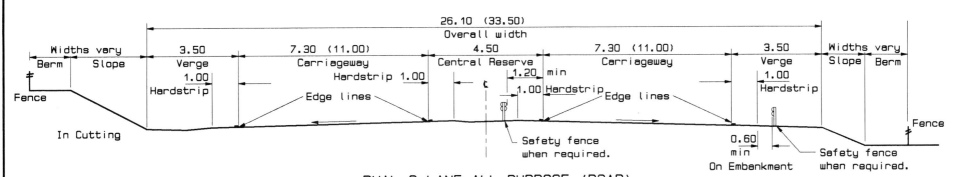

26.10 (33.50)
Overall width

Widths vary
Berm   Slope

3.50
Verge
1.00
Hardstrip

7.30 (11.00)
Carriageway
Hardstrip 1.00

4.50
Central Reserve
1.20 min
1.00 Hardstrip

7.30 (11.00)
Carriageway

3.50
Verge
1.00
Hardstrip

Widths vary
Slope   Berm

Fence

In Cutting

Edge lines
Edge lines

Safety fence when required.

0.60 min
On Embankment

Fence

Safety fence when required.

DUAL 2 LANE ALL PURPOSE (D2AP)

DUAL 3 LANE ALL PURPOSE (D3AP)
As D2AP but with dimensions in brackets
for carriageway and overall width

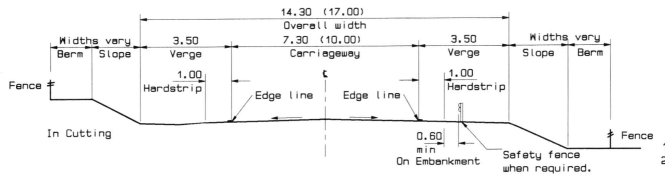

14.30 (17.00)
Overall width

Widths vary
Berm   Slope

3.50
Verge
1.00
Hardstrip

7.30 (10.00)
Carriageway

3.50
Verge
1.00
Hardstrip

Widths vary
Slope   Berm

Fence

In Cutting

Edge line   Edge line

0.60 min
On Embankment

Safety fence when required.

Fence

SINGLE 7.3m CARRIAGEWAY (S2)

WIDE SINGLE 10m CARRIAGEWAY (WS2)
As S2 but with dimensions in brackets
for carriageway and overall width

NOTES
1. ALL DIMENSIONS ARE IN METRES
2. The cross sections shown are typical only.
3. Normal crossfall on balanced carriageways shall be 2.5%
4. The contractor shall erect the fences in the positions indicated on the layout drawings
5. See Drawing A12 for edge and lane line details.

| DEPARTMENT OF TRANSPORT HIGHWAY CONSTRUCTION DETAILS | HIGHWAY CROSS SECTIONS | RURAL ALL-PURPOSE ROADS | Drawing No. **A2** | Date |

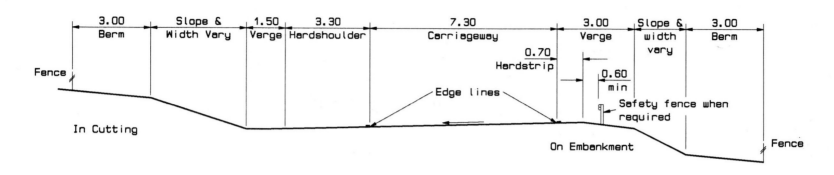

MOTORWAY TO MOTORWAY TWO LANE LINK

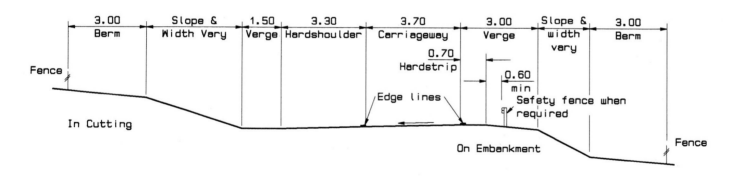

MOTORWAY TO MOTORWAY SINGLE LANE LINK

NOTES
1. ALL DIMENSIONS ARE IN METRES.
2. The cross-sections shown are typical only. The direction of traffic is into the plane of the drawing.
3. Normal crossfall on carriageways shall be 2.5%.
4. Permanent fence lines may vary from the position shown and the Contractor shall erect the fences on the positions indicated on the layout drawings.
5. All edge lines to be 0.20m wide.

DEPARTMENT OF TRANSPORT HIGHWAY CONSTRUCTION DETAILS	HIGHWAY CROSS SECTIONS	RURAL MOTORWAY LINK ROADS	Drawing No. A3	Date

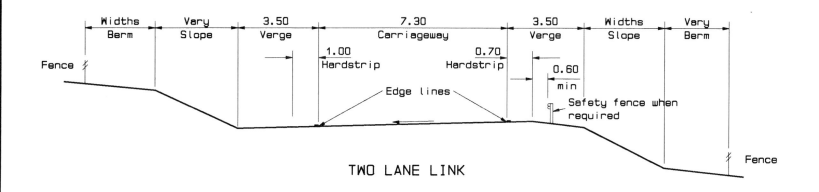

TWO LANE LINK

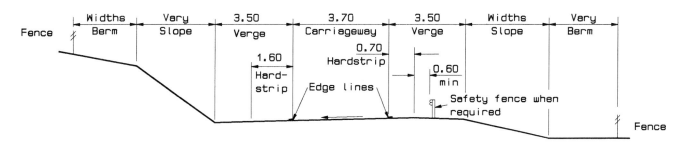

SINGLE LANE LINK

NOTES
1. ALL DIMENSIONS ARE IN METRES.
2. The cross-sections shown are typical only. The direction of traffic is into the plane of the drawing.
3. Normal crossfall on carriageways shall be 2.5%.
4. All edge lines to be 0.15m wide.

DEPARTMENT OF TRANSPORT HIGHWAY CONSTRUCTION DETAILS	HIGHWAY CROSS SECTIONS	RURAL ALL-PURPOSE LINK ROADS	Drawing No. A4	Date

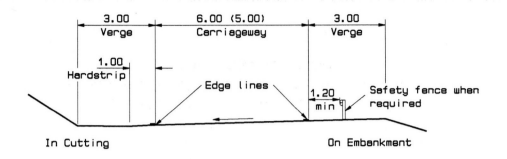

SLIP ROAD - NORMAL CROSSFALL

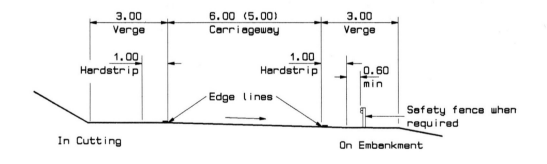

SLIP ROAD - SUPERELEVATED

"LIGHTLY TRAFFICKED" SLIP ROADS
As above but with dimensions in brackets
for carriageway width

NOTES
1. ALL DIMENSIONS ARE IN METRES.
2. The cross-sections shown are typical only. The direction of traffic is into the plane of the drawing.
3. Normal crossfall on carriageways shall be 2.5% superelevated as indicated on layout drawings.
4. Permanent fence lines may vary from the position shown and the Contractor shall erect the fences on the positions indicated on the layout drawings.
5. All edge lines to be 0.20m wide

| DEPARTMENT OF TRANSPORT HIGHWAY CONSTRUCTION DETAILS | HIGHWAY CROSS SECTIONS | RURAL MOTORWAY SLIP ROADS | Drawing No. **A5** | Date |

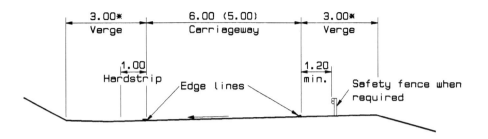

SLIP ROAD - NORMAL CROSSFALL

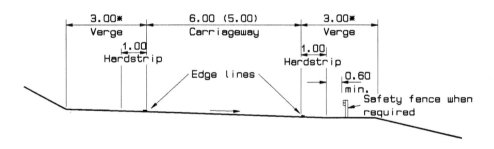

SLIP ROAD - SUPERELEVATED

"LIGHTLY TRAFFICKED" SLIP ROADS
As above but with dimensions in brackets
for carriageway width

NOTES
1. ALL DIMENSIONS ARE IN METRES.
2. The cross-sections shown are typical only. The direction of traffic is into the plane of the drawing.
3. Normal crossfall on carriageways shall be 2.5% superelevated as indicated on layout drawings.
4. All edge lines to be 0.15m wide.
5. * Verges adjacent to highway boundaries to be 3.50m.

| DEPARTMENT OF TRANSPORT
HIGHWAY CONSTRUCTION DETAILS | HIGHWAY CROSS
SECTIONS | RURAL ALL-PURPOSE SLIP ROADS | Drawing No.
A6 | Date |

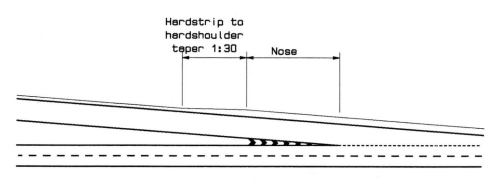

Hardstrip to
hardshoulder
taper 1:30   Nose

MERGE LANE

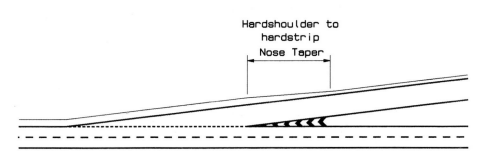

Hardshoulder to
hardstrip
Nose Taper

DIVERGE LANE

| DEPARTMENT OF TRANSPORT HIGHWAY CONSTRUCTION DETAILS | HIGHWAY CROSS SECTIONS | MOTORWAY HARDSHOULDER TO HARDSTRIP TREATMENT | Drawing No. **A7** | Date |

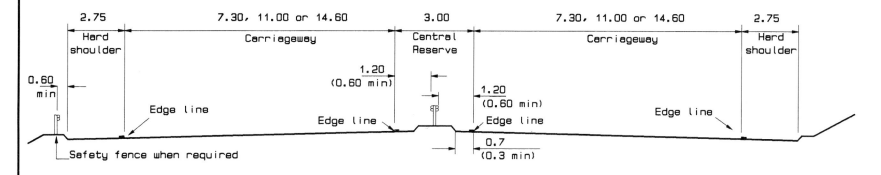

2.75   7.30, 11.00 or 14.60   3.00   7.30, 11.00 or 14.60   2.75

Hard shoulder   Carriageway   Central Reserve   Carriageway   Hard shoulder

0.60 min

1.20 (0.60 min)

1.20 (0.60 min)

Edge line

Edge line

Edge line

Edge line

0.7 (0.3 min)

Safety fence when required

On Embankment

In Cutting

DUAL 2 LANE MOTORWAY (D2M)
DUAL 3 LANE MOTORWAY (D3M)
DUAL 4 LANE MOTORWAY (D4M)

NOTES
1. ALL DIMENSIONS ARE IN METRES.
2. The cross-sections shown are typical only.
3. Normal crossfall on balanced carriageways shall be 2.5%.
4. The central reserve should be bordered by raised kerbs. If road lighting is provided in the central reserve then the required clearances may make a wider central reserve necessary.
5. See Drawing A11 for edge and lane line details.

DEPARTMENT OF TRANSPORT HIGHWAY CONSTRUCTION DETAILS	HIGHWAY CROSS SECTIONS	URBAN MOTORWAYS (UP TO 85 KPH DESIGN SPEED)	Drawing No. **A8**	Date

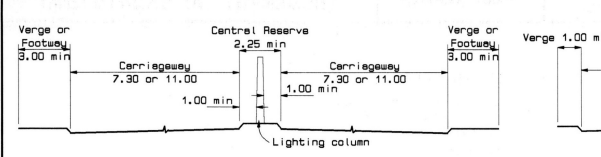

Verge or Footway 3.00 min · Carriageway 7.30 or 11.00 · 1.00 min · Central Reserve 2.25 min · 1.00 min · Carriageway 7.30 or 11.00 · Verge or Footway 3.00 min · Lighting column

With footways

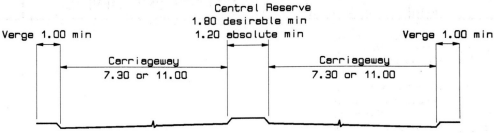

Verge 1.00 min · Carriageway 7.30 or 11.00 · Central Reserve 1.80 desirable min 1.20 absolute min · Carriageway 7.30 or 11.00 · Verge 1.00 min

No footways : lanterns bracketed from buildings or suspended

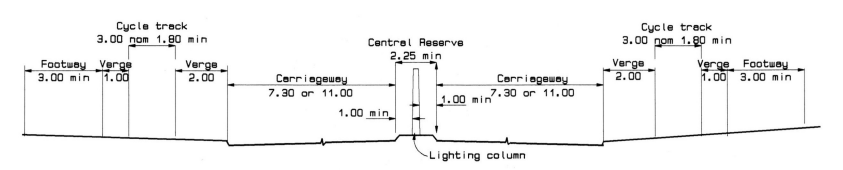

Footway 3.00 min · Verge 1.00 · Cycle track 3.00 nom 1.80 min · Verge 2.00 · Carriageway 7.30 or 11.00 · 1.00 min · Central Reserve 2.25 min · 1.00 min · Carriageway 7.30 or 11.00 · Verge 2.00 · Cycle track 3.00 nom 1.80 min · Verge 1.00 · Footway 3.00 min · Lighting column

With footways and cycle tracks

DUAL CARRIAGEWAYS (D2/3 UAP)

NOTES
1. ALL DIMENSIONS ARE IN METRES.
2. Dimensions of verges and central reserve may vary to allow for the erection of safety fences where required.
3. The cross-sections shown are typical only.
4. Normal crossfall on balanced carriageways shall be 2.5%.

| DEPARTMENT OF TRANSPORT HIGHWAY CONSTRUCTION DETAILS | HIGHWAY CROSS SECTIONS | URBAN ALL PURPOSE ROADS (UP TO 85KPH DESIGN SPEED) | Drawing No. **A9** | Date |

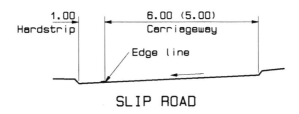

SLIP ROAD

"LIGHTLY TRAFFICKED" SLIP ROADS
As above but with dimensions in brackets
for carriageway width

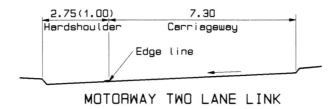

MOTORWAY TWO LANE LINK

ALL PURPOSE TWO LANE LINK
As above but with dimensions in brackets
for hardstrip width

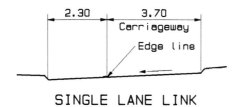

SINGLE LANE LINK

NOTES
1. ALL DIMENSIONS ARE IN METRES.
2. The cross-sections shown are typical only.
   The direction of traffic is into the plane of the drawing.
3. Normal crossfall on carriageways shall be 2.5%.
4. Edge lines on Motorways 0.20m wide, on All Purpose Roads 0.15m wide

| DEPARTMENT OF TRANSPORT HIGHWAY CONSTRUCTION DETAILS | HIGHWAY CROSS SECTIONS | MOTORWAY AND ALL PURPOSE URBAN SLIP ROADS AND LINK ROADS | Drawing No. **A10** | Date |

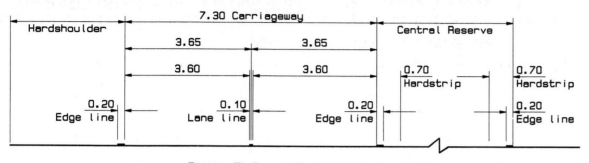

DUAL TWO LANE MOTORWAY (D2M)

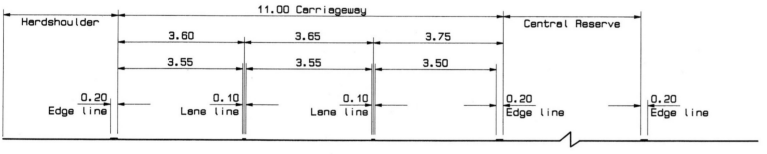

DUAL THREE LANE MOTORWAY (D3M)

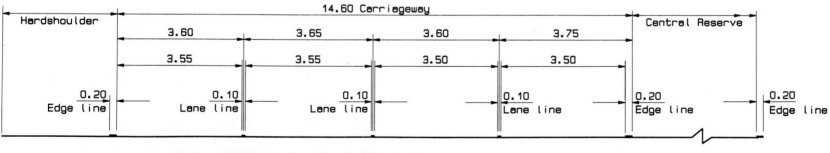

DUAL FOUR LANE MOTORWAY (D4M)

NOTES

1. ALL DIMENSIONS ARE IN METRES.
2. See Drawing No A1 for general cross section details.

DEPARTMENT OF TRANSPORT HIGHWAY CONSTRUCTION DETAILS	HIGHWAY CROSS SECTION	LANE WIDTHS AND CARRIAGEWAY MARKINGS (MOTORWAYS)	Drawing No. **A11**	Date

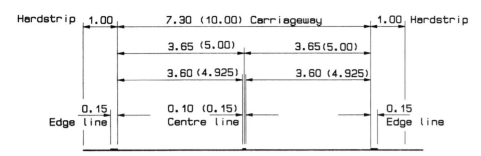

SINGLE 7.30m ALL-PURPOSE (S2)
WIDE SINGLE 10.00m ALL-PURPOSE (WS2)

AS (S2) BUT WITH
DIMENSIONS IN BRACKETS

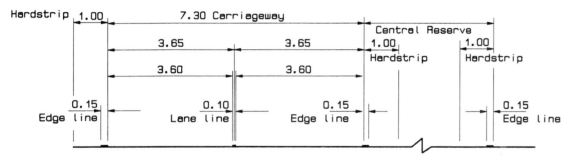

DUAL TWO LANE ALL-PURPOSE (D2AP)

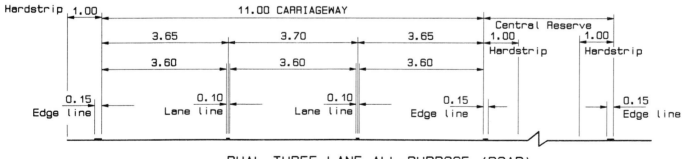

DUAL THREE LANE ALL-PURPOSE (D3AP)

NOTES

1. ALL DIMENSIONS ARE IN METRES.
2. See Drawing No A2 for general cross section details.

| DEPARTMENT OF TRANSPORT HIGHWAY CONSTRUCTION DETAILS | HIGHWAY CROSS SECTION | LANE WIDTHS AND CARRIAGEWAY MARKINGS (RURAL ALL-PURPOSE ROADS) | Drawing No. **A12** | Date |

Series B—
Edge of Pavement Details

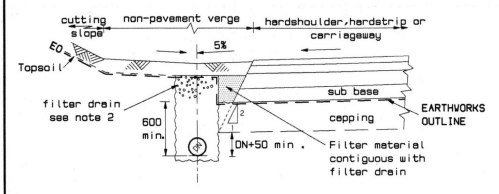

Type 1A (Flexible carriageway).

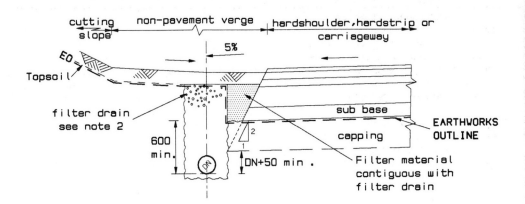

Type 1C (Flexible composite carriageway).

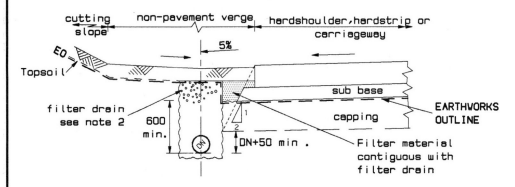

Type 1B (Rigid carriageway).

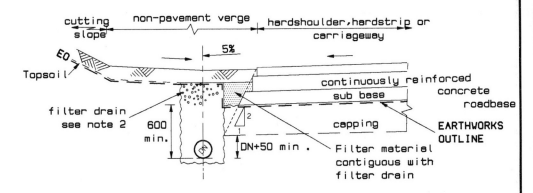

Type 1D (Rigid composite carriageway).

NOTES

1. ALL DIMENSIONS ARE IN MILLIMETRES

2. Alternative treatments to top of filter drains are shown on drawing No.B15. Type V is shown on this drawing.

3. 'DN' represents nominal diameter of the pipe

4. Pipes shall be laid to the levels described in the contract

DEPARTMENT OF TRANSPORT HIGHWAY CONSTRUCTION DETAILS	EDGE OF PAVEMENT DETAILS	CUTTINGS – COMBINED SURFACE AND GROUNDWATER FILTER DRAINS	Drawing No. B1	Date

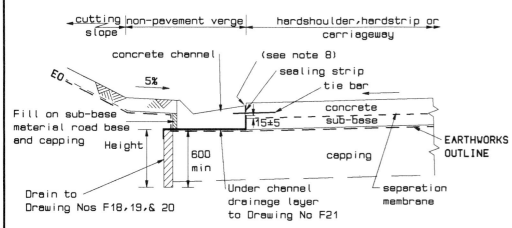

TYPE 2A
(Channel formed on capping or formation layer)

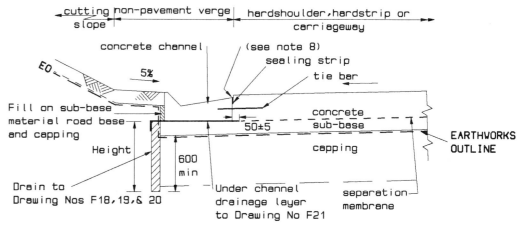

TYPE 2C
(Channel formed on sub-base layer)

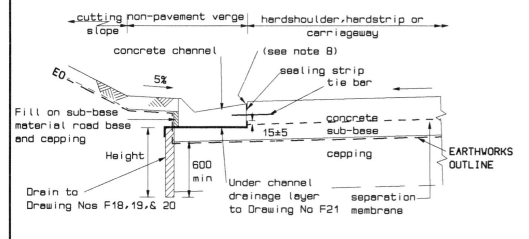

TYPE 2B
(Channel base formed within sub-base layer)

NOTES

1. ALL DIMENSIONS ARE IN MILLIMETRES.
2. For details of concrete channel see Drawing No B14.
3. The sealing strip and the vertical part of under channel drainage layer shown for when channel is cast before pavement. They shall be fixed to pavement edge when pavement cast before channel.
4. Sealing strip to be to Clause 1014 of S.H.W.
5. For details of under-channel drainage layer see Drawing No F21.
6. Channel may be cast in one with the pavement in which case the requirements of NOTES 3 & 4 may be omitted.
7. Channels shall be reinforced when the carriageway slab is reinforced and shall have transverse joints to the same type and spacing as in the carriageway slab.
8. Notwithstanding other tolerances in the specification, the finished level of the channel shall not be higher nor more than 10mm lower than the finished level of the edge of the adjacent carriageway.

| DEPARTMENT OF TRANSPORT HIGHWAY CONSTRUCTION DETAILS | EDGE OF PAVEMENT DETAILS | CUTTINGS – SURFACE WATER CHANNEL FOR RIGID CARRIAGEWAY | Drawing No. B2 | Date |

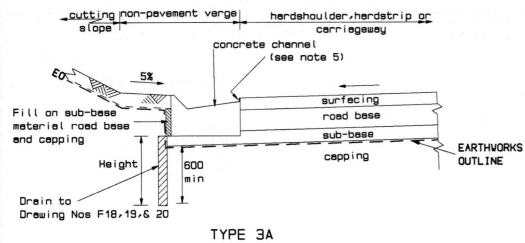

TYPE 3A

(Channel base formed within sub-base layer)

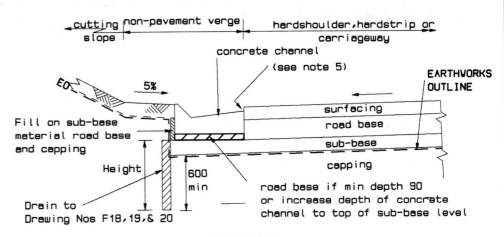

TYPE 3C

(Channel base formed on first road base layer)

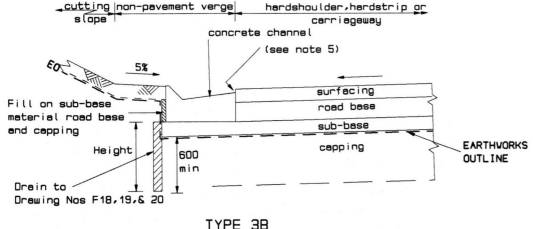

TYPE 3B

(Channel base formed on the sub-base layer)

NOTES

1. ALL DIMENSIONS ARE IN MILLIMETRES.
2. For details of concrete channel see Drawing No B14.
3. Channels may be reinforced or unreinforced. With reinforced channels the reinforcement shall be not less than 4.34kg/m^2 British Standard Mesh.
4. Transverse joints shall be sawn or wet formed to a minimum depth of 25mm below channel invert and sealed in accordance with Clause 1017 of S.H.W. The spacing of joints shall be 5000mm for unreinforced channels and 30000mm for reinforced channels.
5. Notwithstanding other tolerances in the specification the finished level of the channel shall not be higher nor more than 10mm lower than the finished level of the adjacent carriageway.

DEPARTMENT OF TRANSPORT HIGHWAY CONSTRUCTION DETAILS	EDGE OF PAVEMENT DETAILS	CUTTINGS – SURFACE WATER CHANNEL FOR FLEXIBLE CARRIAGEWAY	Drawing No. **B3**	Date

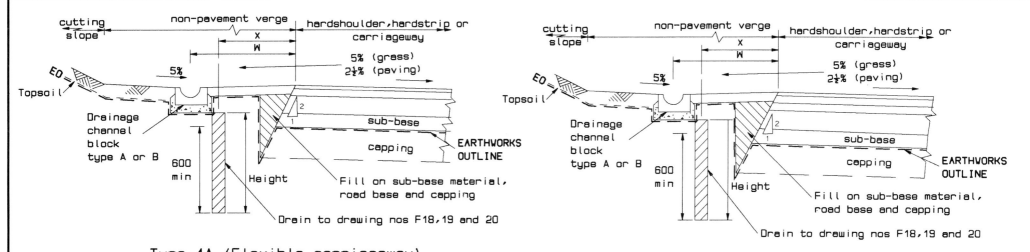

Type 4A (Flexible carriageway).

Type 4C (Flexible composite carriageway).

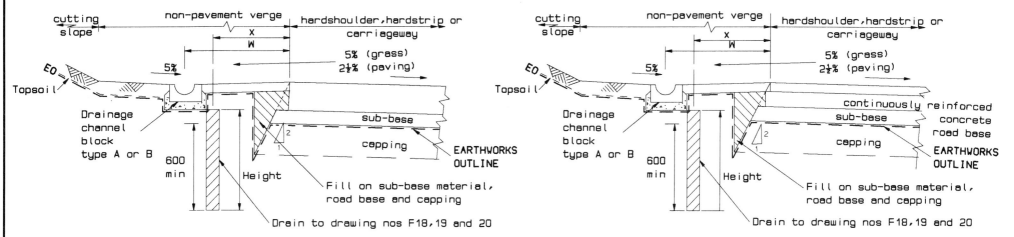

Type 4B (Rigid carriageway).

Type 4D (Rigid composite carriageway).

NOTES

1. ALL DIMENSIONS ARE IN MILLIMETRES.

2. Dimensions X & W to be as described in the contract.

3. Topsoil or Paving in verges shall be as described in the contract.

| DEPARTMENT OF TRANSPORT HIGHWAY CONSTRUCTION DETAILS | EDGE OF PAVEMENT DETAILS | CUTTINGS - DRAINAGE CHANNEL BLOCKS AND DRAINS | Drawing No. B4 | Date |

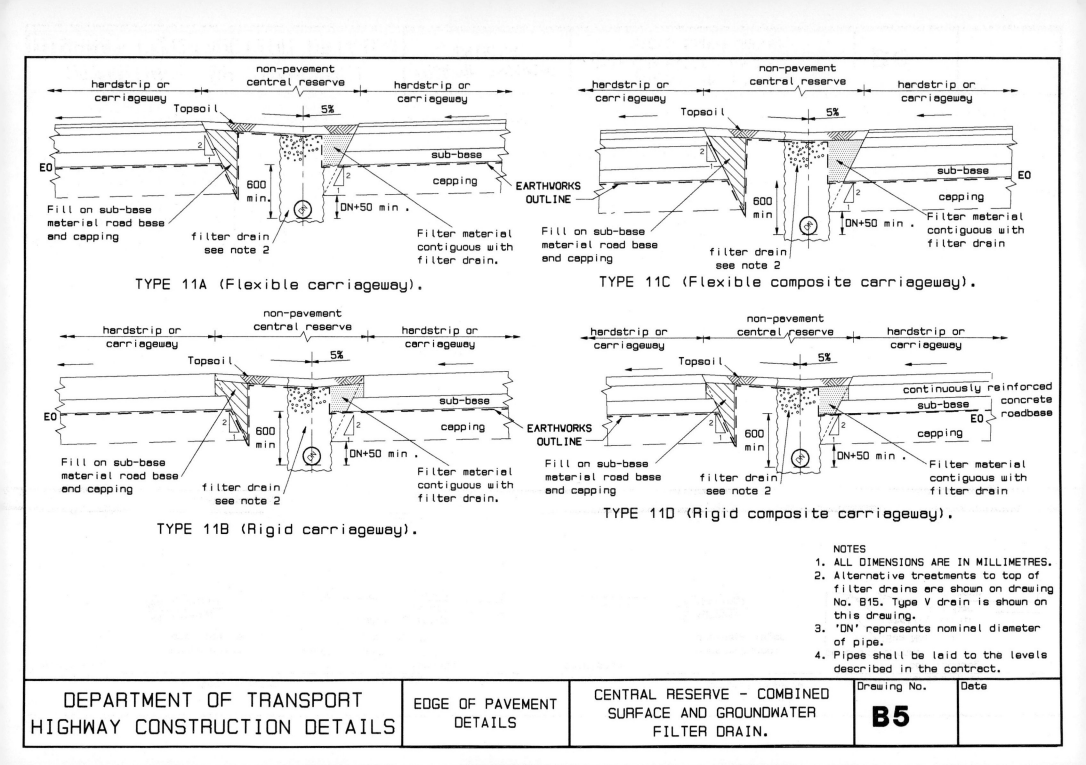

TYPE 11A (Flexible carriageway).

TYPE 11C (Flexible composite carriageway).

TYPE 11B (Rigid carriageway).

TYPE 11D (Rigid composite carriageway).

NOTES
1. ALL DIMENSIONS ARE IN MILLIMETRES.
2. Alternative treatments to top of filter drains are shown on drawing No. B15. Type V drain is shown on this drawing.
3. 'DN' represents nominal diameter of pipe.
4. Pipes shall be laid to the levels described in the contract.

| DEPARTMENT OF TRANSPORT HIGHWAY CONSTRUCTION DETAILS | EDGE OF PAVEMENT DETAILS | CENTRAL RESERVE – COMBINED SURFACE AND GROUNDWATER FILTER DRAIN. | Drawing No. **B5** | Date |

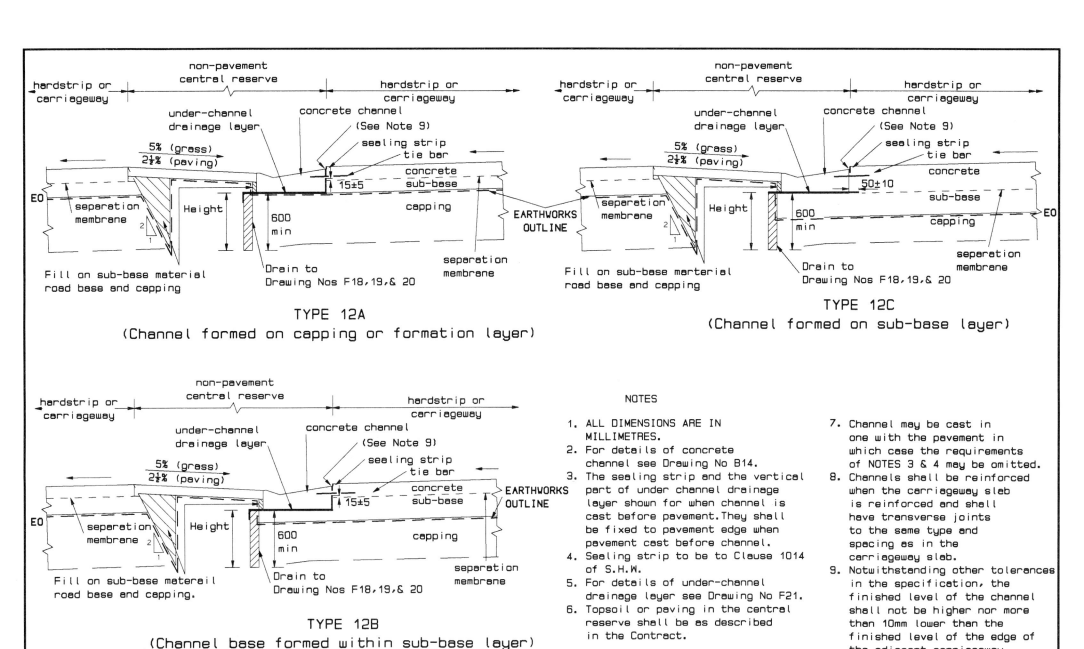

TYPE 12A
(Channel formed on capping or formation layer)

TYPE 12C
(Channel formed on sub-base layer)

TYPE 12B
(Channel base formed within sub-base layer)

NOTES

1. ALL DIMENSIONS ARE IN MILLIMETRES.
2. For details of concrete channel see Drawing No B14.
3. The sealing strip and the vertical part of under channel drainage layer shown for when channel is cast before pavement. They shall be fixed to pavement edge when pavement cast before channel.
4. Sealing strip to be to Clause 1014 of S.H.W.
5. For details of under-channel drainage layer see Drawing No F21.
6. Topsoil or paving in the central reserve shall be as described in the Contract.

7. Channel may be cast in one with the pavement in which case the requirements of NOTES 3 & 4 may be omitted.
8. Channels shall be reinforced when the carriageway slab is reinforced and shall have transverse joints to the same type and spacing as in the carriageway slab.
9. Notwithstanding other tolerances in the specification, the finished level of the channel shall not be higher nor more than 10mm lower than the finished level of the edge of the adjacent carriageway.

DEPARTMENT OF TRANSPORT HIGHWAY CONSTRUCTION DETAILS	EDGE OF PAVEMENT DETAILS	CENTRAL RESERVE - SURFACE WATER CHANNEL FOR RIGID CARRIAGEWAY	Drawing No. B6	Date

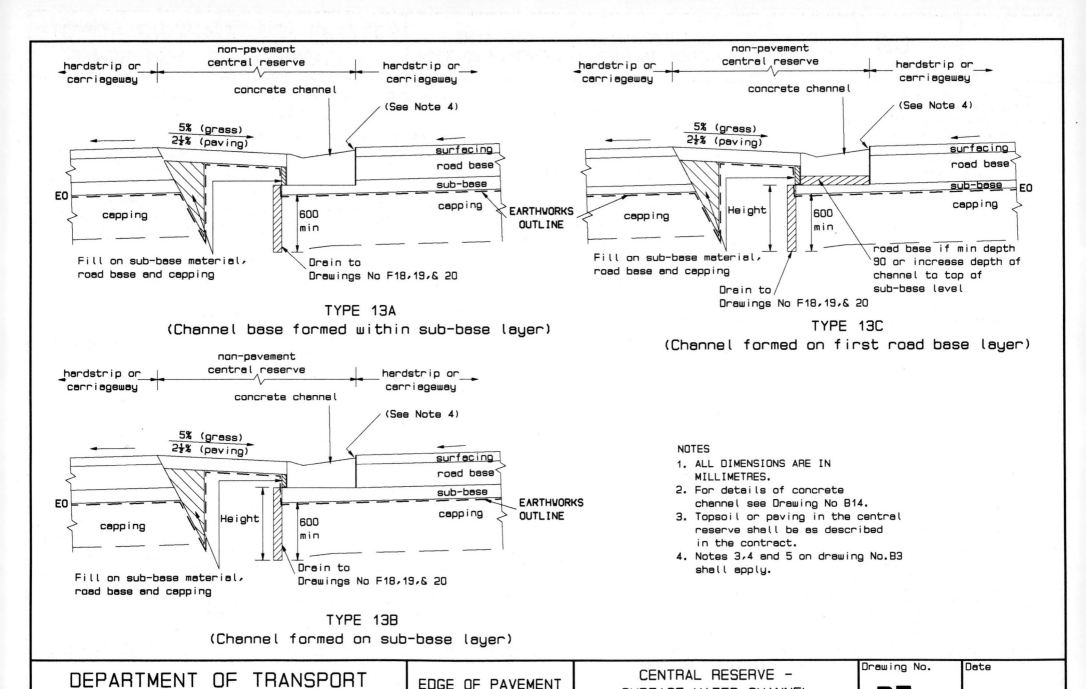

TYPE 13A
(Channel base formed within sub-base layer)

TYPE 13C
(Channel formed on first road base layer)

TYPE 13B
(Channel formed on sub-base layer)

NOTES
1. ALL DIMENSIONS ARE IN MILLIMETRES.
2. For details of concrete channel see Drawing No B14.
3. Topsoil or paving in the central reserve shall be as described in the contract.
4. Notes 3,4 and 5 on drawing No.B3 shall apply.

| DEPARTMENT OF TRANSPORT HIGHWAY CONSTRUCTION DETAILS | EDGE OF PAVEMENT DETAILS | CENTRAL RESERVE - SURFACE WATER CHANNEL FLEXIBLE CARRIAGEWAY | Drawing No. **B7** | Date |

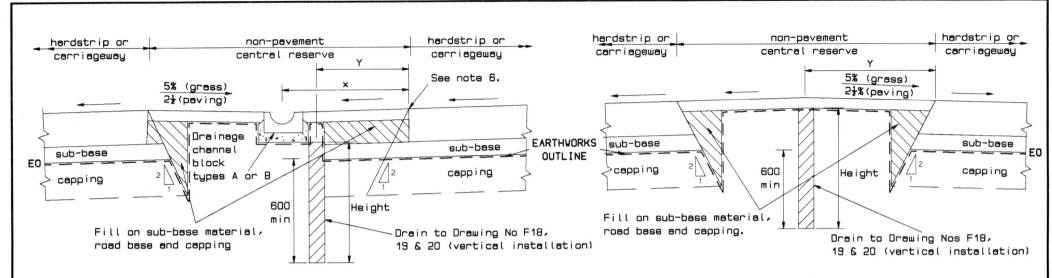

hardstrip or carriageway · non-pavement central reserve · hardstrip or carriageway

5% (grass)
2½ (paving)

Y

X

See note 6.

sub-base

EO

sub-base

capping

EARTHWORKS OUTLINE

capping

Drainage channel block types A or B

2
1

2
1

600 min

Height

Fill on sub-base material, road base and capping

Drain to Drawing No F18, 19 & 20 (vertical installation)

TYPE 14
DRAINAGE CHANNEL BLOCK & DRAIN

hardstrip or carriageway · non-pavement central reserve · hardstrip or carriageway

5% (grass)
2½% (paving)

Y

sub-base

EO

sub-base

capping

EARTHWORKS OUTLINE

capping

600 min

Height

2
1

2
1

Fill on sub-base material, road base and capping.

Drain to Drawing Nos F18, 19 & 20 (vertical installation)

TYPE 16
(Drain in Raised Central Reserve)

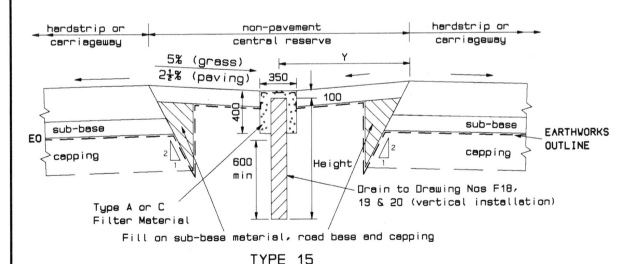

hardstrip or carriageway · non-pavement central reserve · hardstrip or carriageway

5% (grass)
2½% (paving)

350

Y

100

400

sub-base

EO

capping

600 min

Height

2
1

2
1

sub-base

EARTHWORKS OUTLINE

capping

Type A or C Filter Material

Fill on sub-base material, road base and capping

Drain to Drawing Nos F18, 19 & 20 (vertical installation)

TYPE 15
(Drain in Dished Central Reserve)

NOTES

1. ALL DIMENSIONS ARE IN MILLIMETRES.
2. Dimensions X & Y to be as described in the Contract.
3. For details of drainage channel blocks see Drawing No. F15.

4. Flexible carriageway construction is shown. Variations for other constructions to be as shown on Drawing No B1.
5. Topsoil or paving in the central reserve shall be as described in the contract.
6. Where the central reserve is grassed and carriageway surface water is to flow over the edge the surface of the central reserve should be set 40mm below adjacent hardstrip or carriageway

| DEPARTMENT OF TRANSPORT HIGHWAY CONSTRUCTION DETAILS | EDGE OF PAVEMENT DETAILS | CENTRAL RESERVE - DRAINAGE CHANNEL BLOCKS & DRAINS | Drawing No. **B8** | Date |

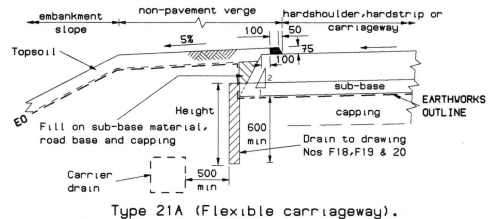

Type 21A (Flexible carriageway).

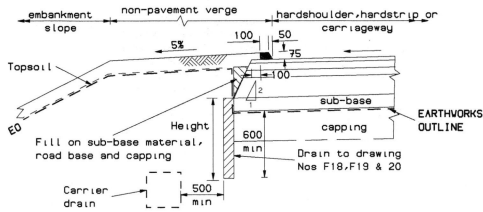

Type 21C (Flexible composite carriageway).

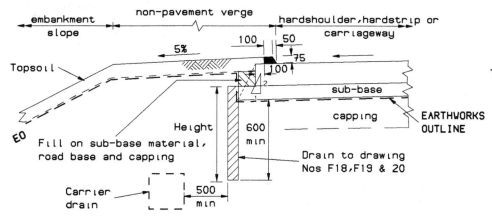

Type 21B (Rigid carriageway).

Type 21D (Rigid composite carriageway).

NOTES
1. ALL DIMENSIONS ARE IN MILLIMETRES.
2. Carrier drains shall be as detailed in the Contract.

| DEPARTMENT OF TRANSPORT HIGHWAY CONSTRUCTION DETAILS | EDGE OF PAVEMENT DETAILS | EMBANKMENTS - CHANNELS FORMED BY KERBS | Drawing No. B9 | Date |

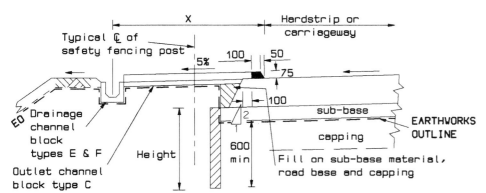

Type 21E (Flexible carriageway).

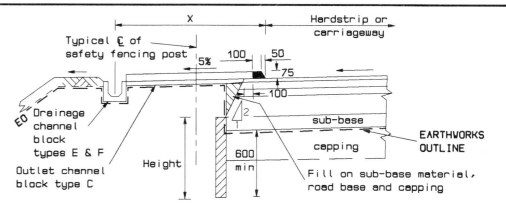

Type 21G (Flexible composite carriageway).

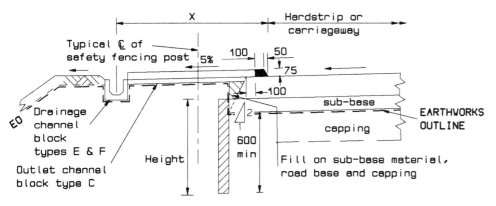

Type 21F (Rigid carriageway).

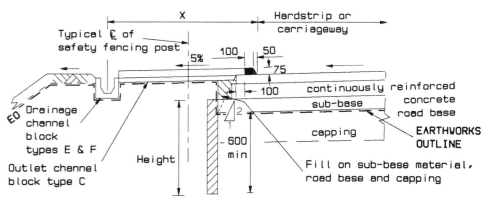

Type 21H (Rigid composite carriageway).

NOTES

1. ALL DIMENSIONS ARE IN MILLIMETRES.
2. Drains shall comply with Drawing Nos F18,19,20.
3. For details of drainage channel blocks see Drawing Nos F15 & F16.
4. Dimension X shall be as described in the Contract.
5. Not applicable on motorways.

| DEPARTMENT OF TRANSPORT HIGHWAY CONSTRUCTION DETAILS | EDGE OF PAVEMENT DETAILS | EMBANKMENTS - EXTERNAL KERBS AND DRAINAGE CHANNEL BLOCKS | Drawing No. B10 | Date |

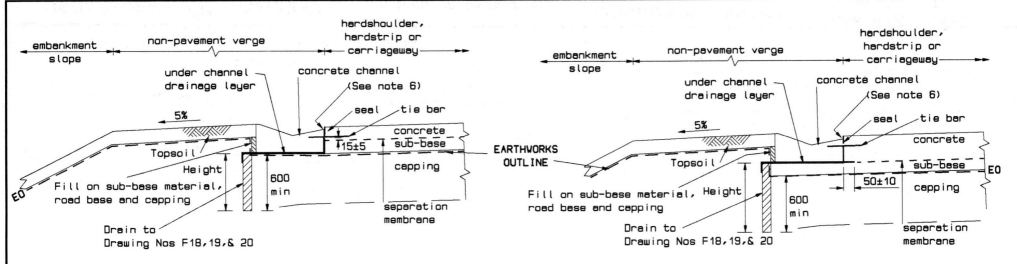

TYPE 22A
(Channel formed on capping or formation layer)

TYPE 22C
(Channel formed on sub-base layer)

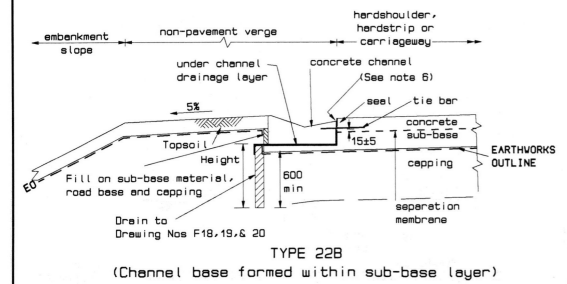

TYPE 22B
(Channel base formed within sub-base layer)

NOTES

1. ALL DIMENSIONS ARE IN MILLIMETRES.
2. For details of concrete channel see Drawing No B14.
3. The sealing strip and the vertical part of under channel drainage layer shown for when channel is cast before pavement. They shall be fixed to pavement edge when pavement cast before channel.
4. Sealing strip to be to Clause 1014 of S.H.W.
5. For details of under-channel drainage layer see Drawing No F21.
6. Notwithstanding other tolerances in the specification, the finished level of the channel shall not be higher nor more than 10mm lower than the finished level of the edge of the adjacent carriageway.
7. Channel may be cast in one with the pavement in which case the requirements of NOTES 3 & 4 may be omitted.
8. Channels shall be reinforced when the carriageway slab is reinforced and shall have transverse joints to the same type and spacing as in the carriageway slab.
9. Safety Fences shall be positioned as described in the contract.

DEPARTMENT OF TRANSPORT HIGHWAY CONSTRUCTION DETAILS	EDGE OF PAVEMENT DETAILS	EMBANKMENTS - SURFACE WATER CHANNEL FOR RIGID CARRIAGEWAYS	Drawing No. **B11**	Date

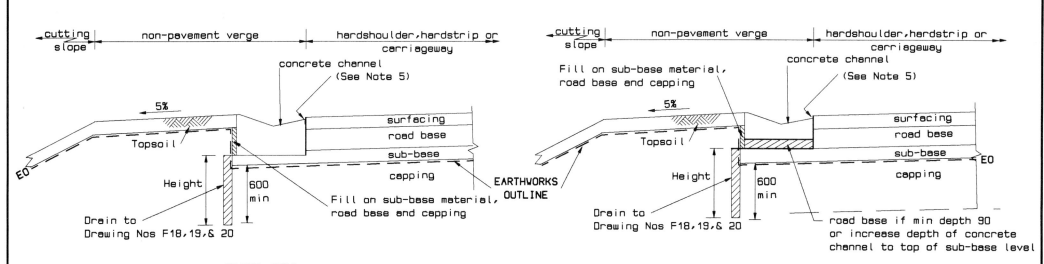

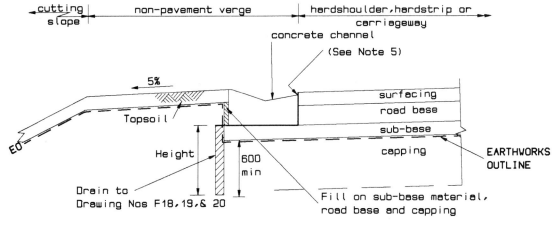

TYPE 23A
(Channel base formed within sub-base layer)

TYPE 23C
(Channel formed on first road base layer)

TYPE 23B
(Channel formed on the sub-base layer)

NOTES

1. ALL DIMENSIONS ARE IN MILLIMETRES.
2. For details of concrete channel see Drawing No B14.
3. Channels may be reinforced or unreinforced. With reinforced channels the reinforcement shall be not less than $4.34 kg/m^2$ British Standard Mesh.
4. Transverse joints shall be sawn or wet formed to a minimum depth of 25mm below channel invert and sealed in accordance with Clause 1017 of S.H.W. The spacing of joints shall be 5000mm for unreinforced channels and 30000mm for reinforced channels.
5. Notwithstanding other tolerances in the specification the finished level of the channel shall not be higher nor more than 10mm lower than the finished level of the edge of the adjacent carriageway.

| DEPARTMENT OF TRANSPORT HIGHWAY CONSTRUCTION DETAILS | EDGE OF PAVEMENT DETAILS | EMBANKMENTS – SURFACE WATER CHANNEL FOR FLEXIBLE CARRIAGEWAY | Drawing No. **B12** | Date |

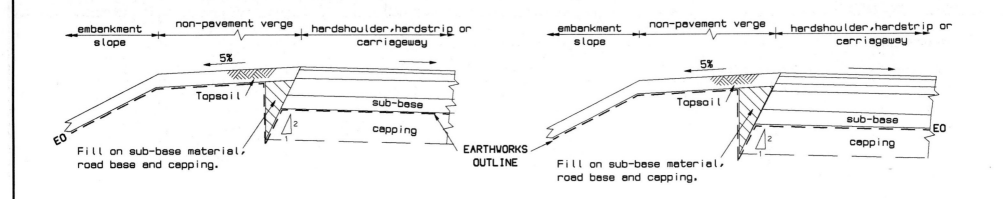

embankment slope | non-pavement verge | hardshoulder,hardstrip or carriageway

5%

Topsoil

EO

Fill on sub-base material, road base and capping.

sub-base

capping

Type 24A (Flexible carriageway).

embankment slope | non-pavement verge | hardshoulder,hardstrip or carriageway

5%

Topsoil

EARTHWORKS OUTLINE

Fill on sub-base material, road base and capping.

sub-base

EO

capping

Type 24C (Flexible composite carriageway).

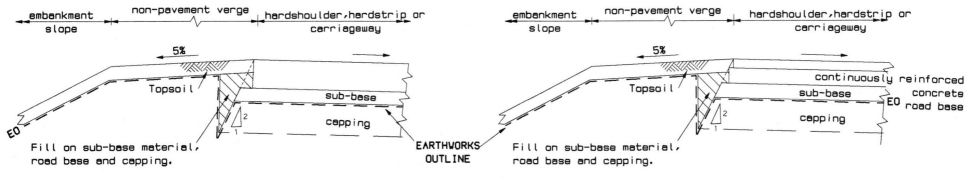

embankment slope | non-pavement verge | hardshoulder,hardstrip or carriageway

5%

Topsoil

EO

Fill on sub-base material, road base and capping.

sub-base

capping

EARTHWORKS OUTLINE

Type 24B (Rigid carriageway).

embankment slope | non-pavement verge | hardshoulder,hardstrip or carriageway

5%

Topsoil

Fill on sub-base material, road base and capping.

continuously reinforced concrete road base

sub-base

EO

capping

Type 24D (Rigid composite carriageway).

| DEPARTMENT OF TRANSPORT HIGHWAY CONSTRUCTION DETAILS | EDGE OF PAVEMENT DETAILS | EMBANKMENTS – VERGE DRAINING OVER EMBANKMENT SLOPE | Drawing No. **B13** | Date |

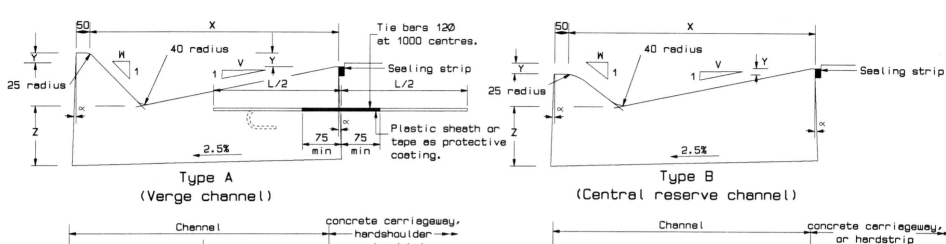

Type A
(Verge channel)

Tie bars 12Ø at 1000 centres.

Sealing strip

Plastic sheath or tape as protective coating.

Type B
(Central reserve channel)

Sealing strip

concrete carriageway, hardshoulder or hardstrip

Type C
(Modified verge channel)

concrete carriageway, or hardstrip

Type D
(Modified central reserve channel)

NOTES

1. ALL DIMENSIONS ARE IN MILLIMETRES.
2. Dimensions V,W,X,Y & Z shall be as described in the Contract.
3. Angle $\alpha=0°$ exept where the edge of the channel is more than 300mm high when $\alpha=0°$ to 2.5°.

4. Modified channel design shall be used when carriageway + channel are slipformed simultaneously.
5. Concrete to channel to be grade C40 to clause 1001 of SHW.

6. Channels may be reinforced or unreinforced. With reinforced channels the reinforcement shall be not less than 4.34Kg/m^2 British Standard Mesh.
7. Transverse joints shall be sawn or wet formed to a minimum depth of 25mm below channel invert and sealed in accordance with Clause 1017 of S.H.W. The spacing of joints shall be 5000mm for unreinforced channels and 30,000mm for reinforced channels.

8. For tie bars in type A or Type B channels with rigid carriageway construction length L to be 1000 for steel grade 250, and 750 for steel grade 460. Minimum cover to steel 50mm.
9. Sealing strip is required with rigid carriageway construction and shall be in accordance with Clause 1017 of the S.H.W.
10. The dimension Y is the difference in level between the outer edges of the channel.

| DEPARTMENT OF TRANSPORT HIGHWAY CONSTRUCTION DETAILS | EDGE OF PAVEMENT DETAILS | CROSS SECTION OF CONCRETE SURFACE WATER CHANNEL | Drawing No. **B14** | Date |

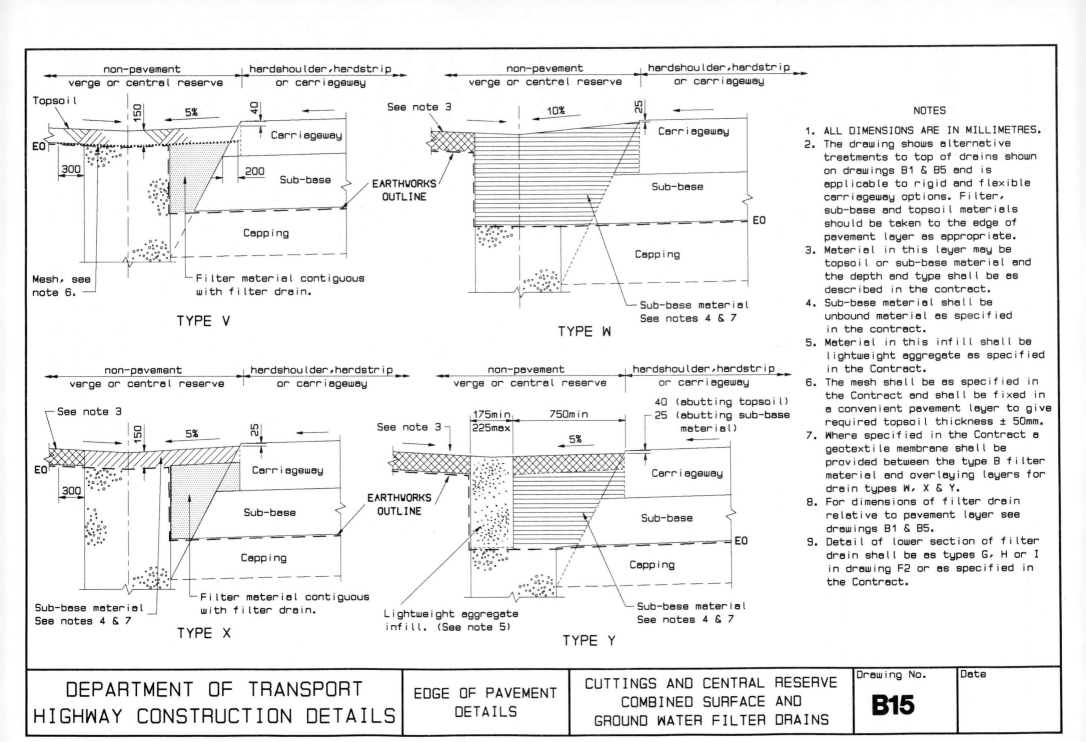

TYPE V

TYPE W

TYPE X

TYPE Y

NOTES

1. ALL DIMENSIONS ARE IN MILLIMETRES.
2. The drawing shows alternative treatments to top of drains shown on drawings B1 & B5 and is applicable to rigid and flexible carriageway options. Filter, sub-base and topsoil materials should be taken to the edge of pavement layer as appropriate.
3. Material in this layer may be topsoil or sub-base material and the depth and type shall be as described in the contract.
4. Sub-base material shall be unbound material as specified in the contract.
5. Material in this infill shall be lightweight aggregate as specified in the Contract.
6. The mesh shall be as specified in the Contract and shall be fixed in a convenient pavement layer to give required topsoil thickness ± 50mm.
7. Where specified in the Contract a geotextile membrane shall be provided between the type B filter material and overlaying layers for drain types W, X & Y.
8. For dimensions of filter drain relative to pavement layer see drawings B1 & B5.
9. Detail of lower section of filter drain shall be as types G, H or I in drawing F2 or as specified in the Contract.

| DEPARTMENT OF TRANSPORT HIGHWAY CONSTRUCTION DETAILS | EDGE OF PAVEMENT DETAILS | CUTTINGS AND CENTRAL RESERVE COMBINED SURFACE AND GROUND WATER FILTER DRAINS | Drawing No. **B15** | Date |

Series C — Concrete Carriageway

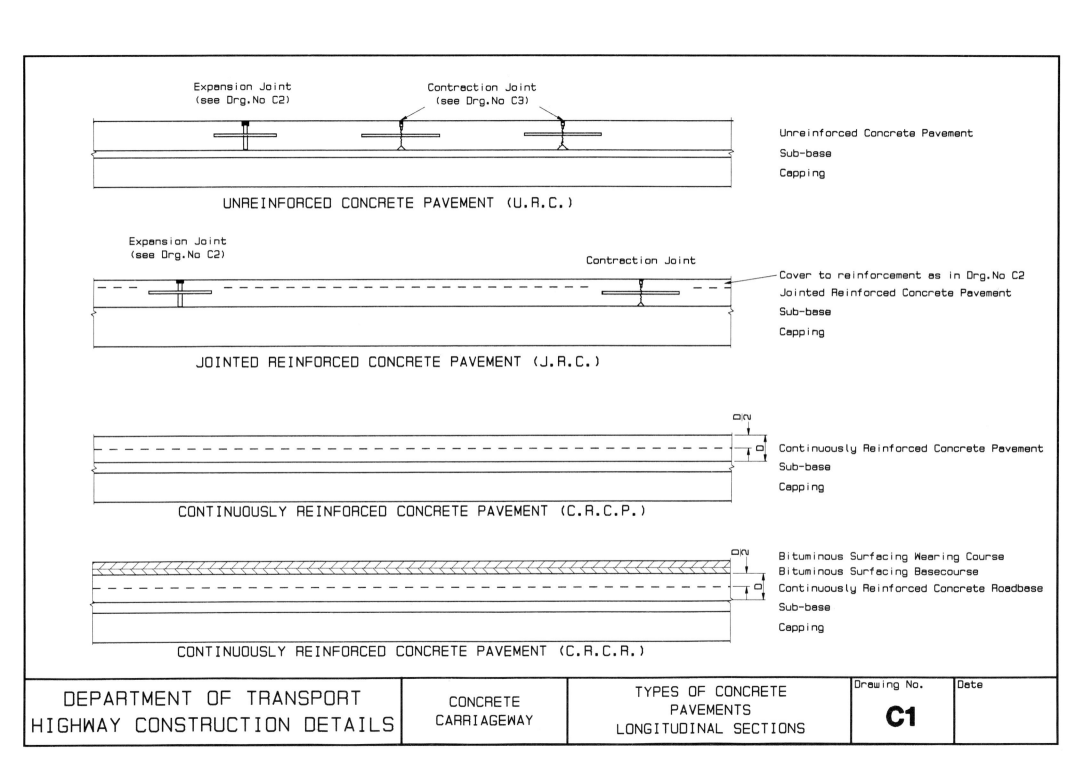

Expansion Joint
(see Drg.No C2)

Contraction Joint
(see Drg.No C3)

Unreinforced Concrete Pavement

Sub-base

Capping

UNREINFORCED CONCRETE PAVEMENT (U.R.C.)

Expansion Joint
(see Drg.No C2)

Contraction Joint

Cover to reinforcement as in Drg.No C2
Jointed Reinforced Concrete Pavement

Sub-base

Capping

JOINTED REINFORCED CONCRETE PAVEMENT (J.R.C.)

D/2

D

Continuously Reinforced Concrete Pavement

Sub-base

Capping

CONTINUOUSLY REINFORCED CONCRETE PAVEMENT (C.R.C.P.)

D/2

D

Bituminous Surfacing Wearing Course
Bituminous Surfacing Basecourse
Continuously Reinforced Concrete Roadbase

Sub-base

Capping

CONTINUOUSLY REINFORCED CONCRETE PAVEMENT (C.R.C.R.)

| DEPARTMENT OF TRANSPORT HIGHWAY CONSTRUCTION DETAILS | CONCRETE CARRIAGEWAY | TYPES OF CONCRETE PAVEMENTS LONGITUDINAL SECTIONS | Drawing No. C1 | Date |

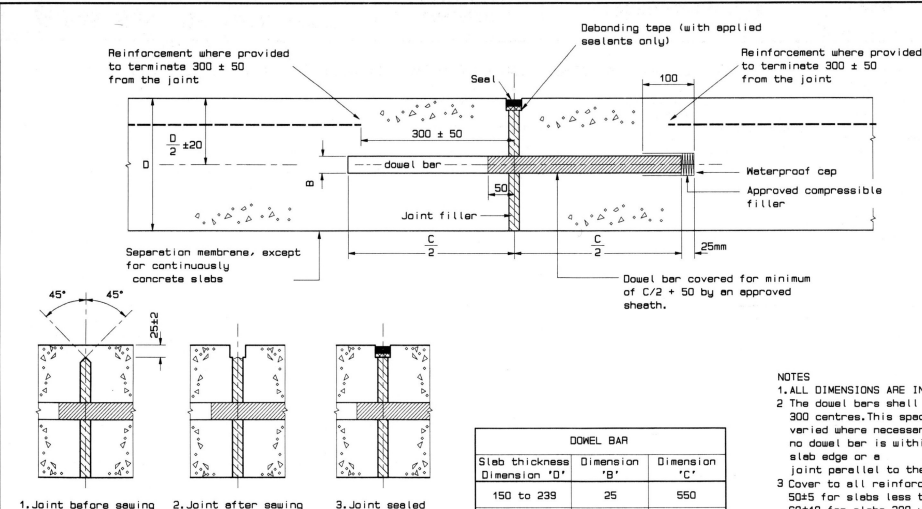

Debonding tape (with applied sealants only)

Reinforcement where provided to terminate 300 ± 50 from the joint

Reinforcement where provided to terminate 300 ± 50 from the joint

Seal

100

$\frac{D}{2}$ ±20

D

B

300 ± 50

dowel bar

50

Waterproof cap

Approved compressible filler

Joint filler

Separation membrane, except for continuously concrete slabs

$\frac{C}{2}$

$\frac{C}{2}$

25mm

Dowel bar covered for minimum of C/2 + 50 by an approved sheath.

45°   45°

25±2

1. Joint before sawing   2. Joint after sawing   3. Joint sealed

SAWN GROOVE FILLER DETAIL

DOWEL BAR		
Slab thickness Dimension 'D'	Dimension 'B'	Dimension 'C'
150 to 239	25	550
240 and over	32	650

NOTES
1. ALL DIMENSIONS ARE IN MILLIMETRES
2 The dowel bars shall be placed at 300 centres. This spacing shall be varied where necessary so that no dowel bar is within 150 of a slab edge or a joint parallel to the bars.
3 Cover to all reinforcement to be 50±5 for slabs less than 200 thick 60±10 for slabs 200 up to 270 thick and 70±20 for slabs 270 thick or more

DEPARTMENT OF TRANSPORT HIGHWAY CONSTRUCTION DETAILS	CONCRETE CARRIAGEWAY	EXPANSION JOINTS Reinforced and unreinforced concrete slabs	Drawing No. C2	Date

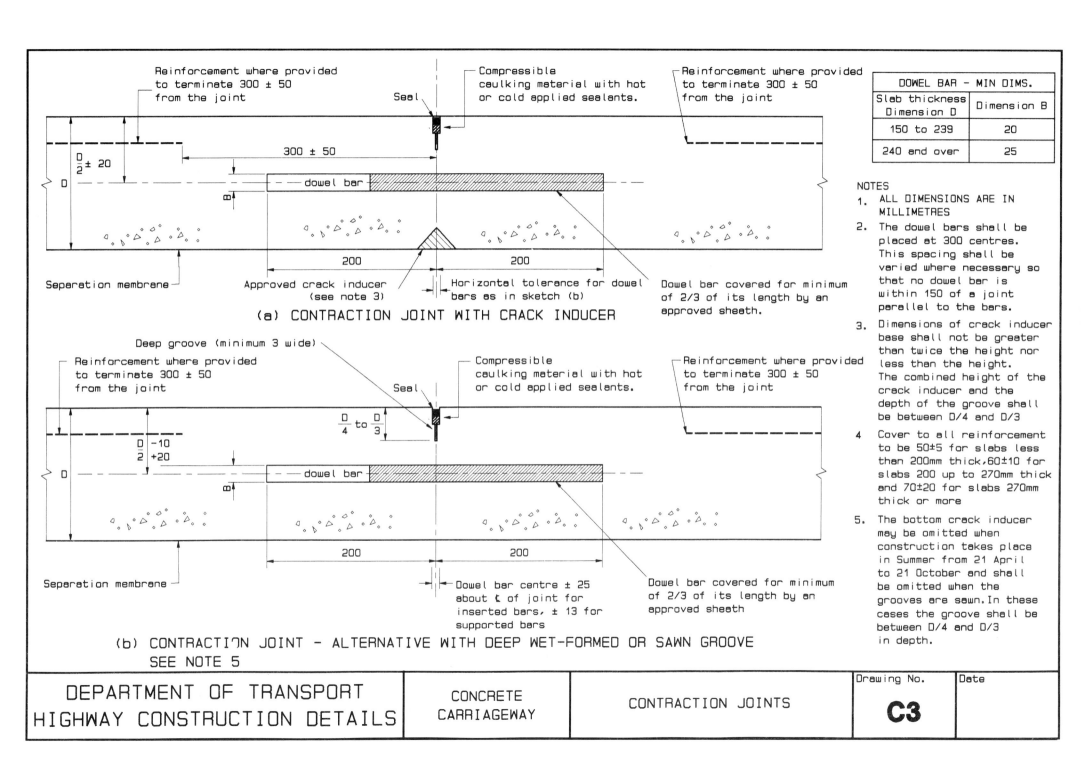

Reinforcement where provided to terminate 300 ± 50 from the joint

Seal

Compressible caulking material with hot or cold applied sealants.

Reinforcement where provided to terminate 300 ± 50 from the joint

DOWEL BAR - MIN DIMS.	
Slab thickness Dimension D	Dimension B
150 to 239	20
240 and over	25

$\frac{D}{2} \pm 20$

D

dowel bar

B

300 ± 50

200   200

Separation membrane

Approved crack inducer (see note 3)

Horizontal tolerance for dowel bars as in sketch (b)

Dowel bar covered for minimum of 2/3 of its length by an approved sheath.

(a) CONTRACTION JOINT WITH CRACK INDUCER

NOTES

1. ALL DIMENSIONS ARE IN MILLIMETRES

2. The dowel bars shall be placed at 300 centres. This spacing shall be varied where necessary so that no dowel bar is within 150 of a joint parallel to the bars.

3. Dimensions of crack inducer base shall not be greater than twice the height nor less than the height. The combined height of the crack inducer and the depth of the groove shall be between D/4 and D/3

4. Cover to all reinforcement to be 50±5 for slabs less than 200mm thick, 60±10 for slabs 200 up to 270mm thick and 70±20 for slabs 270mm thick or more

5. The bottom crack inducer may be omitted when construction takes place in Summer from 21 April to 21 October and shall be omitted when the grooves are sawn. In these cases the groove shall be between D/4 and D/3 in depth.

Deep groove (minimum 3 wide)

Reinforcement where provided to terminate 300 ± 50 from the joint

Seal

Compressible caulking material with hot or cold applied sealants.

Reinforcement where provided to terminate 300 ± 50 from the joint

$\frac{D}{4}$ to $\frac{D}{3}$

$\frac{D}{2} \begin{array}{c} -10 \\ +20 \end{array}$

D

dowel bar

B

200   200

Separation membrane

Dowel bar centre ± 25 about ₵ of joint for inserted bars, ± 13 for supported bars

Dowel bar covered for minimum of 2/3 of its length by an approved sheath

(b) CONTRACTION JOINT - ALTERNATIVE WITH DEEP WET-FORMED OR SAWN GROOVE
SEE NOTE 5

DEPARTMENT OF TRANSPORT HIGHWAY CONSTRUCTION DETAILS	CONCRETE CARRIAGEWAY	CONTRACTION JOINTS	Drawing No. **C3**	Date

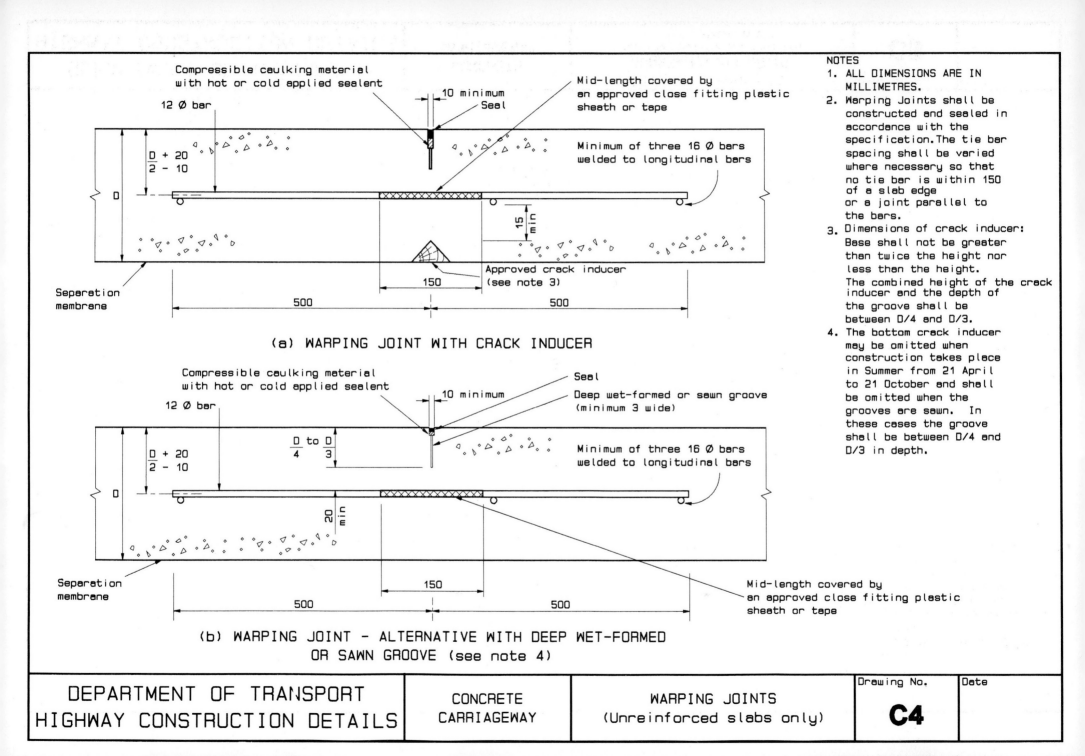

(a) WARPING JOINT WITH CRACK INDUCER

Compressible caulking material with hot or cold applied sealent

12 Ø bar

$\dfrac{D + 20}{2} - 10$

10 minimum

Seal

Mid-length covered by an approved close fitting plastic sheath or tape

Minimum of three 16 Ø bars welded to longitudinal bars

15 min

Approved crack inducer (see note 3)

150

500

500

D

Separation membrane

(b) WARPING JOINT - ALTERNATIVE WITH DEEP WET-FORMED OR SAWN GROOVE (see note 4)

Compressible caulking material with hot or cold applied sealent

12 Ø bar

$\dfrac{D + 20}{2} - 10$

Seal

10 minimum

Deep wet-formed or sawn groove (minimum 3 wide)

$\dfrac{D}{4}$ to $\dfrac{D}{3}$

Minimum of three 16 Ø bars welded to longitudinal bars

20 min

150

500

500

D

Separation membrane

Mid-length covered by an approved close fitting plastic sheath or tape

NOTES
1. ALL DIMENSIONS ARE IN MILLIMETRES.
2. Warping Joints shall be constructed and sealed in accordance with the specification. The tie bar spacing shall be varied where necessary so that no tie bar is within 150 of a slab edge or a joint parallel to the bars.
3. Dimensions of crack inducer: Base shall not be greater than twice the height nor less than the height. The combined height of the crack inducer and the depth of the groove shall be between D/4 and D/3.
4. The bottom crack inducer may be omitted when construction takes place in Summer from 21 April to 21 October and shall be omitted when the grooves are sawn. In these cases the groove shall be between D/4 and D/3 in depth.

| DEPARTMENT OF TRANSPORT HIGHWAY CONSTRUCTION DETAILS | CONCRETE CARRIAGEWAY | WARPING JOINTS (Unreinforced slabs only) | Drawing No. **C4** | Date |

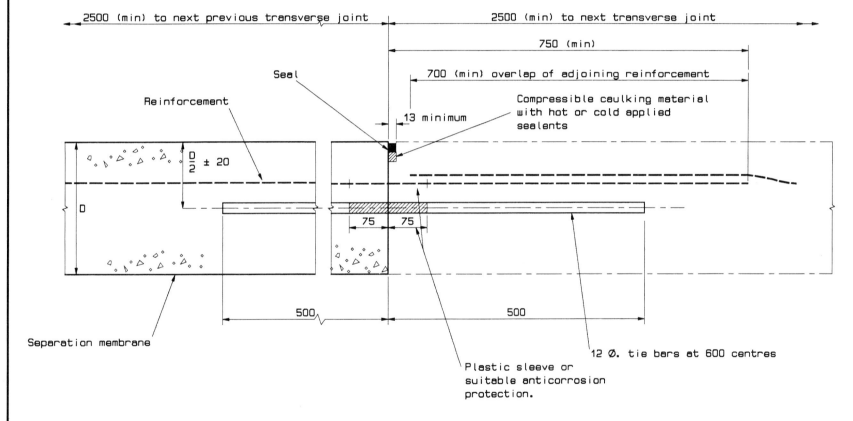

NOTES
1. ALL DIMENSIONS ARE IN MILLIMETRES.
2. The reinforcement cover, measured from the top shall be 50+5 when D is less than 200mm , 60+10 when D is 200 up to 270 and 70+20 when D is 270 or greater.

2500 (min) to next previous transverse joint

2500 (min) to next transverse joint

750 (min)

700 (min) overlap of adjoining reinforcement

Seal

Reinforcement

Compressible caulking material with hot or cold applied sealents

13 minimum

$\frac{D}{2}$ ± 20

D

75   75

Separation membrane

500

500

Plastic sleeve or suitable anticorrosion protection.

12 Ø. tie bars at 600 centres

| DEPARTMENT OF TRANSPORT HIGHWAY CONSTRUCTION DETAILS | CONCRETE CARRIAGEWAY | EMERGENCY TRANSVERSE CONSTRUCTION JOINT (Jointed reinforced concrete slabs only) | Drawing No. C5 | Date |

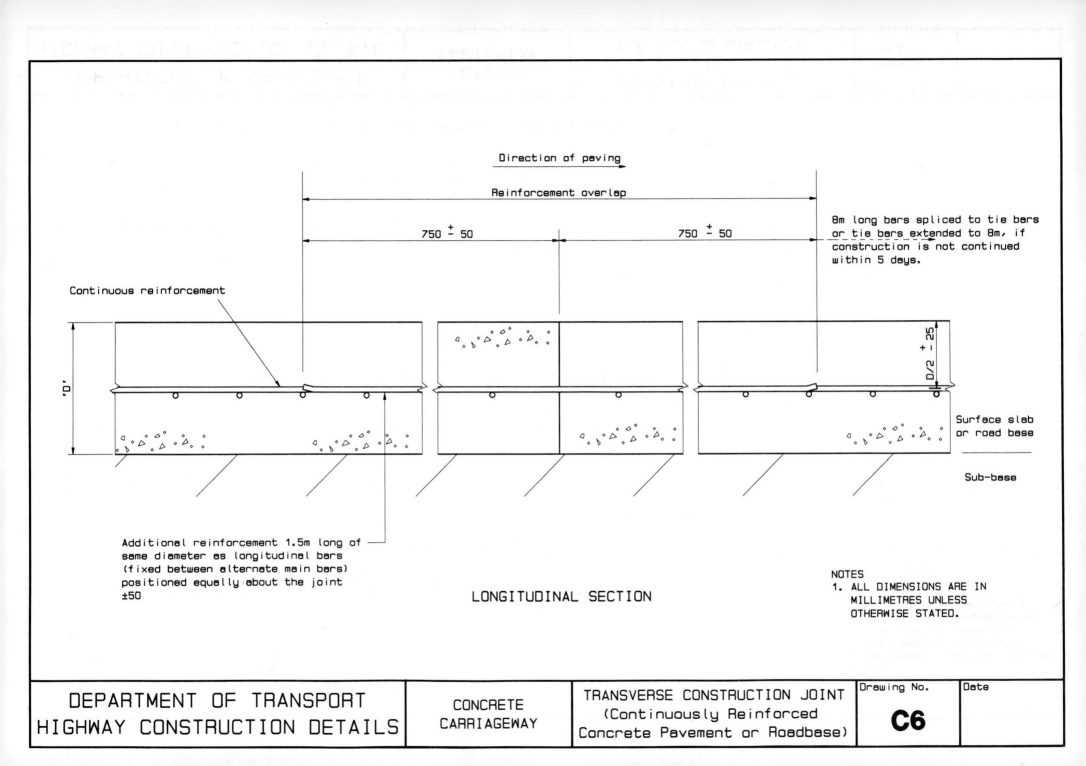

Direction of paving →

Reinforcement overlap

750 ± 50   750 ± 50

8m long bars spliced to tie bars
or tie bars extended to 8m, if
construction is not continued
within 5 days.

Continuous reinforcement

'D'

D/2 + 25

Surface slab
or road base

Sub-base

Additional reinforcement 1.5m long of
same diameter as longitudinal bars
(fixed between alternate main bars)
positioned equally about the joint
±50

LONGITUDINAL SECTION

NOTES
1. ALL DIMENSIONS ARE IN
   MILLIMETRES UNLESS
   OTHERWISE STATED.

| DEPARTMENT OF TRANSPORT HIGHWAY CONSTRUCTION DETAILS | CONCRETE CARRIAGEWAY | TRANSVERSE CONSTRUCTION JOINT (Continuously Reinforced Concrete Pavement or Roadbase) | Drawing No. C6 | Date |

NOTES
1. At Underbridges the roadbase adjacent to the structure shall be a minimum of 5m of flexible roadbase using hot rolled asphalt dense bitumen macadam or dense tarmacadam.
2. The depth of transition slab shall not be less than 200mm. If necessary, the thickness of the last bay of rigid pavement shall be tapered to match, so that the sub-base surface level is continuous without steps.

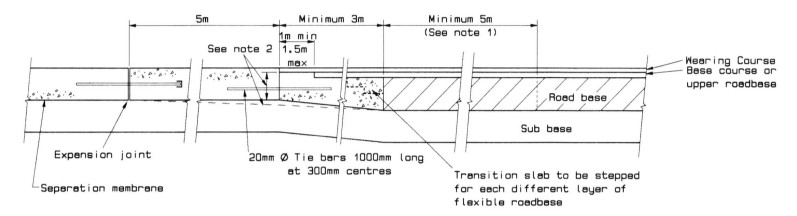

Fig.1 RIGID TO FLEXIBLE CONSTRUCTION (SURFACE SLABS)

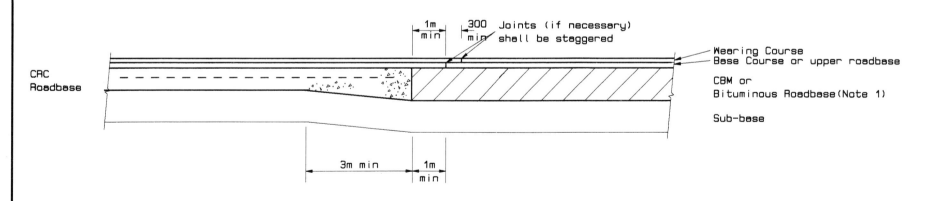

Fig.2 RIGID TO FLEXIBLE CONSTRUCTION (CRC ROADBASE)

| DEPARTMENT OF TRANSPORT HIGHWAY CONSTRUCTION DETAILS | CONCRETE CARRIAGEWAY | TRANSITIONS FROM RIGID TO FLEXIBLE CONSTRUCTION | Drawing No. **C7** | Date |

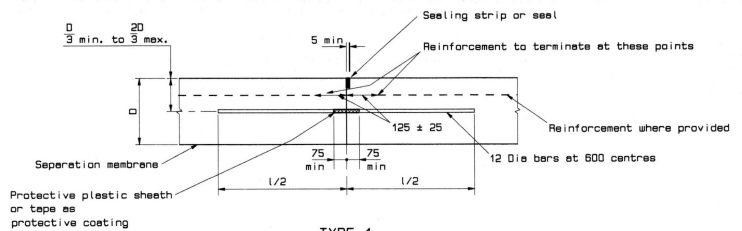

$\frac{D}{3}$ min. to $\frac{2D}{3}$ max.

5 min

Sealing strip or seal

Reinforcement to terminate at these points

D

125 ± 25

Reinforcement where provided

75 min   75 min

12 Dia bars at 600 centres

l/2   l/2

Separation membrane

Protective plastic sheath
or tape as
protective coating

TYPE 1

Longitudinal construction joint between two separately constructed
unreinforced or jointed reinforced slabs

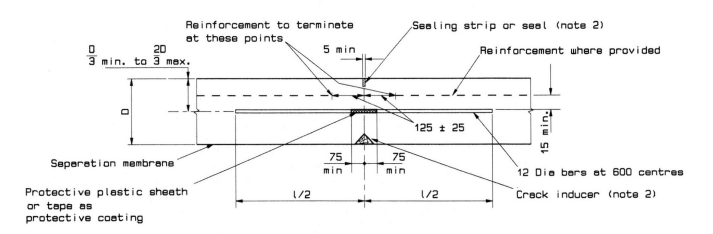

Reinforcement to terminate
at these points

Sealing strip or seal (note 2)

5 min

Reinforcement where provided

$\frac{D}{3}$ min. to $\frac{2D}{3}$ max.

D

125 ± 25

15 min.

75 min   75 min

12 Dia bars at 600 centres

l/2   l/2

Crack inducer (note 2)

Separation membrane

Protective plastic sheath
or tape as
protective coating

TYPE 2

Formed longitudinal joint for slabs more than one lane width
constructed in one operation

NOTES
1. ALL DIMENSIONS ARE IN MILLIMETRES.
2. Dimensions of crack inducer:
   Base shall not be greater than twice the height nor less than the height.
   The combined depth of the sealing strip and bottom crack inducers shall be D3 to D/4.
3. The cover to any reinforcement measured to the top shall be 50 ± 10 when D is less than 200, 60 ± 10 when D is 200 up to 270 and 70 ± 20 when D is 270 or greater.
4. Tie bars length, l to be 1000 for steel grade 250 750 for steel grade 460

| DEPARTMENT OF TRANSPORT HIGHWAY CONSTRUCTION DETAILS | CONCRETE CARRIAGEWAY | LONGITUDINAL JOINTS for U.R.C. or J.R.C.slabs | Drawing No. C8 | Date |

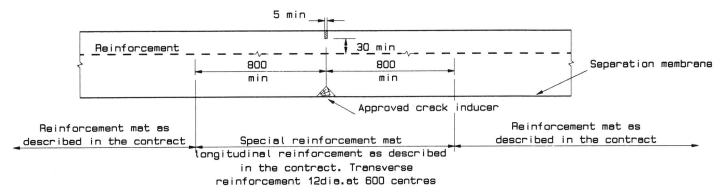

5 min

Reinforcement

30 min

800 min

800 min

Separation membrane

Approved crack inducer

Reinforcement mat as described in the contract

Special reinforcement mat longitudinal reinforcement as described in the contract. Transverse reinforcement 12dia.at 600 centres

Reinforcement mat as described in the contract

LONGITUDINAL JOINT TYPE 3 (Alternative to TYPE 2)

Formed Longitudinal joint for slabs constructed in more than one lane width in one operation.

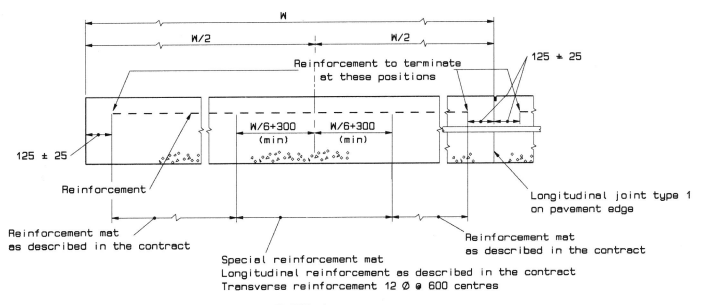

W

W/2

W/2

Reinforcement to terminate at these positions

125 ± 25

125 ± 25

Reinforcement

W/6+300 (min)

W/6+300 (min)

Longitudinal joint type 1 on pavement edge

Reinforcement mat as described in the contract

Reinforcement mat as described in the contract

Special reinforcement mat
Longitudinal reinforcement as described in the contract
Transverse reinforcement 12 Ø @ 600 centres

TYPE 4

Alternative to a longitudinal joint for wide reinforced slabs up to 6m width

NOTES
1. ALL DIMENSIONS ARE IN MILLIMETRES.
2. W equals slab width laid in one operation between 4m and 6m
3. The special transverse reinforcement shall be lapped with or be continuous with the normal specified transverse reinforcement.
4. The combined depth of the sealing strip and the bottom crack inducer shall be D/3 to D/4. Dimensions of bottom crack inducer: Base shall not be greater than twice the height nor less than the height.
5. Cover to reinforcement shall be 50 ± 10 for slabs less than 200 , 60 ± 10 for slabs 200 up to 270 and 70 ± 20 for 270 or greater.

| DEPARTMENT OF TRANSPORT HIGHWAY CONSTRUCTION DETAILS | CONCRETE CARRIAGEWAY | LONGITUDINAL JOINTS Jointed Reinforced Concrete slabs | Drawing No. C9 | Date |

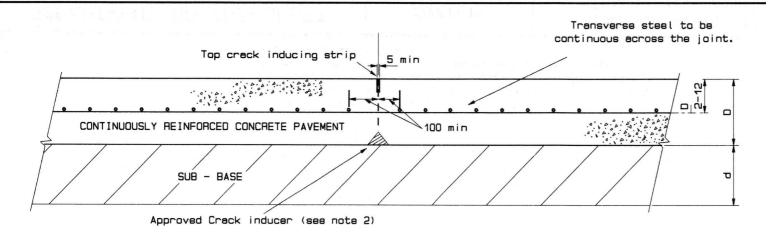

Transverse steel to be
continuous across the joint.

Top crack inducing strip

5 min

2-12

D

CONTINUOUSLY REINFORCED CONCRETE PAVEMENT

100 min

SUB - BASE

d

Approved Crack inducer (see note 2)

FORMED LONGITUDINAL JOINT FOR CRCP

(constructed in 2 or more
lane widths in one operation)

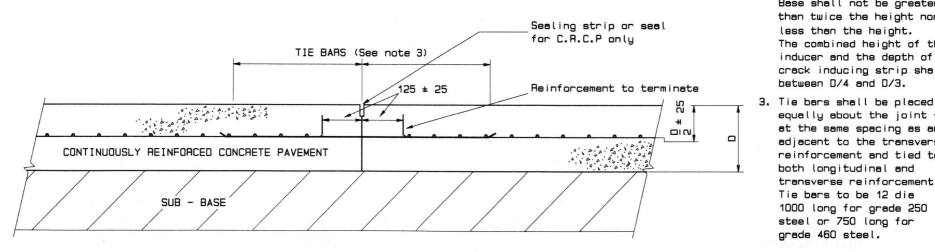

Sealing strip or seal
for C.R.C.P only

TIE BARS (See note 3)

125 ± 25

Reinforcement to terminate

D/2 ± 25

D

CONTINUOUSLY REINFORCED CONCRETE PAVEMENT

SUB - BASE

CRCP or CRCR
BUTT TYPE CONSTRUCTION JOINT
(between separately constructed slabs)

NOTES
1. ALL DIMENSIONS ARE IN
   MILLIMETRES UNLESS
   OTHERWISE STATED.

2. Dimensions of the crack inducer:
   Base shall not be greater
   than twice the height nor
   less than the height.
   The combined height of the crack
   inducer and the depth of the top
   crack inducing strip shall be
   between D/4 and D/3.

3. Tie bars shall be placed
   equally about the joint ± 50
   at the same spacing as and
   adjacent to the transverse
   reinforcement and tied to
   both longitudinal and
   transverse reinforcement.
   Tie bars to be 12 dia
   1000 long for grade 250
   steel or 750 long for
   grade 460 steel.

| DEPARTMENT OF TRANSPORT HIGHWAY CONSTRUCTION DETAILS | CONCRETE CARRIAGEWAY | LONGITUDINAL JOINT (Continuously Reinforced Concrete Pavement or Roadbase) | Drawing No. C10 | Date |

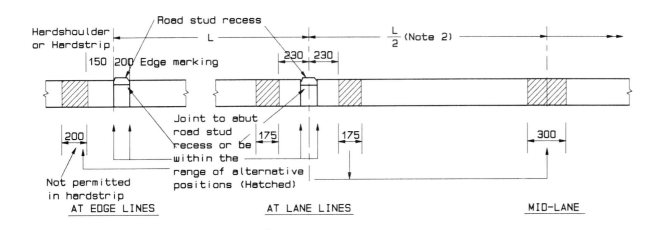

NOTES
1. ALL DIMENSIONS ARE IN
   MILLIMETRES UNLESS
   OTHERWISE STATED.
2. L= Lane width. For dual
   carriageways joint position
   may be at L/2. For position
   of joints in single
   carriageways see following
   Drawings.
3. Maximum slab widths:

Aggregate-	Limestone	All others
URC	5.0m	4.2m
JRC ⎱ CRCP ⎰	7.0m	6.0m

4. For transverse joint arrangements
   in hardstrips see Drg No C26.
5. Road studs recesses not to be
   within 150 min of transverse joints.

PERMITTED ALTERNATIVE LONGITUDINAL JOINT POSITIONS
PAVEMENT SURFACE SLABS

Longitudinal joint
positions.

Joints shall be positioned beside or close to edge or lane markings,
road studs or their recesses, or in mid-lane so that the maximum
width of slab is 4.2m for unreinforced concrete or 6.0m for reinforced
concrete. Permitted alternative joint positions are shown by arrows above.
Tolerances for alternative joint positions are shown by shading.
Joints in CRC Roadbases shall only be construction joints at positions
agreed by the Engineer ,to suit the method of construction, avoiding
positions under the wheeltracks.

Lane markings
and reflective
road studs

Lane and edge markings shall be placed as shown in the contract
drawings. Reflecting road studs shall be placed centrally in lane
markings or adjacent to edge markings unless otherwise shown
in the contract.

Minor adjustments to the lane line position of up to 100mm may
be made where the joint and lane line would conflict or otherwise
fall outside the permitted tolerances, provided that there are no
offset discontinuities in the markings and the adjustments are
approved by the Engineer.

DEPARTMENT OF TRANSPORT HIGHWAY CONSTRUCTION DETAILS	CONCRETE CARRIAGEWAY	PERMITTED ALTERNATIVE LONGITUDINAL JOINT POSITIONS & TOLERANCES	Drawing No. C11	Date

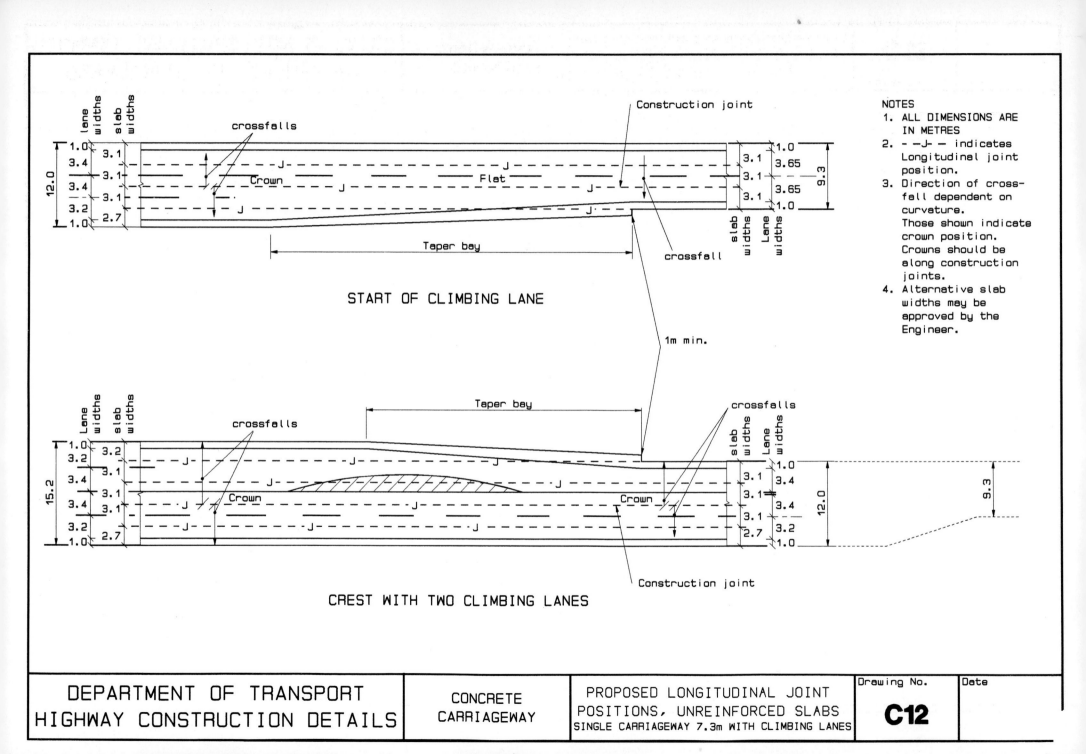

START OF CLIMBING LANE

CREST WITH TWO CLIMBING LANES

Construction joint

crossfalls

Crown

Flat

Taper bay

crossfall

1m min.

NOTES
1. ALL DIMENSIONS ARE IN METRES
2. – –J– – indicates Longitudinal joint position.
3. Direction of cross-fall dependent on curvature. Those shown indicate crown position. Crowns should be along construction joints.
4. Alternative slab widths may be approved by the Engineer.

| DEPARTMENT OF TRANSPORT HIGHWAY CONSTRUCTION DETAILS | CONCRETE CARRIAGEWAY | PROPOSED LONGITUDINAL JOINT POSITIONS, UNREINFORCED SLABS SINGLE CARRIAGEWAY 7.3m WITH CLIMBING LANES | Drawing No. C12 | Date |

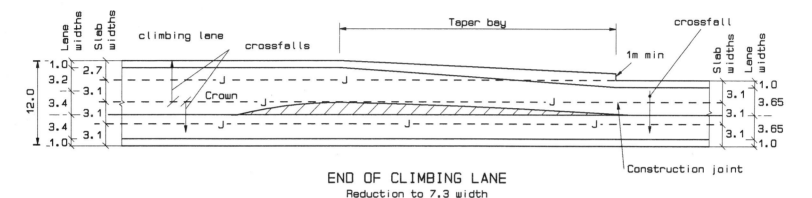

Lane widths
Slab widths
climbing lane
crossfalls
Taper bay
crossfall

12.0

1.0 — 2.7
3.2 — 3.1
3.4 — 3.1
3.4 — 3.1
1.0 — 3.1

J
J
Crown
J
J

1m min
Slab widths
Lane widths

1.0
3.1
3.65
3.1
3.65
3.1
1.0

Construction joint

END OF CLIMBING LANE
Reduction to 7.3 width

NOTES
1. ALL DIMENSIONS ARE
   IN METRES
2. - —J- — indicates
   Longitudinal joint
   position.
3. Direction of cross-
   fall dependent on
   curvature.
4. Alternative slab
   widths may be
   approved by the
   Engineer.
5. Crossfalls depend
   on curvature.
   Those shown indicate
   position of crown for
   normal conditions.
   Crowns should be
   along construction
   joints.

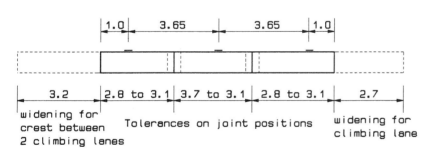

1.0 | 3.65 | 3.65 | 1.0

3.2 | 2.8 to 3.1 | 3.7 to 3.1 | 2.8 to 3.1 | 2.7

widening for
crest between
2 climbing lanes

Tolerances on joint positions

widening for
climbing lane

CROSS SECTION - SINGLE CARRIAGEWAY

| DEPARTMENT OF TRANSPORT HIGHWAY CONSTRUCTION DETAILS | CONCRETE CARRIAGEWAY | PROPOSED LONGITUDINAL JOINT POSITIONS, UNREINFORCED SLABS SINGLE CARRIAGEWAY 7.3m WITH CLIMBING LANES | Drawing No. C13 | Date |

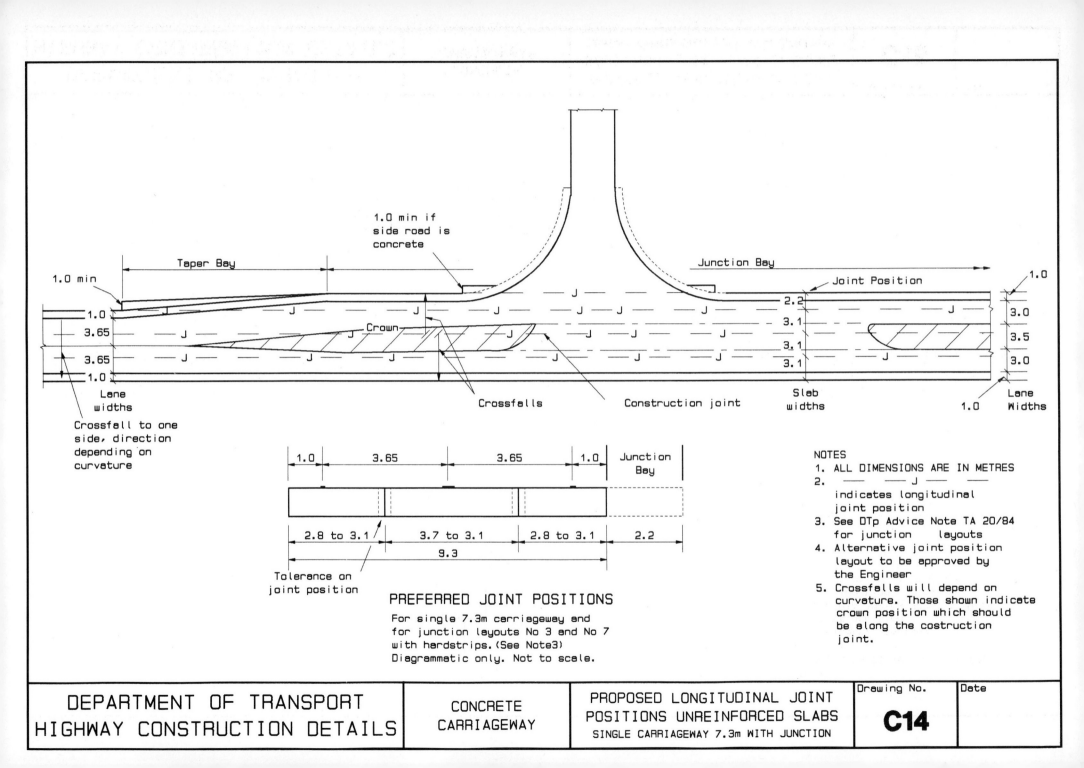

1.0 min if
side road is
concrete

Taper Bay

Junction Bay

Joint Position

1.0 min

1.0

2.2

1.0

J

J

J

J

J

J

J

J

3.65

J

J

Crown

J

J

J

J

J

3.0

3.1

3.5

3.1

3.65

J

J

J

J

J

J

J

3.1

3.0

1.0

Lane
widths

Crossfalls

Construction joint

Slab
widths

1.0

Lane
Widths

Crossfall to one
side, direction
depending on
curvature

1.0   3.65   3.65   1.0   Junction
                                                 Bay

2.8 to 3.1   3.7 to 3.1   2.8 to 3.1   2.2

9.3

Tolerance on
joint position

PREFERRED JOINT POSITIONS

For single 7.3m carriageway and
for junction layouts No 3 and No 7
with hardstrips. (See Note3)
Diagrammatic only. Not to scale.

NOTES
1. ALL DIMENSIONS ARE IN METRES
2. —— —— J ——
   indicates longitudinal
   joint position
3. See DTp Advice Note TA 20/84
   for junction   layouts
4. Alternative joint position
   layout to be approved by
   the Engineer
5. Crossfalls will depend on
   curvature. Those shown indicate
   crown position which should
   be along the costruction
   joint.

| DEPARTMENT OF TRANSPORT HIGHWAY CONSTRUCTION DETAILS | CONCRETE CARRIAGEWAY | PROPOSED LONGITUDINAL JOINT POSITIONS UNREINFORCED SLABS SINGLE CARRIAGEWAY 7.3m WITH JUNCTION | Drawing No. C14 | Date |

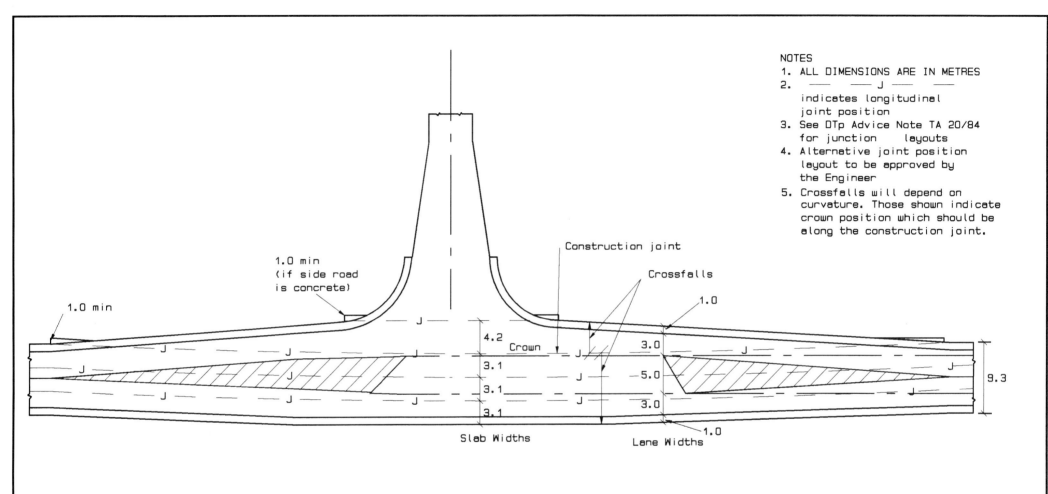

NOTES
1. ALL DIMENSIONS ARE IN METRES
2. ——— ——— J ——— ———
   indicates longitudinal
   joint position
3. See DTp Advice Note TA 20/84
   for junction   layouts
4. Alternative joint position
   layout to be approved by
   the Engineer
5. Crossfalls will depend on
   curvature. Those shown indicate
   crown position which should be
   along the construction joint.

Construction joint

Crossfalls

1.0 min
(if side road
is concrete)

1.0 min

1.0

4.2   Crown

3.1   3.0

J

3.1   5.0

3.1   3.0

3.1   1.0

Slab Widths   Lane Widths

9.3

PROPOSED JOINT POSITIONS
JUNCTION LAYOUT No5 WITH HARDSTRIPS
Diagrammatic only. Not to scale
See Note3.

| DEPARTMENT OF TRANSPORT HIGHWAY CONSTRUCTION DETAILS | CONCRETE CARRIAGEWAY | PROPOSED LONGITUDINAL JOINT POSITIONS UNREINFORCED SLABS SINGLE CARRIAGEWAY 7.3m WITH JUNCTION | Drawing No. C15 | Date |

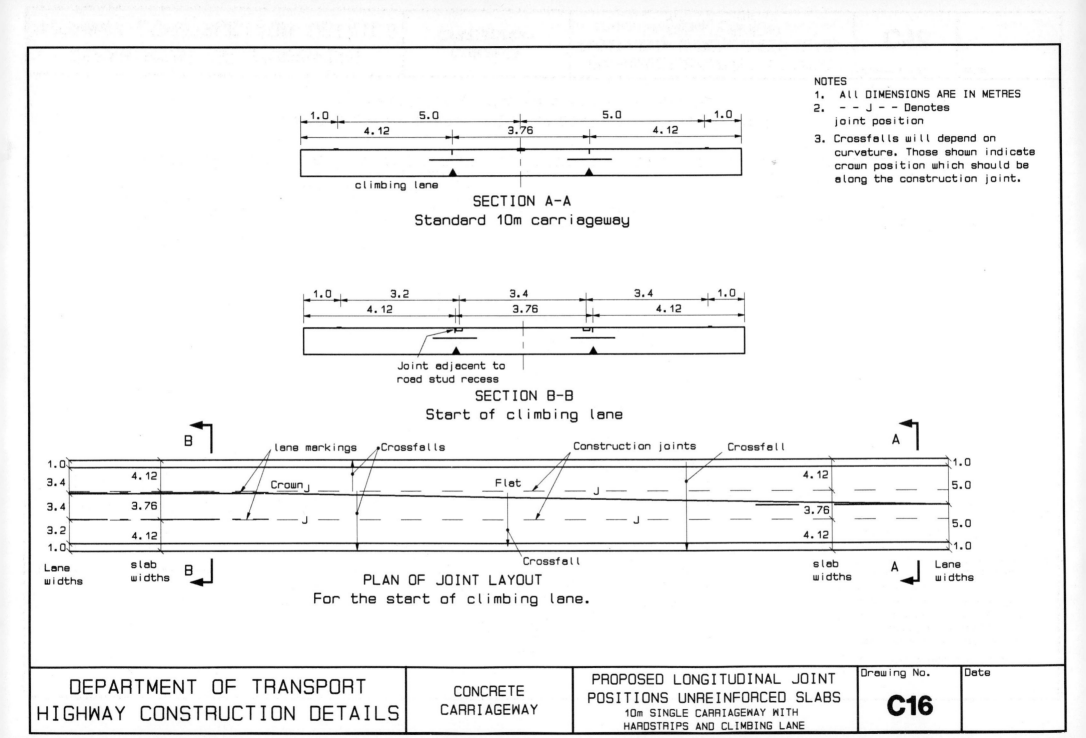

NOTES
1. All DIMENSIONS ARE IN METRES
2. - - J - - Denotes joint position
3. Crossfalls will depend on curvature. Those shown indicate crown position which should be along the construction joint.

SECTION A-A
Standard 10m carriageway

1.0 5.0 5.0 1.0
4.12 3.76 4.12

SECTION B-B
Start of climbing lane

1.0 3.2 3.4 3.4 1.0
4.12 3.76 4.12

climbing lane

Joint adjacent to road stud recess

PLAN OF JOINT LAYOUT
For the start of climbing lane.

lane markings Crossfalls Construction joints Crossfall
Crown J Flat J
J J
Crossfall

Lane widths   slab widths   slab widths   Lane widths

1.0   4.12   4.12   1.0
3.4   5.0
3.4   3.76   3.76
3.2   4.12   4.12   5.0
1.0   1.0

| DEPARTMENT OF TRANSPORT HIGHWAY CONSTRUCTION DETAILS | CONCRETE CARRIAGEWAY | PROPOSED LONGITUDINAL JOINT POSITIONS UNREINFORCED SLABS 10m SINGLE CARRIAGEWAY WITH HARDSTRIPS AND CLIMBING LANE | Drawing No. C16 | Date |

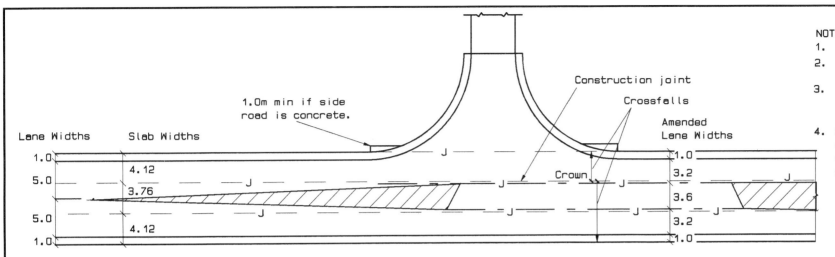

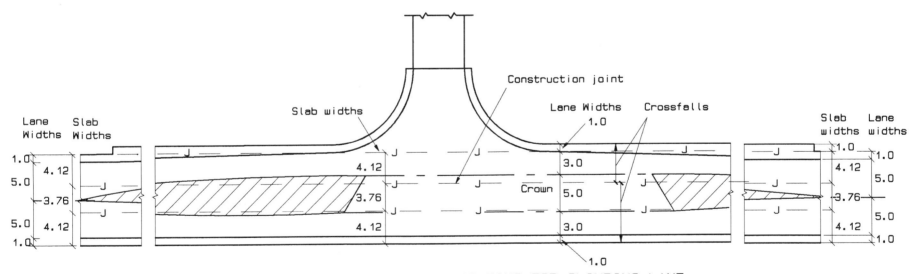

NOTES
1. ALL DIMENSIONS ARE IN METRES
2. See DTp Advice Note TA 20/84 for junction layouts
3. Alternative joint position layouts to be approved by the Engineer.
4. Crossfalls will depend on curvature. Those shown indicate crown position which should be along a construction joint

AMENDED JUNCTION LAYOUT 4 WITH JOINT SPACINGS FOR CLIMBING LANES

JUNCTION LAYOUT 6 WITH JOINT SPACING FOR CLIMBING LANE
Diagrammatic only. Not to scale (See note 2)

| DEPARTMENT OF TRANSPORT HIGHWAY CONSTRUCTION DETAILS | CONCRETE CARRIAGEWAY | PROPOSED LONGITUDINAL JOINT POSITIONS, UNREINFORCED SLABS 10m SINGLE CARRIAGEWAY WITH JUNCTIONS | Drawing No. C17 | Date |

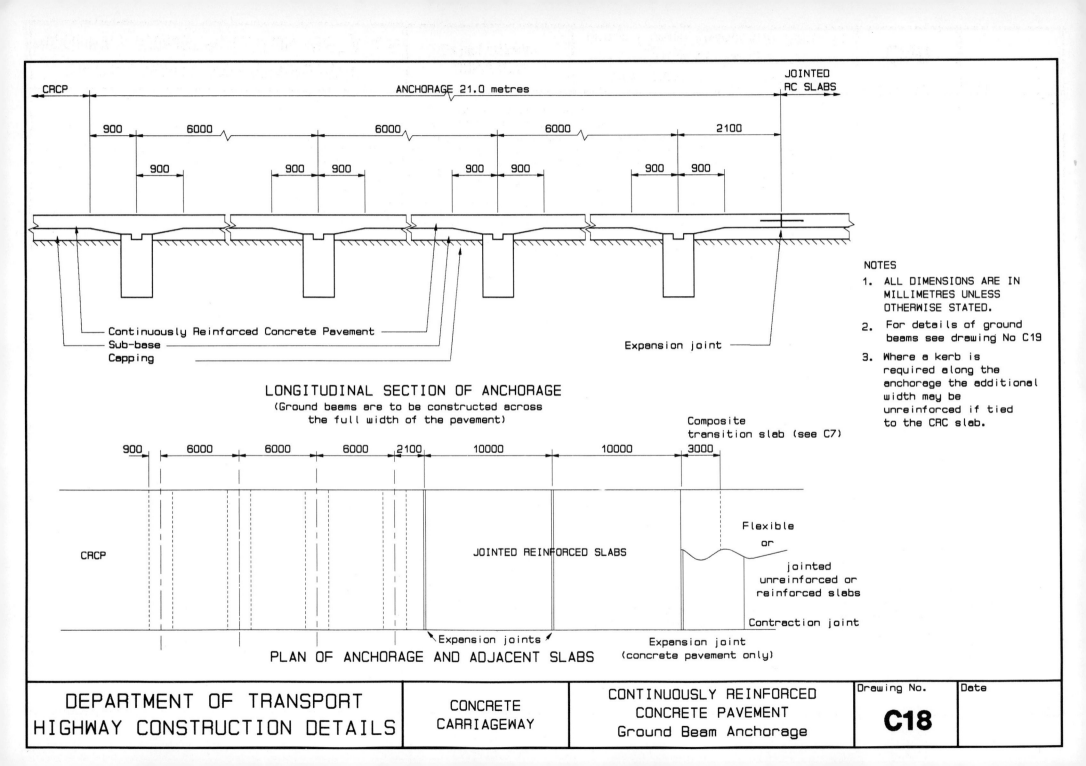

CRCP

ANCHORAGE 21.0 metres

JOINTED RC SLABS

900 6000 6000 6000 2100

900 900 900 900 900 900 900

NOTES

1. ALL DIMENSIONS ARE IN MILLIMETRES UNLESS OTHERWISE STATED.

2. For details of ground beams see drawing No C19

3. Where a kerb is required along the anchorage the additional width may be unreinforced if tied to the CRC slab.

Continuously Reinforced Concrete Pavement
Sub-base
Capping

Expansion joint

LONGITUDINAL SECTION OF ANCHORAGE
(Ground beams are to be constructed across the full width of the pavement)

Composite transition slab (see C7)

900 6000 6000 6000 2100 10000 10000 3000

CRCP

JOINTED REINFORCED SLABS

Flexible
or
jointed unreinforced or reinforced slabs

Contraction joint

Expansion joints

Expansion joint (concrete pavement only)

PLAN OF ANCHORAGE AND ADJACENT SLABS

| DEPARTMENT OF TRANSPORT HIGHWAY CONSTRUCTION DETAILS | CONCRETE CARRIAGEWAY | CONTINUOUSLY REINFORCED CONCRETE PAVEMENT Ground Beam Anchorage | Drawing No. C18 | Date |

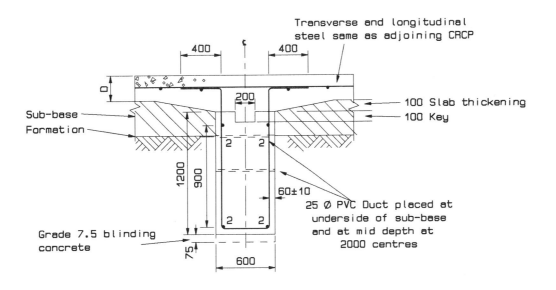

NOTES
1. ALL DIMENSIONS ARE IN MILLIMETRES UNLESS OTHERWISE STATED.
2. Concrete in ground beams to be Grade C30 cast in trench below formation level or sub-base surface
3. Reinforcement shall be in accordance with BS4449 or BS4461 and be securely fixed at all bar intersections.
4. Reinforcement bending dimensions to BS4466 and the specification.
5. Beam reinforcement cover to be 60 ± 10mm.

Transverse and longitudinal steel same as adjoining CRCP

100 Slab thickening

100 Key

Sub-base

Formation

25 Ø PVC Duct placed at underside of sub-base and at mid depth at 2000 centres

Grade 7.5 blinding concrete

GROUND BEAM

(4 No. in anchorage)

BENDING SCHEDULE FOR REINFORCEMENT

MEMBER	BAR Mk	TYPE & SIZE	No OF Mbrs	No IN EACH	TOTAL No	LENGTH OF EACH #	SHAPE CODE	A*	B*	C*	D*	E*	E/R*
BEAMS	1	R16	4	**	**	3900	53	400	1375	480	1375	–	–
do	2	R16	4	4	16	**	20	**	–	–	–	–	–

** Varies with width of anchorage
* Specified to nearest 5mm
# Specified to nearest 25mm

DEPARTMENT OF TRANSPORT HIGHWAY CONSTRUCTION DETAILS	CONCRETE CARRIAGEWAY	CONTINUOUSLY REINFORCED CONCRETE PAVEMENT Ground Beam Anchorage Details	Drawing No. C19	Date

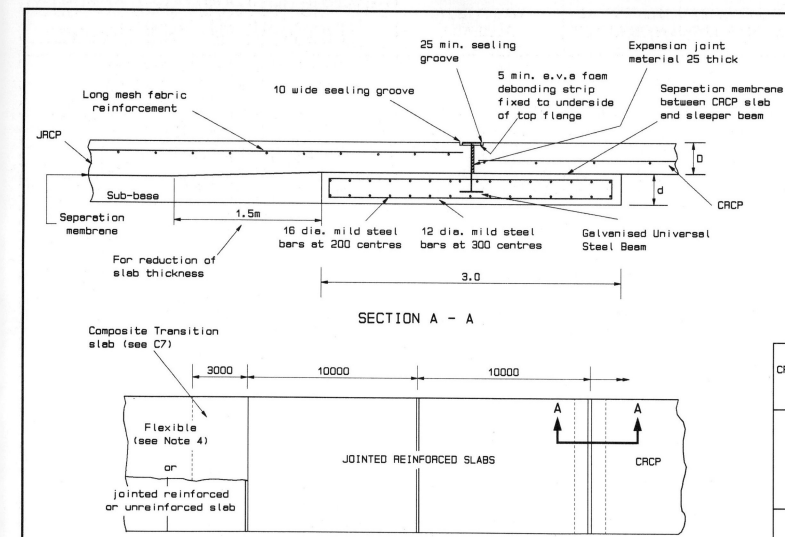

25 min. sealing groove

10 wide sealing groove

5 min. e.v.a foam debonding strip fixed to underside of top flange

Expansion joint material 25 thick

Separation membrane between CRCP slab and sleeper beam

Long mesh fabric reinforcement

JRCP

Sub-base

Separation membrane

For reduction of slab thickness

1.5m

16 dia. mild steel bars at 200 centres

12 dia. mild steel bars at 300 centres

Galvanised Universal Steel Beam

CRCP

D

d

3.0

SECTION A - A

NOTES
1. ALL DIMENSIONS ARE IN MILLIMETRES UNLESS OTHERWISE STATED.
2. This type of anchorage is an alternative to the ground beam anchorage (see C18 and C19) for CRCP surface slabs only.
3. Minimum cover to sleeper beam reinforcement to be 50.
4. At Underbridges the road base adjacent to the structure shall be a minimum of 5m of flexible road base using bituminous or tar binders.

Composite Transition slab (see C7)

3000

10000

10000

Flexible (see Note 4)

or

jointed reinforced or unreinforced slab

JOINTED REINFORCED SLABS

CRCP

A

A

Expansion joint to concrete pavement only

Expansion joint

Universal Steel Beam Anchorage

PLAN OF SLAB

CRCP Slab Depth D	min Sleeper Beam Depth d	BS4 Universal Beam Size
200	210	
210	200	305 × 127 48Kg/m
220	190	
230	180	
240	220	356 × 171 67Kg/m
250	210	

DEPARTMENT OF TRANSPORT HIGHWAY CONSTRUCTION DETAILS	CONCRETE CARRIAGEWAY	CONTINUOUSLY REINFORCED CONCRETE PAVEMENT SURFACE SLABS UNIVERSAL STEEL BEAM ANCHORAGE	Drawing No. **C20**	Date

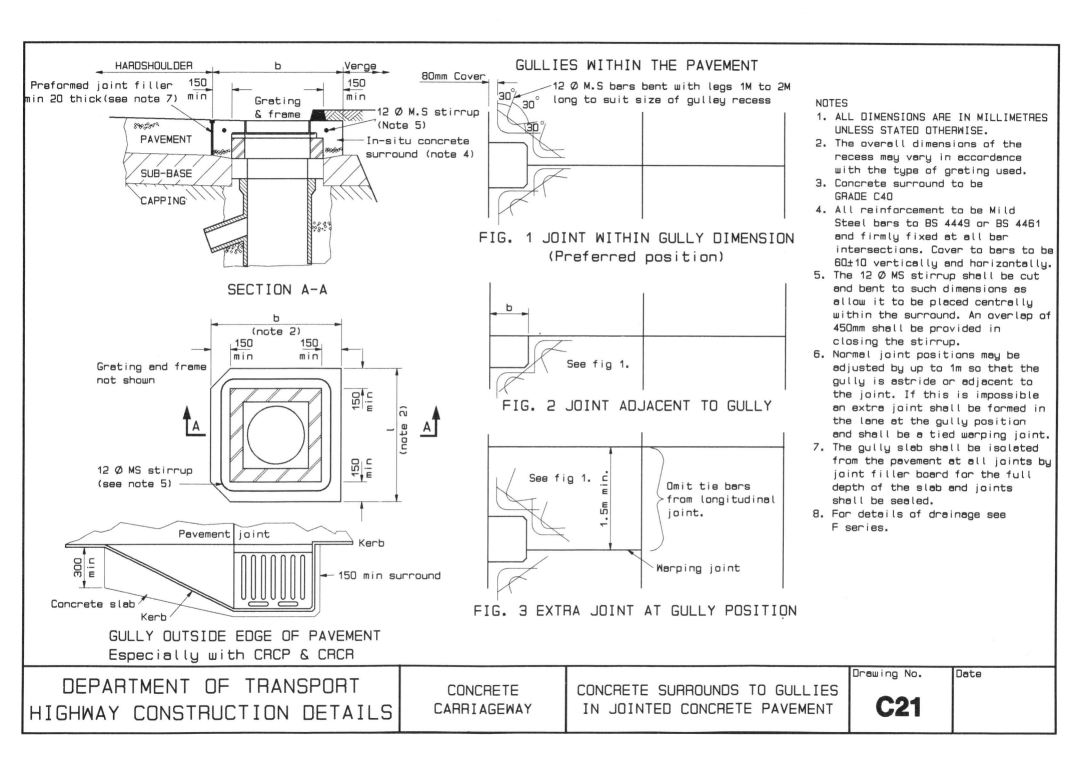

HARDSHOULDER | b | Verge

Preformed joint filler min 20 thick (see note 7)

150 min

150 min

Grating & frame

12 Ø M.S stirrup (Note 5)

PAVEMENT

In-situ concrete surround (note 4)

SUB-BASE

CAPPING

SECTION A-A

b
(note 2)

150 min | 150 min

Grating and frame not shown

150 min
150 min
l (note 2)

12 Ø MS stirrup (see note 5)

A | A

Pavement joint

Kerb

300 min

150 min surround

Concrete slab

Kerb

GULLY OUTSIDE EDGE OF PAVEMENT
Especially with CRCP & CRCR

GULLIES WITHIN THE PAVEMENT

80mm Cover

12 Ø M.S bars bent with legs 1M to 2M long to suit size of gulley recess

30° 30° 30° 30°

FIG. 1 JOINT WITHIN GULLY DIMENSION
(Preferred position)

b

See fig 1.

FIG. 2 JOINT ADJACENT TO GULLY

See fig 1.

1.5m min.

Omit tie bars from longitudinal joint.

Warping joint

FIG. 3 EXTRA JOINT AT GULLY POSITION

NOTES
1. ALL DIMENSIONS ARE IN MILLIMETRES UNLESS STATED OTHERWISE.
2. The overall dimensions of the recess may vary in accordance with the type of grating used.
3. Concrete surround to be GRADE C40
4. All reinforcement to be Mild Steel bars to BS 4449 or BS 4461 and firmly fixed at all bar intersections. Cover to bars to be 60±10 vertically and horizontally.
5. The 12 Ø MS stirrup shall be cut and bent to such dimensions as allow it to be placed centrally within the surround. An overlap of 450mm shall be provided in closing the stirrup.
6. Normal joint positions may be adjusted by up to 1m so that the gully is astride or adjacent to the joint. If this is impossible an extra joint shall be formed in the lane at the gully position and shall be a tied warping joint.
7. The gully slab shall be isolated from the pavement at all joints by joint filler board for the full depth of the slab and joints shall be sealed.
8. For details of drainage see F series.

| DEPARTMENT OF TRANSPORT HIGHWAY CONSTRUCTION DETAILS | CONCRETE CARRIAGEWAY | CONCRETE SURROUNDS TO GULLIES IN JOINTED CONCRETE PAVEMENT | Drawing No. C21 | Date |

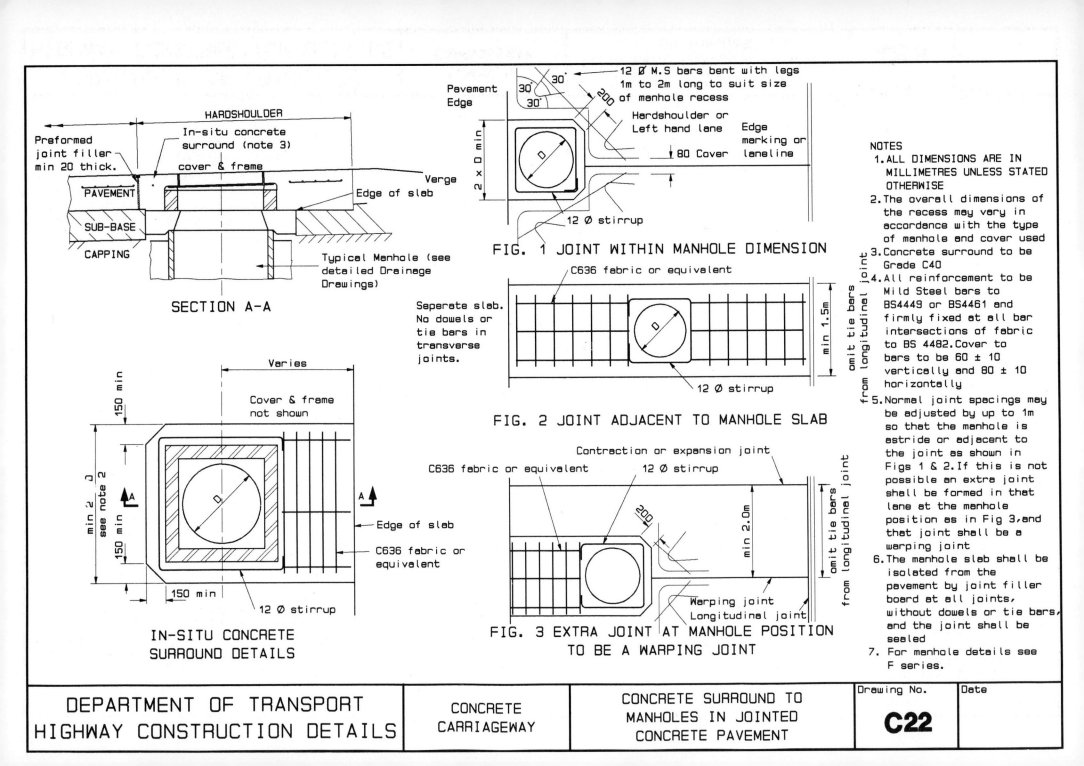

SECTION A-A

HARDSHOULDER

Preformed joint filler min 20 thick.
In-situ concrete surround (note 3)
cover & frame
Verge
Edge of slab
PAVEMENT
SUB-BASE
CAPPING
Typical Manhole (see detailed Drainage Drawings)

FIG. 1 JOINT WITHIN MANHOLE DIMENSION

12 Ø M.S bars bent with legs 1m to 2m long to suit size of manhole recess
Pavement Edge
Hardshoulder or Left hand lane
Edge marking or laneline
80 Cover
2 x D min
12 Ø stirrup

FIG. 2 JOINT ADJACENT TO MANHOLE SLAB

C636 fabric or equivalent
Seperate slab. No dowels or tie bars in transverse joints.
min 1.5m
omit tie bars from longitudinal joint
12 Ø stirrup

IN-SITU CONCRETE SURROUND DETAILS

Varies
Cover & frame not shown
150 min
min 2 D see note 2
150 min
150 min
Edge of slab
C636 fabric or equivalent
12 Ø stirrup

FIG. 3 EXTRA JOINT AT MANHOLE POSITION TO BE A WARPING JOINT

Contraction or expansion joint
C636 fabric or equivalent
12 Ø stirrup
200
min 2.0m
omit tie bars from longitudinal joint
Warping joint
Longitudinal joint

NOTES
1. ALL DIMENSIONS ARE IN MILLIMETRES UNLESS STATED OTHERWISE
2. The overall dimensions of the recess may vary in accordance with the type of manhole and cover used
3. Concrete surround to be Grade C40
4. All reinforcement to be Mild Steel bars to BS4449 or BS4461 and firmly fixed at all bar intersections of fabric to BS 4482. Cover to bars to be 60 ± 10 vertically and 80 ± 10 horizontally
5. Normal joint spacings may be adjusted by up to 1m so that the manhole is astride or adjacent to the joint as shown in Figs 1 & 2. If this is not possible an extra joint shall be formed in that lane at the manhole position as in Fig 3, and that joint shall be a warping joint
6. The manhole slab shall be isolated from the pavement by joint filler board at all joints, without dowels or tie bars, and the joint shall be sealed
7. For manhole details see F series.

| DEPARTMENT OF TRANSPORT HIGHWAY CONSTRUCTION DETAILS | CONCRETE CARRIAGEWAY | CONCRETE SURROUND TO MANHOLES IN JOINTED CONCRETE PAVEMENT | Drawing No. **C22** | Date |

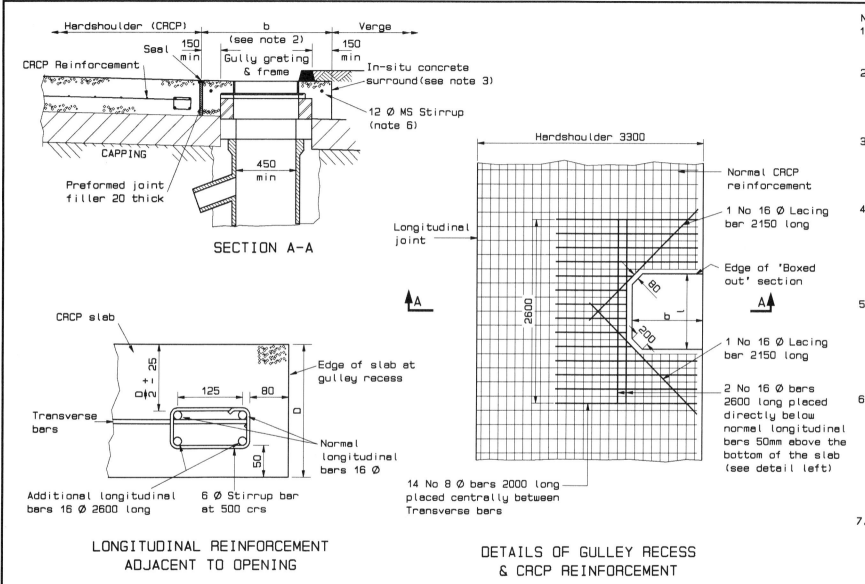

NOTES

1. ALL DIMENSIONS ARE IN MILLIMETRES UNLESS OTHERWISE STATED.
2. The overall dimensions of the opening may vary in accordance with the type of gully grating used.
3. Concrete surround to be C30 or C40 as for the pavement, in accordance with the specification.
4. Normal transverse reinforcement near opening to be strenghtened by additional 8 Ø bars placed centrally between the transverse bars.
5. All reinforcement to CRCP Slab to be Grade 460 deformed bars in accordance with BS4449 or BS4461 and firmly fixed at all bar intersections.
6. The 12 Ø stirrup shall be cut and bent to such dimensions as allow it to be located centrally within the surround 450 overlap shall be provided in closing the stirrup.
7. For gulley details see F series

SECTION A-A

Hardshoulder (CRCP) · b (see note 2) · Verge
Seal · 150 min · Gully grating & frame · 150 min
CRCP Reinforcement · In-situ concrete surround (see note 3)
12 Ø MS Stirrup (note 6)
CAPPING
Preformed joint filler 20 thick
450 min

LONGITUDINAL REINFORCEMENT ADJACENT TO OPENING

CRCP slab
Edge of slab at gulley recess
Transverse bars
Normal longitudinal bars 16 Ø
Additional longitudinal bars 16 Ø 2600 long
6 Ø Stirrup bar at 500 crs
25, +¹ ₀², 125, 80, 50

DETAILS OF GULLEY RECESS & CRCP REINFORCEMENT

Hardshoulder 3300
Normal CRCP reinforcement
Longitudinal joint
1 No 16 Ø Lacing bar 2150 long
Edge of 'Boxed out' section
2600
80, b, 200
A
1 No 16 Ø Lacing bar 2150 long
2 No 16 Ø bars 2600 long placed directly below normal longitudinal bars 50mm above the bottom of the slab (see detail left)
14 No 8 Ø bars 2000 long placed centrally between Transverse bars

| DEPARTMENT OF TRANSPORT HIGHWAY CONSTRUCTION DETAILS | CONCRETE CARRIAGEWAY | GULLIES IN CONTINUOUSLY REINFORCED CONCRETE PAVEMENT OR ROADBASE | Drawing No. C23 | Date |

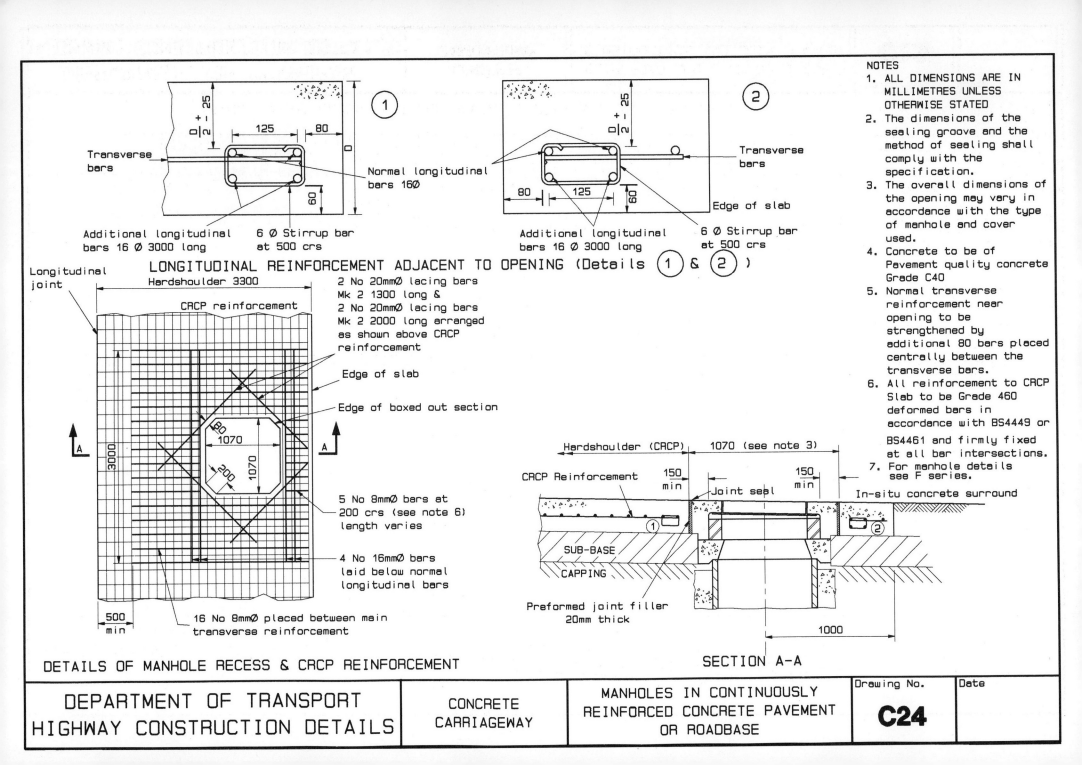

NOTES

1. ALL DIMENSIONS ARE IN MILLIMETRES UNLESS OTHERWISE STATED
2. The dimensions of the sealing groove and the method of sealing shall comply with the specification.
3. The overall dimensions of the opening may vary in accordance with the type of manhole and cover used.
4. Concrete to be of Pavement quality concrete Grade C40
5. Normal transverse reinforcement near opening to be strengthened by additional 80 bars placed centrally between the transverse bars.
6. All reinforcement to CRCP Slab to be Grade 460 deformed bars in accordance with BS4449 or BS4461 and firmly fixed at all bar intersections.
7. For manhole details see F series.

Transverse bars

Normal longitudinal bars 16Ø

Additional longitudinal bars 16 Ø 3000 long

6 Ø Stirrup bar at 500 crs

Edge of slab

LONGITUDINAL REINFORCEMENT ADJACENT TO OPENING (Details ① & ②)

Longitudinal joint

Hardshoulder 3300

CRCP reinforcement

2 No 20mmØ lacing bars Mk 2 1300 long &
2 No 20mmØ lacing bars Mk 2 2000 long arranged as shown above CRCP reinforcement

Edge of slab

Edge of boxed out section

80
1070
200
1070

5 No 8mmØ bars at 200 crs (see note 6) length varies

4 No 16mmØ bars laid below normal longitudinal bars

500 min

16 No 8mmØ placed between main transverse reinforcement

DETAILS OF MANHOLE RECESS & CRCP REINFORCEMENT

Hardshoulder (CRCP)   1070 (see note 3)

CRCP Reinforcement

150 min

Joint seal

150 min

In-situ concrete surround

SUB-BASE

CAPPING

Preformed joint filler 20mm thick

1000

SECTION A-A

| DEPARTMENT OF TRANSPORT HIGHWAY CONSTRUCTION DETAILS | CONCRETE CARRIAGEWAY | MANHOLES IN CONTINUOUSLY REINFORCED CONCRETE PAVEMENT OR ROADBASE | Drawing No. **C24** | Date |

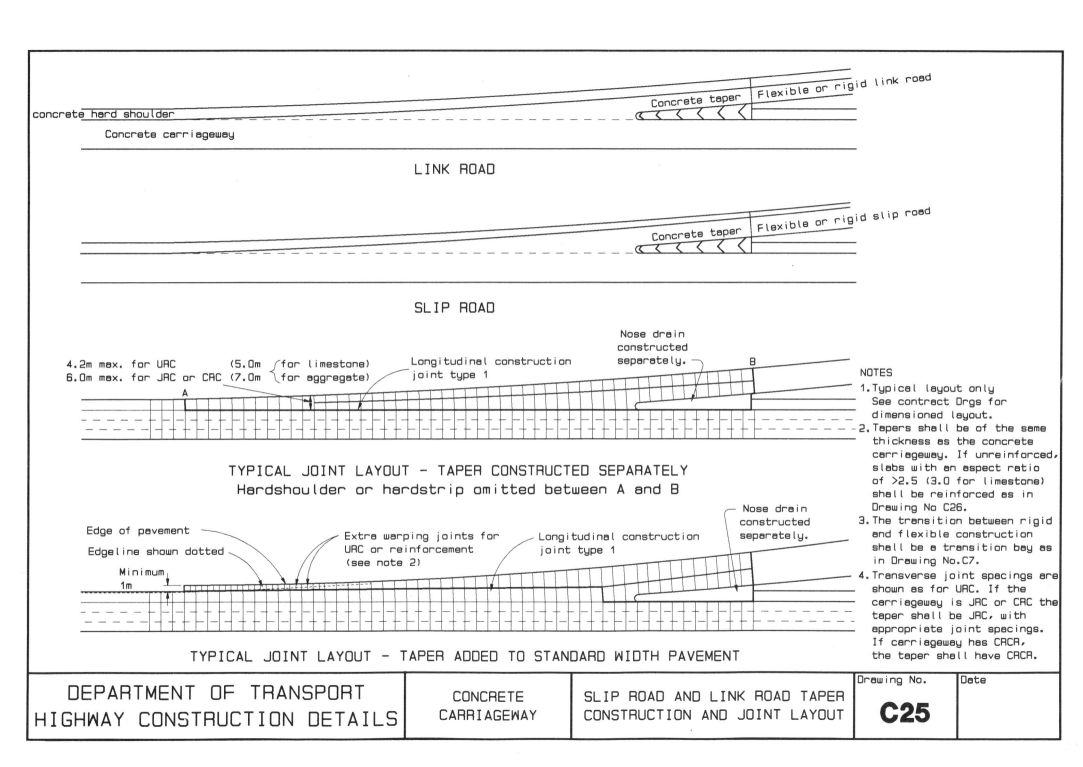

concrete hard shoulder

Concrete carriageway

Concrete taper

Flexible or rigid link road

LINK ROAD

Concrete taper

Flexible or rigid slip road

SLIP ROAD

4.2m max. for URC
6.0m max. for JRC or CRC

(5.0m {for limestone)
(7.0m {for aggregate)

Longitudinal construction
joint type 1

Nose drain
constructed
separately.

A

B

TYPICAL JOINT LAYOUT - TAPER CONSTRUCTED SEPARATELY
Hardshoulder or hardstrip omitted between A and B

Edge of pavement

Edgeline shown dotted

Extra warping joints for
URC or reinforcement
(see note 2)

Longitudinal construction
joint type 1

Nose drain
constructed
separately.

Minimum
1m

TYPICAL JOINT LAYOUT - TAPER ADDED TO STANDARD WIDTH PAVEMENT

NOTES

1. Typical layout only
See contract Drgs for
dimensioned layout.

2. Tapers shall be of the same
thickness as the concrete
carriageway. If unreinforced,
slabs with an aspect ratio
of >2.5 (3.0 for limestone)
shall be reinforced as in
Drawing No C26.

3. The transition between rigid
and flexible construction
shall be a transition bay as
in Drawing No.C7.

4. Transverse joint spacings are
shown as for URC. If the
carriageway is JRC or CRC the
taper shall be JRC, with
appropriate joint spacings.
If carriageway has CRCR,
the taper shall have CRCR.

| DEPARTMENT OF TRANSPORT HIGHWAY CONSTRUCTION DETAILS | CONCRETE CARRIAGEWAY | SLIP ROAD AND LINK ROAD TAPER CONSTRUCTION AND JOINT LAYOUT | Drawing No. C25 | Date |

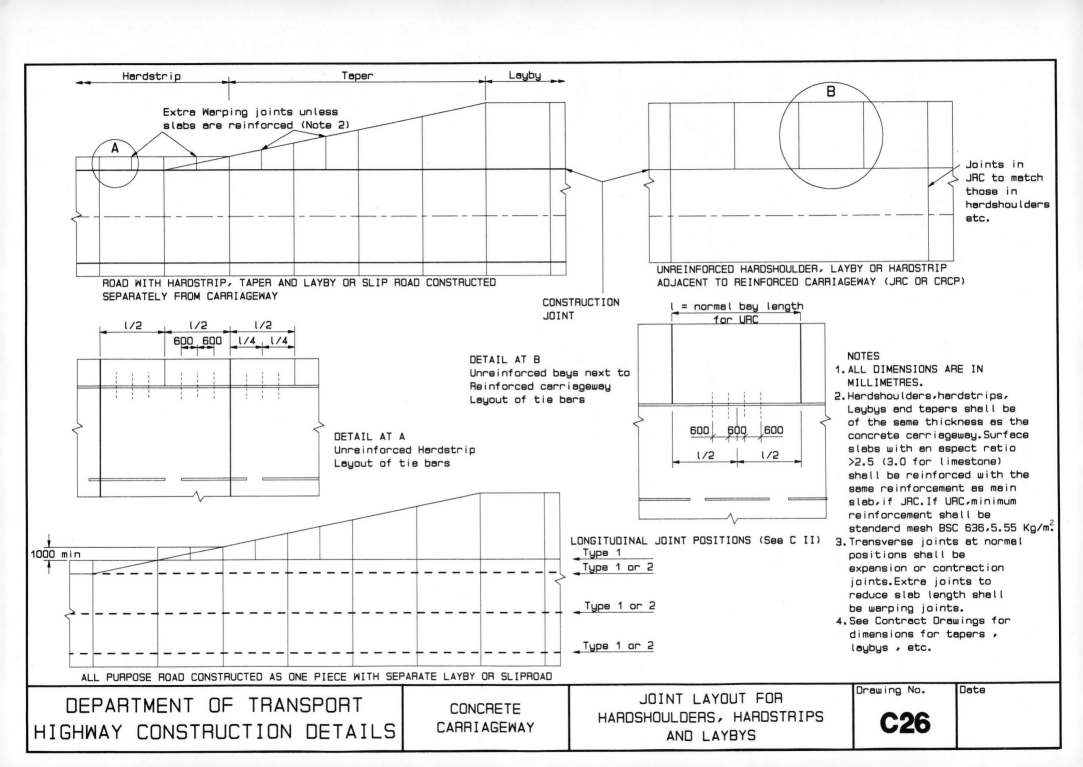

Hardstrip | Taper | Layby

Extra Warping joints unless
slabs are reinforced (Note 2)

A

B

Joints in
JRC to match
those in
hardshoulders
etc.

ROAD WITH HARDSTRIP, TAPER AND LAYBY OR SLIP ROAD CONSTRUCTED
SEPARATELY FROM CARRIAGEWAY

UNREINFORCED HARDSHOULDER, LAYBY OR HARDSTRIP
ADJACENT TO REINFORCED CARRIAGEWAY (JRC OR CRCP)

CONSTRUCTION
JOINT

$l/2$ | $l/2$ | $l/2$
600 | 600 | $l/4$ | $l/4$

DETAIL AT A
Unreinforced Hardstrip
Layout of tie bars

DETAIL AT B
Unreinforced bays next to
Reinforced carriageway
Layout of tie bars

l = normal bay length
for URC

600 | 600 | 600
$l/2$ | $l/2$

1000 min

Type 1
Type 1 or 2

Type 1 or 2

Type 1 or 2

LONGITUDINAL JOINT POSITIONS (See C II)

ALL PURPOSE ROAD CONSTRUCTED AS ONE PIECE WITH SEPARATE LAYBY OR SLIPROAD

NOTES
1. ALL DIMENSIONS ARE IN
   MILLIMETRES.
2. Hardshoulders, hardstrips,
   Laybys and tapers shall be
   of the same thickness as the
   concrete carriageway. Surface
   slabs with an aspect ratio
   >2.5 (3.0 for limestone)
   shall be reinforced with the
   same reinforcement as main
   slab, if JRC. If URC, minimum
   reinforcement shall be
   standard mesh BSC 636, 5.55 Kg/m^2.
3. Transverse joints at normal
   positions shall be
   expansion or contraction
   joints. Extra joints to
   reduce slab length shall
   be warping joints.
4. See Contract Drawings for
   dimensions for tapers,
   laybys, etc.

| DEPARTMENT OF TRANSPORT HIGHWAY CONSTRUCTION DETAILS | CONCRETE CARRIAGEWAY | JOINT LAYOUT FOR HARDSHOULDERS, HARDSTRIPS AND LAYBYS | Drawing No. **C26** | Date |

Series D — Carriageway Markings for Rural Motorways

WHITE (bidirectional)

Spacing	
18 metres	Main carriageway and 7.3 m link road lane markings (General use)
9 metres	(1) Main carriageway and 7.3 m link road lane markings where radius is less than 450 m.
	(2) Main carriageway and 7.3 m link road lane markings where fog is prevalent.
8 metres	Where carriageways diverge see Drawing No. D5

RED (unidirectional)

Spacing	
18 metres	Nearside edge of carriageways* (General use)
9 metres	(1) Nearside edge of carriageways* where radius is less than 450 m.
	(2) Nearside edge of carriageways* where fog is prevalent.
	(3) Nearside edge of merge and diverge see Drawing No. D2.
3 metres	At both sides of nose at edge of carriageway* see Drawing No. D2.

* (Main, Slip and Link Roads)

AMBER/RED (bidirectional) Amber reflectors to face oncoming traffic in normal conditions

Spacing	
18 metres	Offside edge of carriageways* (General use)
9 metres	(1) Adjacent to offside hatching when number of lanes reduced.
	(2) Offside edge of carriageways* where radius is less than 450 m.
	(3) Offside edge of carriageways* where fog is prevalent.
	(EXCEPTION: When adjoining chevron markings for nose at a merge or diverge , see Drawing No. D2.

* (Main, Slip and Link Roads)

GREEN (unidirectional)

Spacing	
8 metres	Across merging/diverging tapers at standard junctions See Drawing No. D2.

Studs should not be used in the following cases:
(a) To divide lanes on a 6.0m carriageway
(b) In permanent positions in the constructed
carriageway where temporary ends occur and
where the studs will conflict with temporary arrangements

DEPARTMENT OF TRANSPORT HIGHWAY CONSTRUCTION DETAILS	CARRIAGEWAY MARKINGS FOR RURAL MOTORWAYS	GENERAL NOTES FOR REFLECTING ROAD STUDS	Drawing No. D1	Date

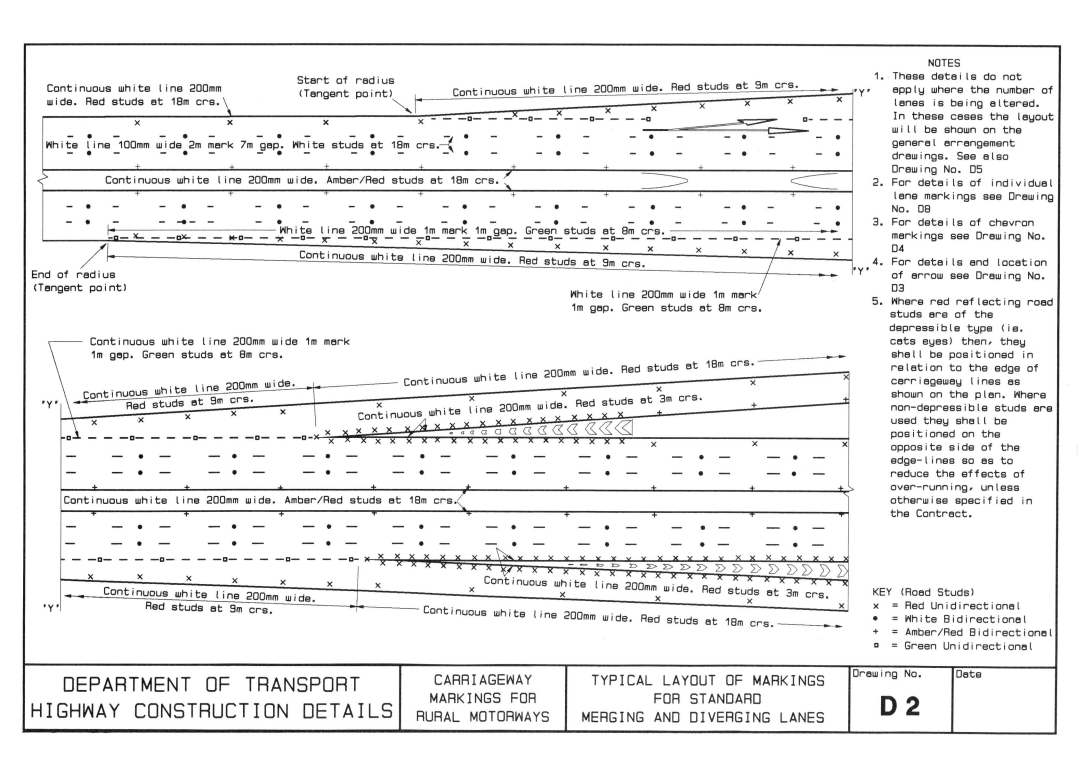

Continuous white line 200mm wide. Red studs at 18m crs.

Start of radius (Tangent point)

Continuous white line 200mm wide. Red studs at 9m crs.

'Y'

White line 100mm wide 2m mark 7m gap. White studs at 18m crs.

Continuous white line 200mm wide. Amber/Red studs at 18m crs.

White line 200mm wide 1m mark 1m gap. Green studs at 8m crs.

Continuous white line 200mm wide. Red studs at 9m crs.

End of radius (Tangent point)

White line 200mm wide 1m mark 1m gap. Green studs at 8m crs.

'Y'

Continuous white line 200mm wide 1m mark 1m gap. Green studs at 8m crs.

Continuous white line 200mm wide. Red studs at 18m crs.

Continuous white line 200mm wide. Red studs at 9m crs.

Continuous white line 200mm wide. Red studs at 3m crs.

'Y'

Continuous white line 200mm wide.

Continuous white line 200mm wide. Amber/Red studs at 18m crs.

Continuous white line 200mm wide. Red studs at 3m crs.

Continuous white line 200mm wide. Red studs at 9m crs.

'Y'

Continuous white line 200mm wide. Red studs at 18m crs.

Continuous white line 200mm wide. Red studs at 3m crs.

NOTES

1. These details do not apply where the number of lanes is being altered. In these cases the layout will be shown on the general arrangement drawings. See also Drawing No. D5

2. For details of individual lane markings see Drawing No. D8

3. For details of chevron markings see Drawing No. D4

4. For details and location of arrow see Drawing No. D3

5. Where red reflecting road studs are of the depressible type (ie. cats eyes) then, they shall be positioned in relation to the edge of carriageway lines as shown on the plan. Where non-depressible studs are used they shall be positioned on the opposite side of the edge-lines so as to reduce the effects of over-running, unless otherwise specified in the Contract.

KEY (Road Studs)

x = Red Unidirectional
● = White Bidirectional
+ = Amber/Red Bidirectional
▫ = Green Unidirectional

DEPARTMENT OF TRANSPORT HIGHWAY CONSTRUCTION DETAILS	CARRIAGEWAY MARKINGS FOR RURAL MOTORWAYS	TYPICAL LAYOUT OF MARKINGS FOR STANDARD MERGING AND DIVERGING LANES	Drawing No. **D 2**	Date

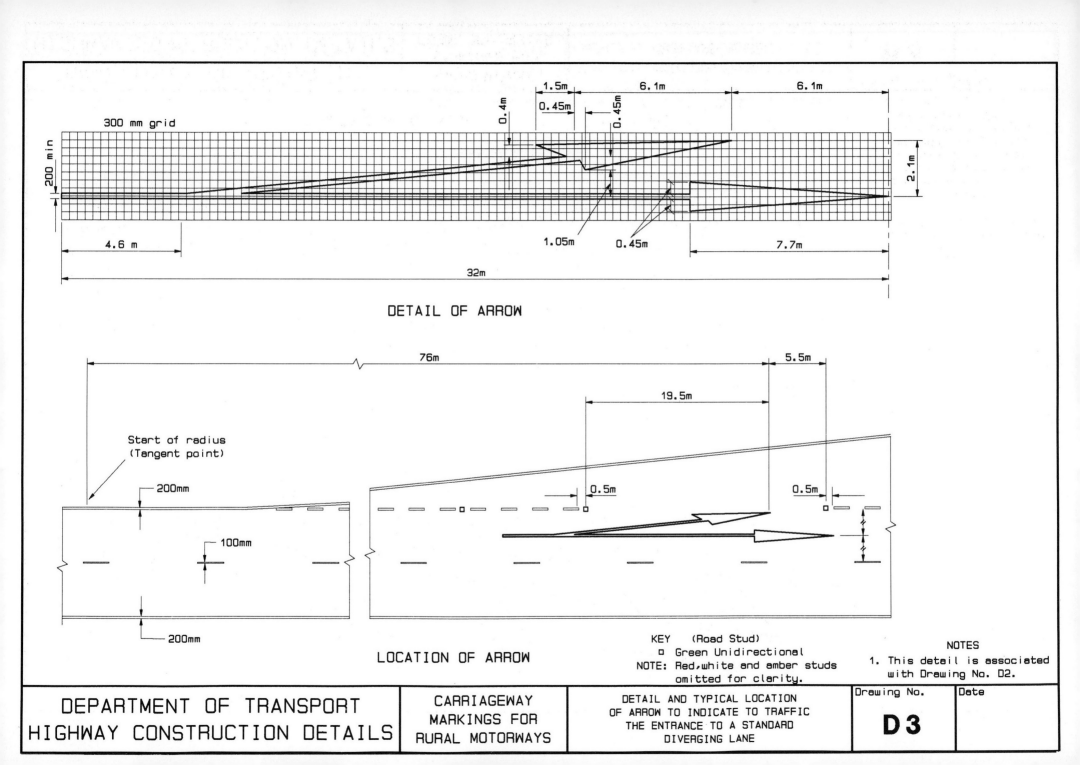

DETAIL OF ARROW

LOCATION OF ARROW

KEY   (Road Stud)
□ Green Unidirectional
NOTE: Red,white and amber studs
      omitted for clarity.

NOTES
1. This detail is associated
   with Drawing No. D2.

| DEPARTMENT OF TRANSPORT HIGHWAY CONSTRUCTION DETAILS | CARRIAGEWAY MARKINGS FOR RURAL MOTORWAYS | DETAIL AND TYPICAL LOCATION OF ARROW TO INDICATE TO TRAFFIC THE ENTRANCE TO A STANDARD DIVERGING LANE | Drawing No. D3 | Date |

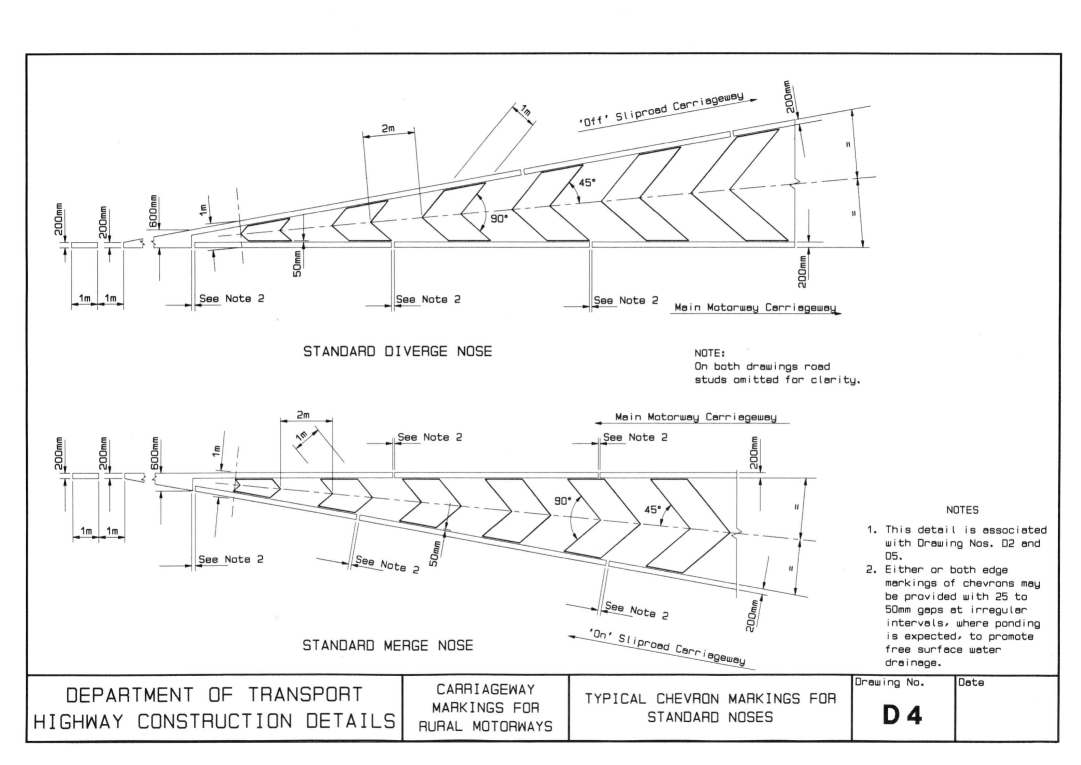

STANDARD DIVERGE NOSE

'Off' Sliproad Carriageway

Main Motorway Carriageway

See Note 2

NOTE:
On both drawings road
studs omitted for clarity.

STANDARD MERGE NOSE

Main Motorway Carriageway

'On' Sliproad Carriageway

NOTES

1. This detail is associated
with Drawing Nos. D2 and
D5.
2. Either or both edge
markings of chevrons may
be provided with 25 to
50mm gaps at irregular
intervals, where ponding
is expected, to promote
free surface water
drainage.

| DEPARTMENT OF TRANSPORT HIGHWAY CONSTRUCTION DETAILS | CARRIAGEWAY MARKINGS FOR RURAL MOTORWAYS | TYPICAL CHEVRON MARKINGS FOR STANDARD NOSES | Drawing No. **D4** | Date |

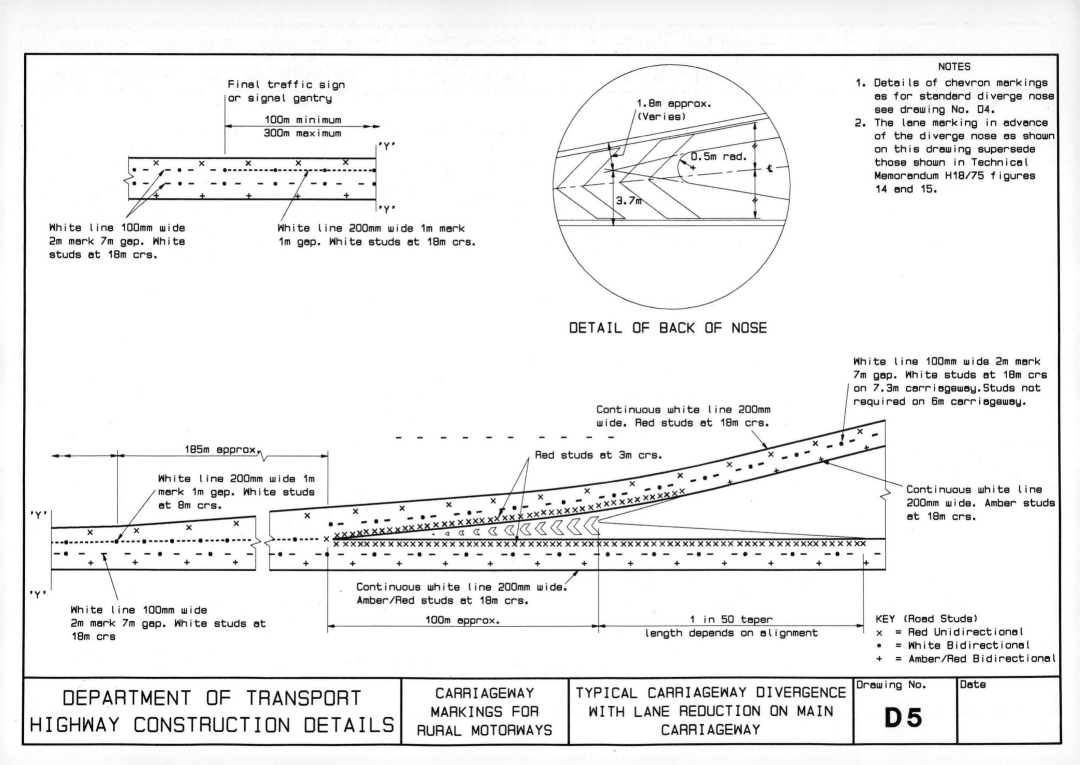

Final traffic sign
or signal gantry

100m minimum
300m maximum

'Y'

'Y'

White line 100mm wide
2m mark 7m gap. White
studs at 18m crs.

White line 200mm wide 1m mark
1m gap. White studs at 18m crs.

1.8m approx.
(Varies)

0.5m rad.

3.7m

DETAIL OF BACK OF NOSE

NOTES

1. Details of chevron markings
   as for standard diverge nose
   see drawing No. D4.
2. The lane marking in advance
   of the diverge nose as shown
   on this drawing supersede
   those shown in Technical
   Memorandum H18/75 figures
   14 and 15.

White line 100mm wide 2m mark
7m gap. White studs at 18m crs
on 7.3m carriageway. Studs not
required on 6m carriageway.

Continuous white line 200mm
wide. Red studs at 18m crs.

Red studs at 3m crs.

Continuous white line
200mm wide. Amber studs
at 18m crs.

185m approx

White line 200mm wide 1m
mark 1m gap. White studs
at 8m crs.

'Y'

'Y'

White line 100mm wide
2m mark 7m gap. White studs at
18m crs

Continuous white line 200mm wide.
Amber/Red studs at 18m crs.

100m approx.

1 in 50 taper
length depends on alignment

KEY (Road Studs)
x = Red Unidirectional
• = White Bidirectional
+ = Amber/Red Bidirectional

DEPARTMENT OF TRANSPORT
HIGHWAY CONSTRUCTION DETAILS

CARRIAGEWAY
MARKINGS FOR
RURAL MOTORWAYS

TYPICAL CARRIAGEWAY DIVERGENCE
WITH LANE REDUCTION ON MAIN
CARRIAGEWAY

Drawing No.
D5

Date

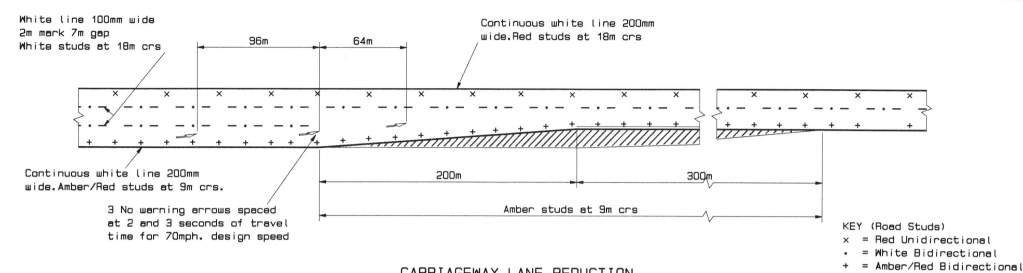

White line 100mm wide
2m mark 7m gap
White studs at 18m crs.

96m

64m

Continuous white line 200mm
wide. Red studs at 18m crs

Continuous white line 200mm
wide. Amber/Red studs at 9m crs.

3 No warning arrows spaced
at 2 and 3 seconds of travel
time for 70mph. design speed

200m

300m

Amber studs at 9m crs

KEY (Road Studs)
× = Red Unidirectional
• = White Bidirectional
+ = Amber/Red Bidirectional

CARRIAGEWAY LANE REDUCTION

3 to 2 lanes. Termination of offside lane shown,
Reverse hatching for termination of nearside lane
(in this case the nearside studs will be red at 9m
centres adjacent to the hatching)

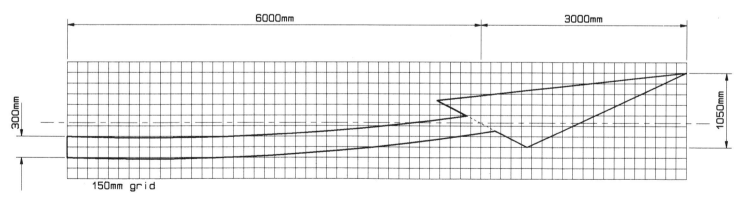

6000mm

3000mm

300mm

1050mm

150mm grid

DETAIL OF WARNING ARROW

NOTES
1. For details of hatched
   marking see Drawing No. D7.
2. Wherever possible lane
   reduction should take place
   at interchanges (see
   Drawing No. D5).

| DEPARTMENT OF TRANSPORT HIGHWAY CONSTRUCTION DETAILS | CARRIAGEWAY MARKINGS FOR RURAL MOTORWAYS | TYPICAL LANE REDUCTION (3 TO 2 LANE) AND DETAIL OF WARNING ARROW | Drawing No. **D6** | Date |

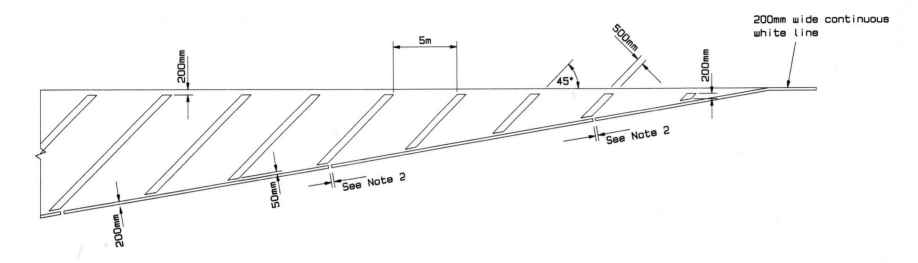

200mm wide continuous
white line

5m

500mm

45°

200mm

200mm

50mm

200mm

See Note 2

See Note 2

MARKING FOR REDUCTION IN
NUMBER OF LANES

NOTES

1. This detail is to be read in
   conjuction with drawing No.
   D6.
2. Edge markings may be
   provided with 25 to 50 mm
   gaps at irregular
   intervals, where ponding
   is expected, to promote
   free surface water
   drainage.

DEPARTMENT OF TRANSPORT	CARRIAGEWAY	TYPICAL DETAILS OF MARKINGS	Drawing No.	Date
HIGHWAY CONSTRUCTION DETAILS	MARKINGS FOR RURAL MOTORWAYS	FOR REDUCTION IN NUMBER OF LANES	D7	

Series E — Distance Marker Posts

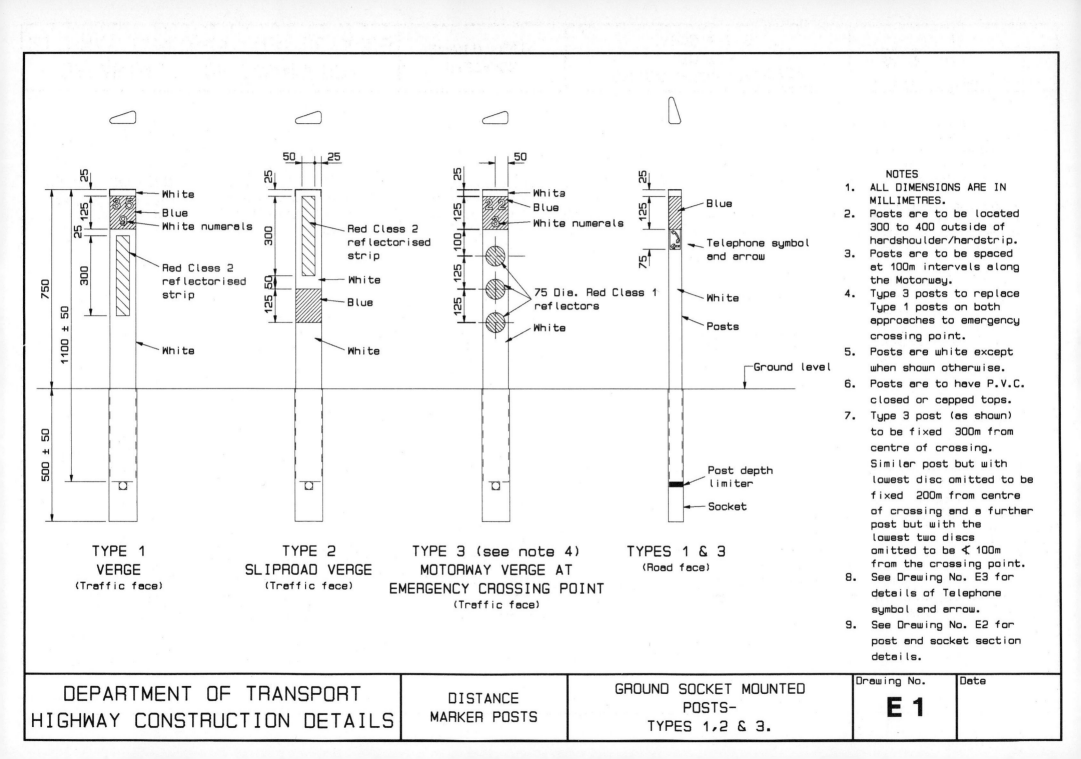

TYPE 1
VERGE
(Traffic face)

TYPE 2
SLIPROAD VERGE
(Traffic face)

TYPE 3 (see note 4)
MOTORWAY VERGE AT
EMERGENCY CROSSING POINT
(Traffic face)

TYPES 1 & 3
(Road face)

Type 1 labels: White / Blue / White numerals / Red Class 2 reflectorised strip / White

Type 2 labels: Red Class 2 reflectorised strip / White / Blue / White

Type 3 labels: White / Blue / White numerals / 75 Dia. Red Class 1 reflectors / White

Types 1 & 3 labels: Blue / Telephone symbol and arrow / White / Posts / Post depth limiter / Socket

Ground level

NOTES
1. ALL DIMENSIONS ARE IN MILLIMETRES.
2. Posts are to be located 300 to 400 outside of hardshoulder/hardstrip.
3. Posts are to be spaced at 100m intervals along the Motorway.
4. Type 3 posts to replace Type 1 posts on both approaches to emergency crossing point.
5. Posts are white except when shown otherwise.
6. Posts are to have P.V.C. closed or capped tops.
7. Type 3 post (as shown) to be fixed 300m from centre of crossing. Similar post but with lowest disc omitted to be fixed 200m from centre of crossing and a further post but with the lowest two discs omitted to be ≮ 100m from the crossing point.
8. See Drawing No. E3 for details of Telephone symbol and arrow.
9. See Drawing No. E2 for post and socket section details.

| DEPARTMENT OF TRANSPORT HIGHWAY CONSTRUCTION DETAILS | DISTANCE MARKER POSTS | GROUND SOCKET MOUNTED POSTS- TYPES 1,2 & 3. | Drawing No. **E1** | Date |

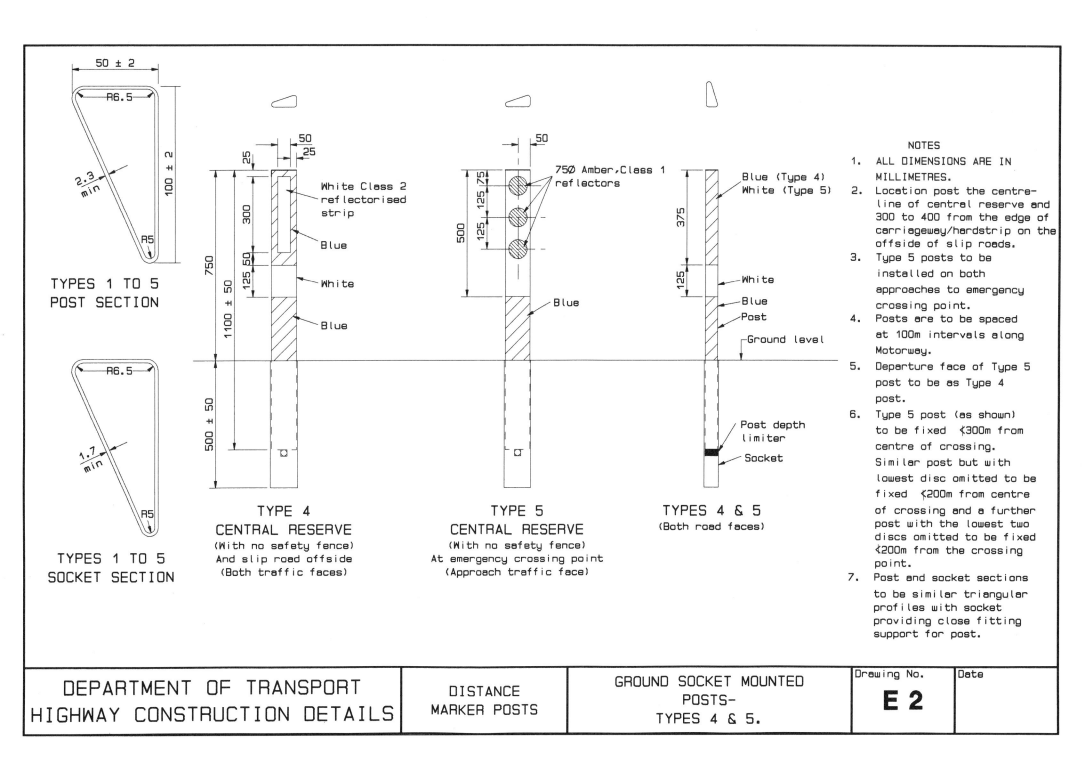

TYPES 1 TO 5
POST SECTION

TYPES 1 TO 5
SOCKET SECTION

50 ± 2
R6.5
2.3 min
100 ± 2
R5

R6.5
1.7 min
R5

25
50
50
25
300
750
125 50
1100 ± 50
125
500 ± 50

White Class 2
reflectorised
strip

Blue

White

Blue

TYPE 4
CENTRAL RESERVE
(With no safety fence)
And slip road offside
(Both traffic faces)

50
75
125
125
125
500

750⌀ Amber, Class 1
reflectors

Blue

TYPE 5
CENTRAL RESERVE
(With no safety fence)
At emergency crossing point
(Approach traffic face)

375
125

Blue (Type 4)
White (Type 5)

White

Blue

Post

Ground level

Post depth
limiter

Socket

TYPES 4 & 5
(Both road faces)

NOTES

1. ALL DIMENSIONS ARE IN
   MILLIMETRES.
2. Location post the centre-
   line of central reserve and
   300 to 400 from the edge of
   carriageway/hardstrip on the
   offside of slip roads.
3. Type 5 posts to be
   installed on both
   approaches to emergency
   crossing point.
4. Posts are to be spaced
   at 100m intervals along
   Motorway.
5. Departure face of Type 5
   post to be as Type 4
   post.
6. Type 5 post (as shown)
   to be fixed ⟨300m from
   centre of crossing.
   Similar post but with
   lowest disc omitted to be
   fixed ⟨200m from centre
   of crossing and a further
   post with the lowest two
   discs omitted to be fixed
   ⟨200m from the crossing
   point.
7. Post and socket sections
   to be similar triangular
   profiles with socket
   providing close fitting
   support for post.

| DEPARTMENT OF TRANSPORT HIGHWAY CONSTRUCTION DETAILS | DISTANCE MARKER POSTS | GROUND SOCKET MOUNTED POSTS- TYPES 4 & 5. | Drawing No. E 2 | Date |

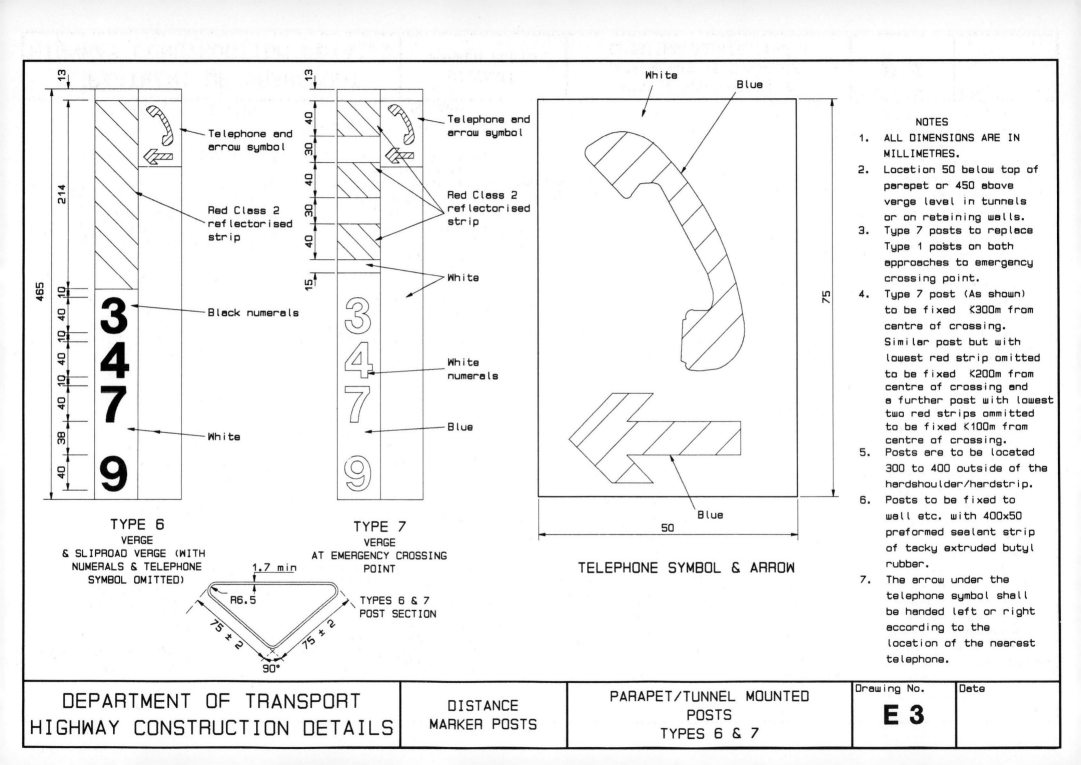

TYPE 6
VERGE
& SLIPROAD VERGE (WITH
NUMERALS & TELEPHONE
SYMBOL OMITTED)

Telephone and arrow symbol
Red Class 2 reflectorised strip
Black numerals
White

TYPE 7
VERGE
AT EMERGENCY CROSSING
POINT

Telephone and arrow symbol
Red Class 2 reflectorised strip
White
White numerals
Blue

TYPES 6 & 7
POST SECTION
1.7 min
R6.5
75 ± 2
75 ± 2
90°

TELEPHONE SYMBOL & ARROW

White
Blue
Blue
75
50

NOTES
1. ALL DIMENSIONS ARE IN MILLIMETRES.
2. Location 50 below top of parapet or 450 above verge level in tunnels or on retaining walls.
3. Type 7 posts to replace Type 1 posts on both approaches to emergency crossing point.
4. Type 7 post (As shown) to be fixed <300m from centre of crossing. Similar post but with lowest red strip omitted to be fixed <200m from centre of crossing and a further post with lowest two red strips ommitted to be fixed <100m from centre of crossing.
5. Posts are to be located 300 to 400 outside of the hardshoulder/hardstrip.
6. Posts to be fixed to wall etc. with 400x50 preformed sealant strip of tacky extruded butyl rubber.
7. The arrow under the telephone symbol shall be handed left or right according to the location of the nearest telephone.

DEPARTMENT OF TRANSPORT
HIGHWAY CONSTRUCTION DETAILS

DISTANCE
MARKER POSTS

PARAPET/TUNNEL MOUNTED
POSTS
TYPES 6 & 7

Drawing No.
E 3

Date

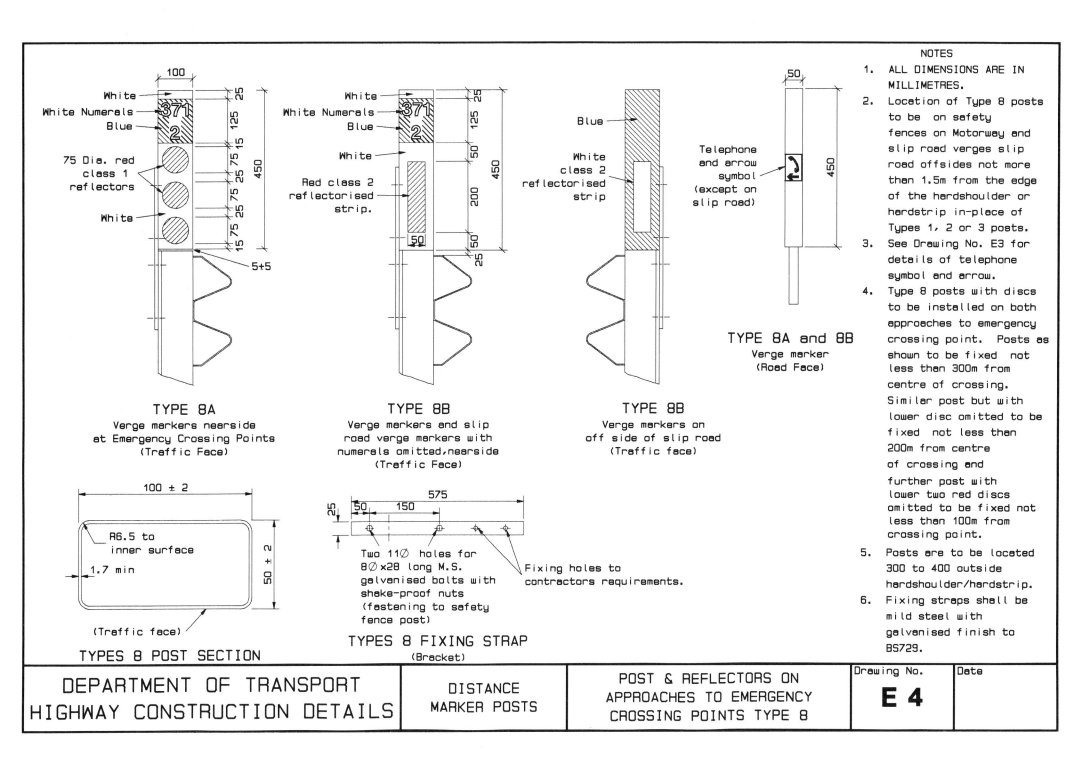

NOTES

1. ALL DIMENSIONS ARE IN MILLIMETRES.

2. Location of Type 8 posts to be on safety fences on Motorway and slip road verges slip road offsides not more than 1.5m from the edge of the hardshoulder or hardstrip in-place of Types 1, 2 or 3 posts.

3. See Drawing No. E3 for details of telephone symbol and arrow.

4. Type 8 posts with discs to be installed on both approaches to emergency crossing point. Posts as shown to be fixed not less than 300m from centre of crossing. Similar post but with lower disc omitted to be fixed not less than 200m from centre of crossing and further post with lower two red discs omitted to be fixed not less than 100m from crossing point.

5. Posts are to be located 300 to 400 outside hardshoulder/hardstrip.

6. Fixing straps shall be mild steel with galvanised finish to BS729.

TYPE 8A
Verge markers nearside at Emergency Crossing Points
(Traffic Face)

TYPE 8B
Verge markers and slip road verge markers with numerals omitted, nearside
(Traffic Face)

TYPE 8B
Verge markers on off side of slip road
(Traffic face)

TYPE 8A and 8B
Verge marker
(Road Face)

White
White Numerals
Blue
75 Dia. red class 1 reflectors
White

White
White Numerals
Blue
White
Red class 2 reflectorised strip.

Blue
White class 2 reflectorised strip

Telephone and arrow symbol (except on slip road)

TYPES 8 POST SECTION
R6.5 to inner surface
1.7 min
(Traffic face)

TYPES 8 FIXING STRAP
(Bracket)
Two 11⌀ holes for 8⌀ x28 long M.S. galvanised bolts with shake-proof nuts (fastening to safety fence post)
Fixing holes to contractors requirements.

| DEPARTMENT OF TRANSPORT HIGHWAY CONSTRUCTION DETAILS | DISTANCE MARKER POSTS | POST & REFLECTORS ON APPROACHES TO EMERGENCY CROSSING POINTS TYPE 8 | Drawing No. E 4 | Date |

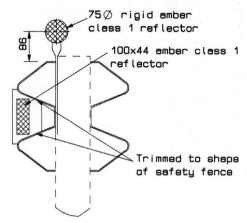

75⌀ rigid amber class 1 reflector

86

100x44 amber class 1 reflector

Trimmed to shape of safety fence

(Tensioned Safety Fence)

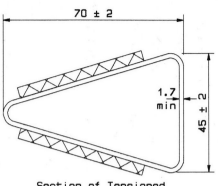

70 ± 2

1.7 min

45 ± 2

Section of Tensioned Safety Fence Version

TYPE 9
Central Reserve at
Emergency Crossing Points
(Traffic face)

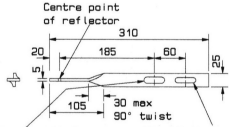

Centre point of reflector

310

20   185   60

5   25

105   30 max 90° twist

One 12x40 long slotted hole for 10⌀ x40 long hexagon head M.S. bolt complete with 2 no. washers and self-locking nut, all galvanised finish, to secure strap to clamp plate and open box safety fence beam

One 10x40 long slotted hole for 8⌀ x30 long hexagon head M.S. bolt complete with 2 no. washers and self-locking nut, all galvanised finish, to secure strap to tensioned guard rail safety fence beam

TYPE 9A FIXING STRAP
(Bracket)

NOTES
1. ALL DIMENSIONS ARE IN MILLIMETRES.
2. Fixing straps shall be mild steel with galvanised finish to BS729.
3. Either Type 9 wedge shape or disc shape markers can be used on tensioned safety fences. Disc shape markers must be under open box beam safety fences.
4. One disc or wedge must be located not less than 100m from the centre of the the emergency crossing point Two discs or wedges between 1.6m and 4.0m apart to be located not less than 200m from, and three discs or wedges between 1.6m and 4.0m apart to be located not less than 300m from, the center of the crossing respectively.
5. Type 9, advance warning markers shall be secured to the safety fence beam with a separate bolt and nut. The use of the beam to post bolt shall not be permitted.

| DEPARTMENT OF TRANSPORT HIGHWAY CONSTRUCTION DETAILS | DISTANCE MARKER POSTS | DISCS & REFLECTORS ON APPROACHES TO EMERGENCY CROSSING POINTS TYPE 9 | Drawing No. E5 | Date |

Series F — Drainage

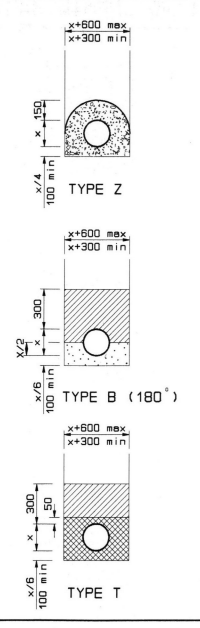

TYPE Z

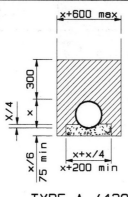

TYPE A (120°)

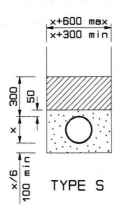

TYPE S

TYPE B (180°)

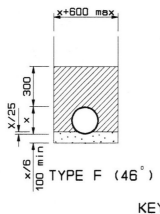

TYPE F (46°)

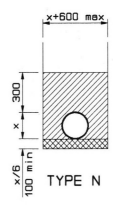

TYPE N

TYPE T

KEY

 Granular material to S.H.W. Clause 503.3(i).

 Concrete to S.H.W.Clause 503.3 (iii)

 Material to S.H.W. Clause 503.3(ii). e.g. sand

Class 8 material to S.H.W.. Clause 503.3(iv).

NOTES
1. ALL DIMENSIONS ARE IN MILLIMETRES.
2. This drawing is to be read in conjunction with Appendix 5/1
3. Dimension X is the external diameter of the pipe.
4. The minimum or maximum width of the trench applies on and below a line 300mm above the outside top of the pipe. Above the 300mm line the trench backfill material shall be as described in the Contract.
5. The concrete bed or surround may extend to the sides of the trench or be of minimum width. Class 8 material is to be used to fill any voids so formed.
6. For Type Z trench the concrete cover may be formed to a radius batter or horizontal surface .Min cover of concrete shall be 150.

| DEPARTMENT OF TRANSPORT HIGHWAY CONSTRUCTION DETAILS | DRAINAGE | SURFACE WATER DRAINS - TRENCH & BEDDING DETAILS | Drawing No. F1 | Date |

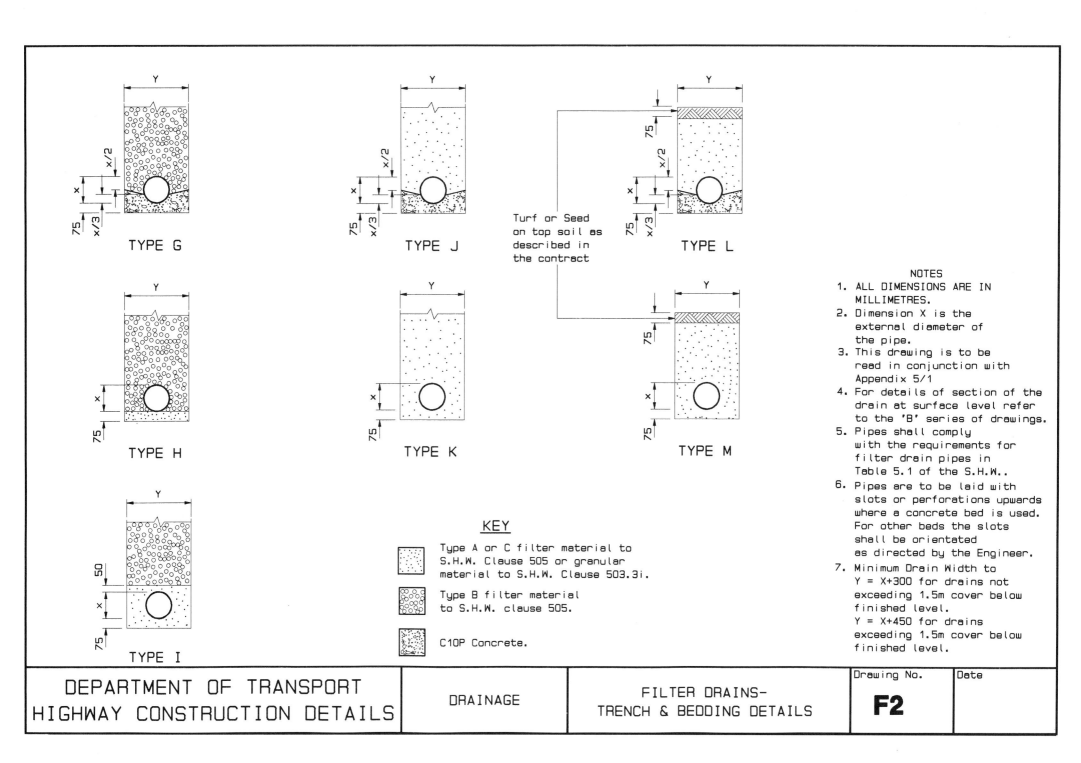

TYPE G

TYPE J

Turf or Seed
on top soil as
described in
the contract

TYPE L

TYPE H

TYPE K

TYPE M

TYPE I

KEY

Type A or C filter material to
S.H.W. Clause 505 or granular
material to S.H.W. Clause 503.3i.

Type B filter material
to S.H.W. clause 505.

C10P Concrete.

NOTES

1. ALL DIMENSIONS ARE IN MILLIMETRES.
2. Dimension X is the external diameter of the pipe.
3. This drawing is to be read in conjunction with Appendix 5/1
4. For details of section of the drain at surface level refer to the 'B' series of drawings.
5. Pipes shall comply with the requirements for filter drain pipes in Table 5.1 of the S.H.W..
6. Pipes are to be laid with slots or perforations upwards where a concrete bed is used. For other beds the slots shall be orientated as directed by the Engineer.
7. Minimum Drain Width to Y = X+300 for drains not exceeding 1.5m cover below finished level. Y = X+450 for drains exceeding 1.5m cover below finished level.

| DEPARTMENT OF TRANSPORT HIGHWAY CONSTRUCTION DETAILS | DRAINAGE | FILTER DRAINS- TRENCH & BEDDING DETAILS | Drawing No. **F2** | Date |

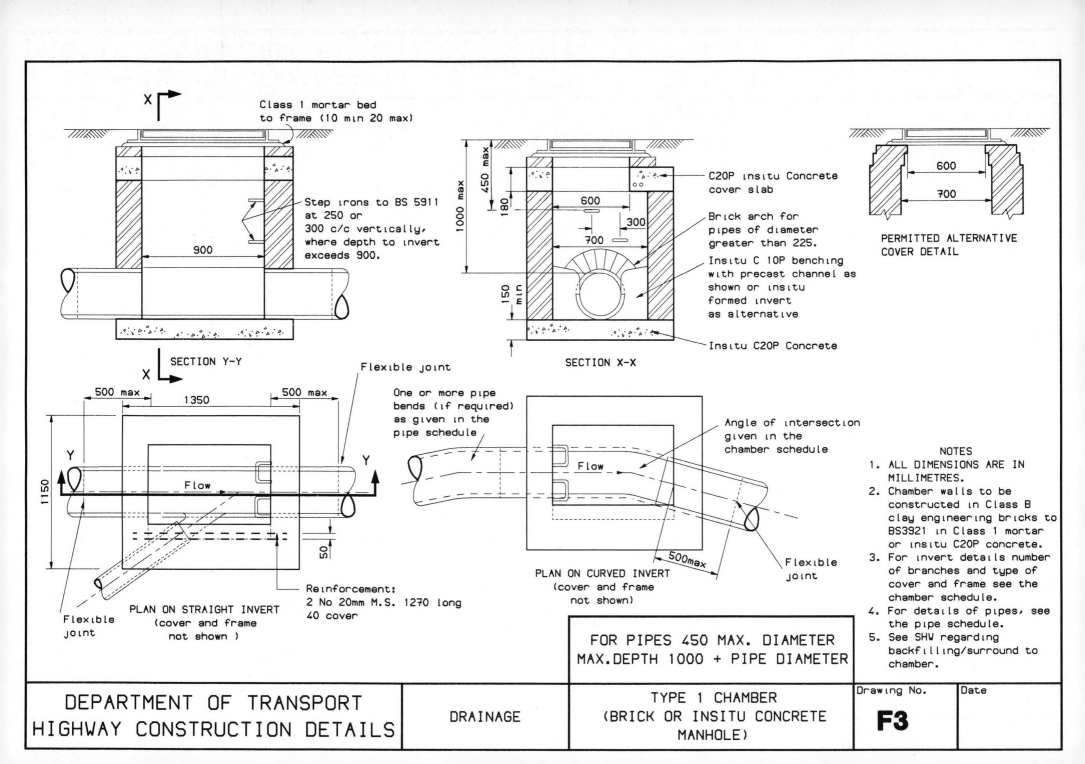

Class 1 mortar bed
to frame (10 min 20 max)

Step irons to BS 5911
at 250 or
300 c/c vertically,
where depth to invert
exceeds 900.

900

SECTION Y-Y

X

1000 max
450 max
180
150 min

C20P insitu Concrete
cover slab

600
300
700

Brick arch for
pipes of diameter
greater than 225.

Insitu C 10P benching
with precast channel as
shown or insitu
formed invert
as alternative

Insitu C20P Concrete

SECTION X-X

600
700

PERMITTED ALTERNATIVE
COVER DETAIL

500 max
1350
500 max
1150
50

Flow

Flexible joint

One or more pipe
bends (if required)
as given in the
pipe schedule

Angle of intersection
given in the
chamber schedule

Flow

500max

Flexible
joint

PLAN ON CURVED INVERT
(cover and frame
not shown)

Flexible
Joint

PLAN ON STRAIGHT INVERT
(cover and frame
not shown)

Reinforcement:
2 No 20mm M.S. 1270 long
40 cover

NOTES
1. ALL DIMENSIONS ARE IN
   MILLIMETRES.
2. Chamber walls to be
   constructed in Class B
   clay engineering bricks to
   BS3921 in Class 1 mortar
   or insitu C20P concrete.
3. For invert details number
   of branches and type of
   cover and frame see the
   chamber schedule.
4. For details of pipes, see
   the pipe schedule.
5. See SHW regarding
   backfilling/surround to
   chamber.

FOR PIPES 450 MAX. DIAMETER
MAX. DEPTH 1000 + PIPE DIAMETER

DEPARTMENT OF TRANSPORT
HIGHWAY CONSTRUCTION DETAILS

DRAINAGE

TYPE 1 CHAMBER
(BRICK OR INSITU CONCRETE
MANHOLE)

Drawing No.
F3

Date

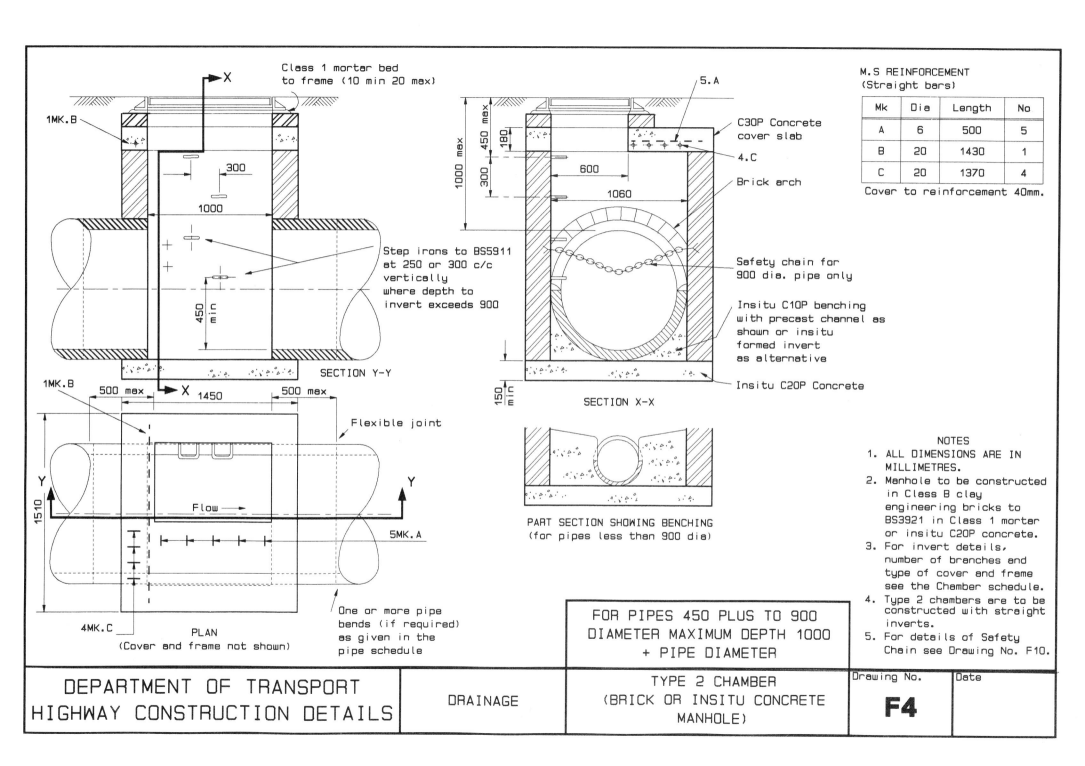

Class 1 mortar bed
to frame (10 min 20 max)

1MK.B

300

1000

450 min

SECTION Y-Y

1MK.B

500 max   1450   500 max

Flow

1510

5MK.A

4MK.C

PLAN
(Cover and frame not shown)

Flexible joint

One or more pipe
bends (if required)
as given in the
pipe schedule

Step irons to BS5911
at 250 or 300 c/c
vertically
where depth to
invert exceeds 900

5.A

C30P Concrete
cover slab

4.C

Brick arch

Safety chain for
900 dia. pipe only

Insitu C10P benching
with precast channel as
shown or insitu
formed invert
as alternative

Insitu C20P Concrete

1000 max   450 max   180   300

600

1060

150 min

SECTION X-X

PART SECTION SHOWING BENCHING
(for pipes less than 900 dia)

M.S REINFORCEMENT
(Straight bars)

Mk	Dia	Length	No
A	6	500	5
B	20	1430	1
C	20	1370	4

Cover to reinforcement 40mm.

NOTES
1. ALL DIMENSIONS ARE IN
   MILLIMETRES.
2. Manhole to be constructed
   in Class B clay
   engineering bricks to
   BS3921 in Class 1 mortar
   or insitu C20P concrete.
3. For invert details,
   number of branches and
   type of cover and frame
   see the Chamber schedule.
4. Type 2 chambers are to be
   constructed with straight
   inverts.
5. For details of Safety
   Chain see Drawing No. F10.

FOR PIPES 450 PLUS TO 900
DIAMETER MAXIMUM DEPTH 1000
+ PIPE DIAMETER

DEPARTMENT OF TRANSPORT
HIGHWAY CONSTRUCTION DETAILS

DRAINAGE

TYPE 2 CHAMBER
(BRICK OR INSITU CONCRETE
MANHOLE)

Drawing No.

F4

Date

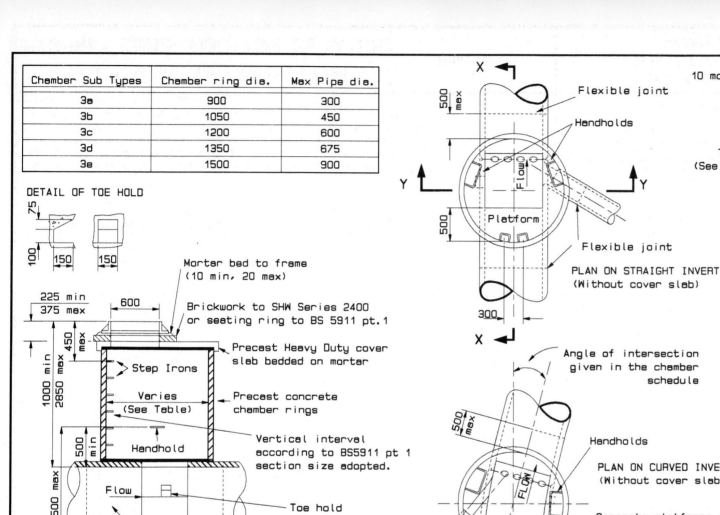

Chamber Sub Types	Chamber ring dia.	Max Pipe dia.
3a	900	300
3b	1050	450
3c	1200	600
3d	1350	675
3e	1500	900

DETAIL OF TOE HOLD

75
100 150   150

Mortar bed to frame
(10 min, 20 max)

Brickwork to SHW Series 2400
or seating ring to BS 5911 pt.1

Precast Heavy Duty cover
slab bedded on mortar

Step Irons

Varies
(See Table)

Precast concrete
chamber rings

Handhold

Vertical interval
according to BS5911 pt 1
section size adopted.

225 min / 375 max
600
450 max
1000 min
2850 max
500 min
1500 max

Flow

Toe hold

SECTION X-X

Integral insitu C20p concrete base walls benching & base
slab with precast channel as shown or insitu formed invert
as alternative. Walls to extend 50 beyond outer faces of chamber
ring. Alternatively precast concrete chamber rings maybe bedded
in mortar or an insitu C20p concrete base slab 300 mm greater in
diameter than chamber rings.

X

500 max

Flexible joint

Handholds

Flow

Platform

500

300

Flexible joint

PLAN ON STRAIGHT INVERT
(Without cover slab)

X

Angle of intersection
given in the chamber
schedule

500 max

Handholds

PLAN ON CURVED INVERT
(Without cover slab)

FLOW

Concrete platforms shall
be level with top of pipe

One or more pipe bends
(if required) as given
in the pipe schedule

10 mortar bed

Benching slope:
1:10 maximum
1:12 minimum

75 rad.

Toe hold
(See Note 6)

50.0

Safety chain for
900 dia.
pipes only

150

SECTION Y-Y

NOTES
1. ALL DIMENSIONS ARE IN
   MILLIMETRES.
2. Chamber walls and cover
   slab to be constructed in
   precast concrete to
   BS5911 Part 1.
3. For invert details,
   number of branches,
   length of ladder and type
   of cover and frame see
   the Chamber schedule.
4. Mortar to be class 1 to
   SHWSeries 2400
5. For details of Safety
   Chain and Handholds see
   Drawing Number F10.
6. Toe Hold required where
   pipe is 500 diameter or
   greater.
7. Handholds required where
   chamber is 1200 diameter
   or greater.

FOR PIPES 900 MAX DIAMETER
1000 TO 2850 DEPTH
+ PIPE DIAMETER

DEPARTMENT OF TRANSPORT
HIGHWAY CONSTRUCTION DETAILS

DRAINAGE

TYPE 3 CHAMBER
(PRECAST CONCRETE
MANHOLE)

Drawing No.
F5

Date

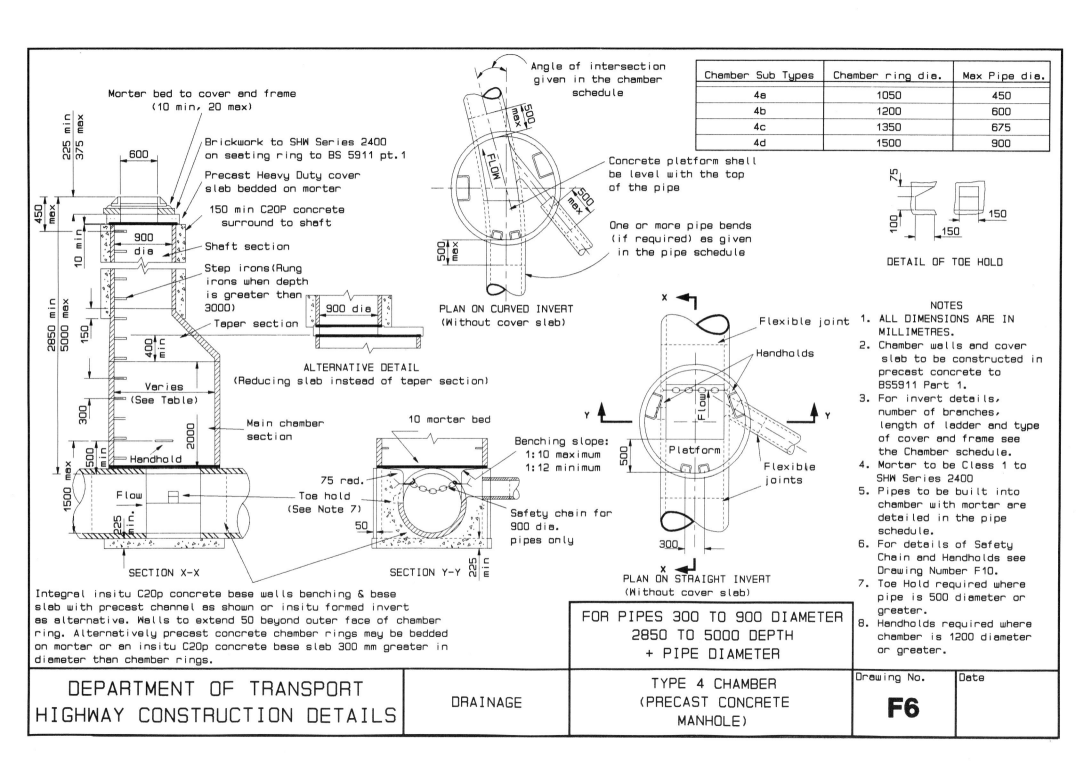

Chamber Sub Types	Chamber ring dia.	Max Pipe dia.
4a	1050	450
4b	1200	600
4c	1350	675
4d	1500	900

Mortar bed to cover and frame (10 min, 20 max)

Brickwork to SHW Series 2400 on seating ring to BS 5911 pt.1

Precast Heavy Duty cover slab bedded on mortar

150 min C20P concrete surround to shaft

Shaft section

Step irons (Rung irons when depth is greater than 3000)

Taper section

Main chamber section

Handhold

Flow

Toe hold (See Note 7)

SECTION X-X

10 mortar bed

Benching slope:
1:10 maximum
1:12 minimum

75 rad.

Safety chain for 900 dia. pipes only

SECTION Y-Y

Angle of intersection given in the chamber schedule

FLOW

Concrete platform shall be level with the top of the pipe

One or more pipe bends (if required) as given in the pipe schedule

PLAN ON CURVED INVERT
(Without cover slab)

900 dia

ALTERNATIVE DETAIL
(Reducing slab instead of taper section)

DETAIL OF TOE HOLD

Flexible joint

Handholds

Platform

Flexible joints

PLAN ON STRAIGHT INVERT
(Without cover slab)

NOTES
1. ALL DIMENSIONS ARE IN MILLIMETRES.
2. Chamber walls and cover slab to be constructed in precast concrete to BS5911 Part 1.
3. For invert details, number of branches, length of ladder and type of cover and frame see the Chamber schedule.
4. Mortar to be Class 1 to SHW Series 2400
5. Pipes to be built into chamber with mortar are detailed in the pipe schedule.
6. For details of Safety Chain and Handholds see Drawing Number F10.
7. Toe Hold required where pipe is 500 diameter or greater.
8. Handholds required where chamber is 1200 diameter or greater.

Integral insitu C20p concrete base walls benching & base slab with precast channel as shown or insitu formed invert as alternative. Walls to extend 50 beyond outer face of chamber ring. Alternatively precast concrete chamber rings may be bedded on mortar or an insitu C20p concrete base slab 300 mm greater in diameter than chamber rings.

FOR PIPES 300 TO 900 DIAMETER
2850 TO 5000 DEPTH
+ PIPE DIAMETER

DEPARTMENT OF TRANSPORT
HIGHWAY CONSTRUCTION DETAILS

DRAINAGE

TYPE 4 CHAMBER
(PRECAST CONCRETE MANHOLE)

Drawing No.
F6

Date

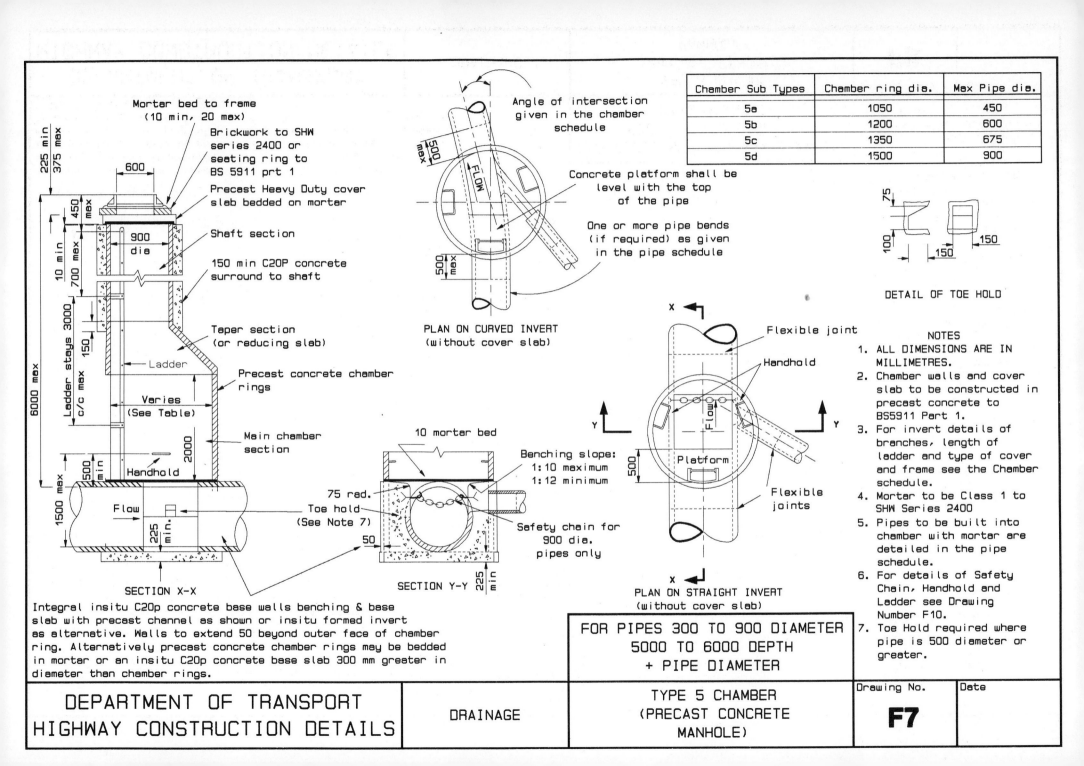

Chamber Sub Types	Chamber ring dia.	Max Pipe dia.
5a	1050	450
5b	1200	600
5c	1350	675
5d	1500	900

Mortar bed to frame
(10 min, 20 max)

Brickwork to SHW series 2400 or seating ring to BS 5911 prt 1

Precast Heavy Duty cover slab bedded on mortar

Shaft section

150 min C20P concrete surround to shaft

Taper section (or reducing slab)

Ladder

Precast concrete chamber rings

Varies (See Table)

Main chamber section

Handhold

Flow

Toe hold (See Note 7)

225 min.

SECTION X-X

Integral insitu C20p concrete base walls benching & base slab with precast channel as shown or insitu formed invert as alternative. Walls to extend 50 beyond outer face of chamber ring. Alternatively precast concrete chamber rings may be bedded in mortar or an insitu C20p concrete base slab 300 mm greater in diameter than chamber rings.

225 min / 375 max
600
450 max
900 dia
10 min / 700 max
150
2000
500 min
1500 max
6000 max
Ladder stays 3000 c/c max
50

Angle of intersection given in the chamber schedule

500 max

FLOW

500 max

Concrete platform shall be level with the top of the pipe

One or more pipe bends (if required) as given in the pipe schedule

PLAN ON CURVED INVERT
(without cover slab)

10 mortar bed

Benching slope:
1:10 maximum
1:12 minimum

75 rad.

Safety chain for 900 dia. pipes only

50

225 min

SECTION Y-Y

75
100
150
150

DETAIL OF TOE HOLD

Flexible joint

Handhold

FLOW

Platform

500

Flexible joints

X

Y

Y

X

PLAN ON STRAIGHT INVERT
(without cover slab)

NOTES

1. ALL DIMENSIONS ARE IN MILLIMETRES.
2. Chamber walls and cover slab to be constructed in precast concrete to BS5911 Part 1.
3. For invert details of branches, length of ladder and type of cover and frame see the Chamber schedule.
4. Mortar to be Class 1 to SHW Series 2400
5. Pipes to be built into chamber with mortar are detailed in the pipe schedule.
6. For details of Safety Chain, Handhold and Ladder see Drawing Number F10.
7. Toe Hold required where pipe is 500 diameter or greater.

FOR PIPES 300 TO 900 DIAMETER
5000 TO 6000 DEPTH
+ PIPE DIAMETER

DEPARTMENT OF TRANSPORT
HIGHWAY CONSTRUCTION DETAILS

DRAINAGE

TYPE 5 CHAMBER
(PRECAST CONCRETE MANHOLE)

Drawing No.
F7

Date

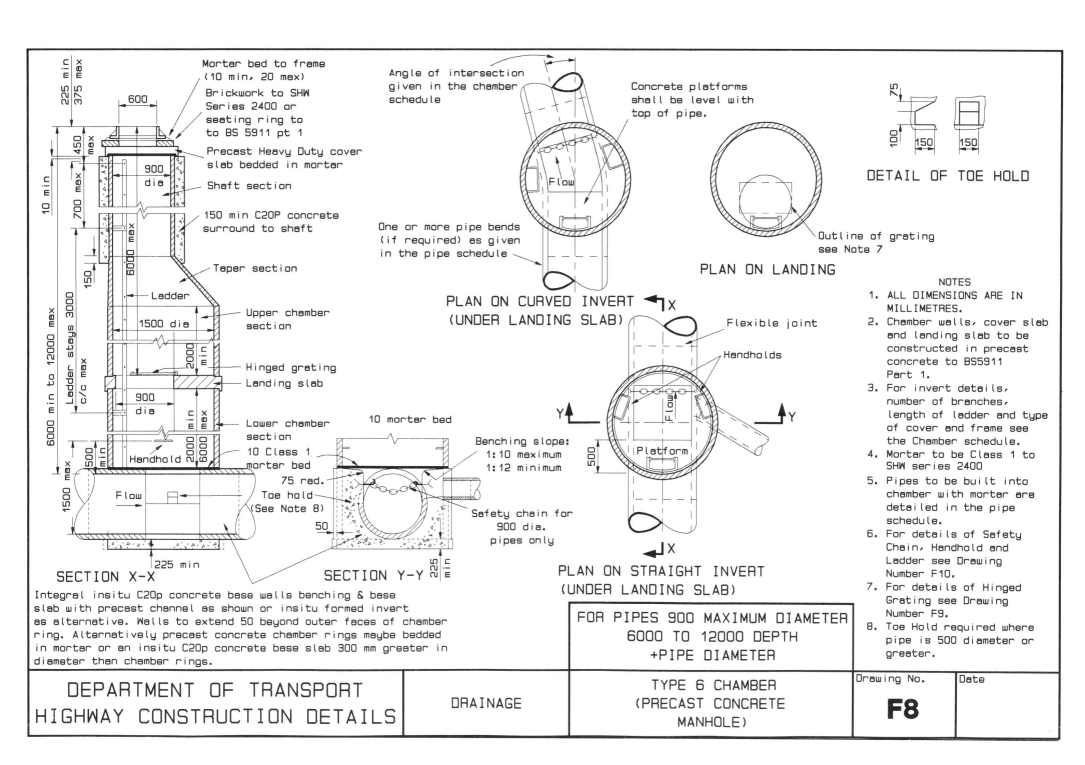

Mortar bed to frame (10 min, 20 max)

Brickwork to SHW Series 2400 or seating ring to to BS 5911 pt 1

Precast Heavy Duty cover slab bedded in mortar

Shaft section

150 min C20P concrete surround to shaft

Taper section

Ladder

Upper chamber section

Hinged grating
Landing slab

Lower chamber section

10 Class 1 mortar bed

75 rad.

Toe hold (See Note 8)

Handhold

225 min

SECTION X-X

Integral insitu C20p concrete base walls benching & base slab with precast channel as shown or insitu formed invert as alternative. Walls to extend 50 beyond outer faces of chamber ring. Alternatively precast concrete chamber rings maybe bedded in mortar or an insitu C20p concrete base slab 300 mm greater in diameter than chamber rings.

225 min / 375 max
450 max
700 max
10 min
6000 max
150
6000 min to 12000 max
Ladder stays 3000 c/c max
600
900 dia
1500 dia
2000 min
900 dia
2000 min / 6000 max
500 min
1500 max

Flow

10 mortar bed

Benching slope:
1:10 maximum
1:12 minimum

Safety chain for 900 dia. pipes only

50
225 min

SECTION Y-Y

Angle of intersection given in the chamber schedule

Concrete platforms shall be level with top of pipe.

Flow

One or more pipe bends (if required) as given in the pipe schedule

PLAN ON CURVED INVERT
(UNDER LANDING SLAB)

Outline of grating see Note 7

PLAN ON LANDING

Flexible joint

Handholds

Flow

Platform

500

Y   Y

X   X

PLAN ON STRAIGHT INVERT
(UNDER LANDING SLAB)

75
100
150   150

DETAIL OF TOE HOLD

NOTES
1. ALL DIMENSIONS ARE IN MILLIMETRES.
2. Chamber walls, cover slab and landing slab to be constructed in precast concrete to BS5911 Part 1.
3. For invert details, number of branches, length of ladder and type of cover and frame see the Chamber schedule.
4. Mortar to be Class 1 to SHW series 2400
5. Pipes to be built into chamber with mortar are detailed in the pipe schedule.
6. For details of Safety Chain, Handhold and Ladder see Drawing Number F10.
7. For details of Hinged Grating see Drawing Number F9.
8. Toe Hold required where pipe is 500 diameter or greater.

FOR PIPES 900 MAXIMUM DIAMETER
6000 TO 12000 DEPTH
+PIPE DIAMETER

| DEPARTMENT OF TRANSPORT HIGHWAY CONSTRUCTION DETAILS | DRAINAGE | TYPE 6 CHAMBER (PRECAST CONCRETE MANHOLE) | Drawing No. **F8** | Date |

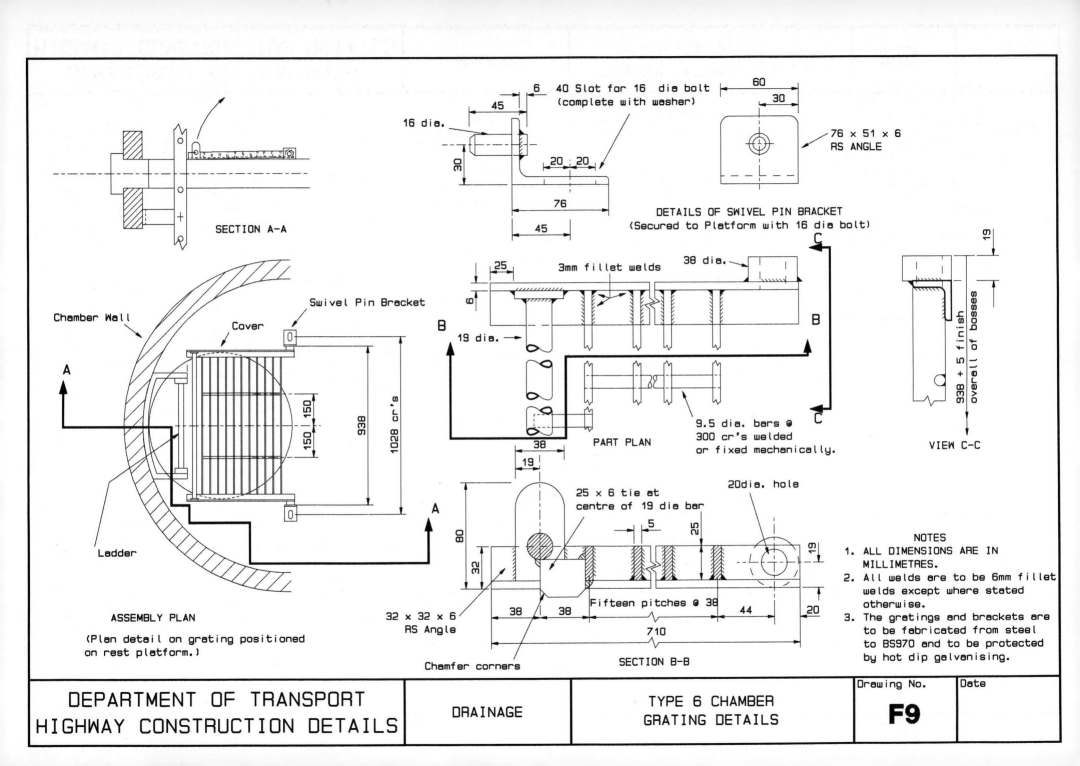

SECTION A-A

16 dia.

45 | 6 | 40 Slot for 16 dia bolt
(complete with washer)

30

76

45

20 | 20

60

30

76 × 51 × 6
RS ANGLE

DETAILS OF SWIVEL PIN BRACKET
(Secured to Platform with 16 dia bolt)

Chamber Wall

Swivel Pin Bracket

Cover

A

Ladder

150 | 150 | 150 | 150

938

1028 cr's

ASSEMBLY PLAN

(Plan detail on grating positioned
on rest platform.)

25

3mm fillet welds

38 dia.

6

19 dia.

B

C

C

B

38

PART PLAN

9.5 dia. bars @
300 cr's welded
or fixed mechanically.

VIEW C-C

938 + 5 finish
overall of bosses

19

80

32

19

25 × 6 tie at
centre of 19 dia bar

5

25

20dia. hole

19

32 × 32 × 6
RS Angle

38 | 38

Fifteen pitches @ 38

44

20

710

Chamfer corners

SECTION B-B

NOTES

1. ALL DIMENSIONS ARE IN
MILLIMETRES.

2. All welds are to be 6mm fillet
welds except where stated
otherwise.

3. The gratings and brackets are
to be fabricated from steel
to BS970 and to be protected
by hot dip galvanising.

| DEPARTMENT OF TRANSPORT HIGHWAY CONSTRUCTION DETAILS | DRAINAGE | TYPE 6 CHAMBER GRATING DETAILS | Drawing No. F9 | Date |

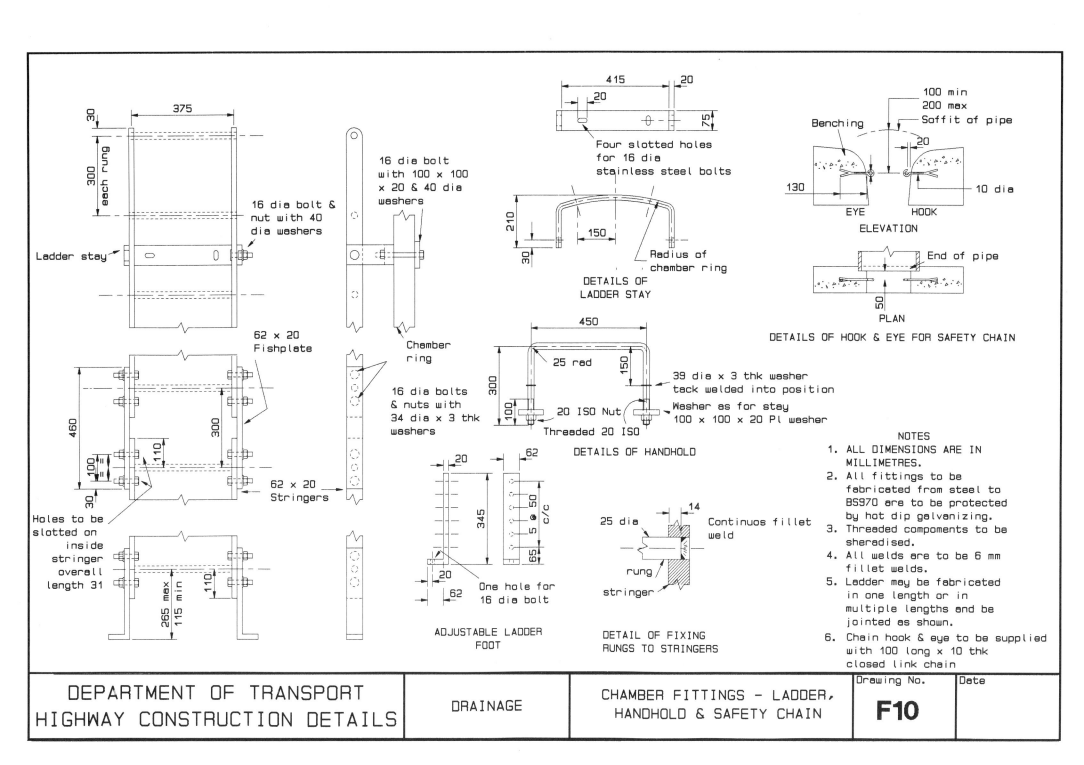

415 · 20
20
75
Four slotted holes
for 16 dia
stainless steel bolts

210
150
30
Radius of
chamber ring

DETAILS OF
LADDER STAY

375
30
300 each rung

16 dia bolt &
nut with 40
dia washers

Ladder stay

62 x 20
Fishplate

460
300
110
100
30

Holes to be
slotted on
inside
stringer
overall
length 31

265 max
115 min
110

16 dia bolt
with 100 x 100
x 20 & 40 dia
washers

Chamber
ring

16 dia bolts
& nuts with
34 dia x 3 thk
washers

62 x 20
Stringers

450
25 rad
150
300
100
39 dia x 3 thk washer
tack welded into position
20 ISO Nut
Threaded 20 ISO
Washer as for stay
100 x 100 x 20 Pl washer

DETAILS OF HANDHOLD

20 · 62
345
5 @ 50 c/c
65
One hole for
16 dia bolt
62
20

ADJUSTABLE LADDER
FOOT

14
25 dia
Continuos fillet
weld
rung
stringer

DETAIL OF FIXING
RUNGS TO STRINGERS

100 min
200 max
Soffit of pipe
Benching
20
130
10 dia
EYE   HOOK

ELEVATION

End of pipe
50

PLAN

DETAILS OF HOOK & EYE FOR SAFETY CHAIN

NOTES
1. ALL DIMENSIONS ARE IN
   MILLIMETRES.
2. All fittings to be
   fabricated from steel to
   BS970 are to be protected
   by hot dip galvanizing.
3. Threaded compoments to be
   sheradised.
4. All welds are to be 6 mm
   fillet welds.
5. Ladder may be fabricated
   in one length or in
   multiple lengths and be
   jointed as shown.
6. Chain hook & eye to be supplied
   with 100 long x 10 thk
   closed link chain

DEPARTMENT OF TRANSPORT HIGHWAY CONSTRUCTION DETAILS	DRAINAGE	CHAMBER FITTINGS - LADDER, HANDHOLD & SAFETY CHAIN	Drawing No. F10	Date

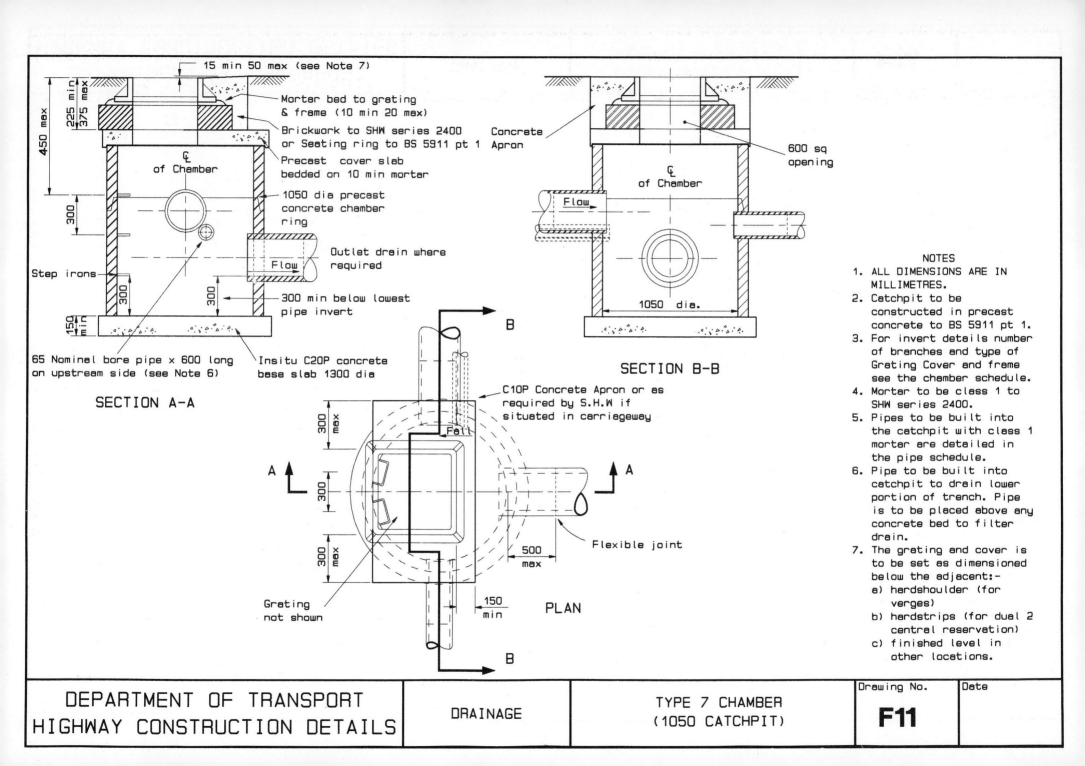

SECTION A-A

15 min 50 max (see Note 7)

225 min 375 max

450 max

C of Chamber

300

Step irons

300

300

150 min

65 Nominal bore pipe x 600 long on upstream side (see Note 6)

Insitu C20P concrete base slab 1300 dia

Flow

Mortar bed to grating & frame (10 min 20 max)

Brickwork to SHW series 2400 or Seating ring to BS 5911 pt 1

Precast cover slab bedded on 10 min mortar

1050 dia precast concrete chamber ring

Outlet drain where required

300 min below lowest pipe invert

SECTION B-B

Concrete Apron

600 sq opening

C of Chamber

Flow

1050 dia.

PLAN

B

A

A

B

300 max

300

300 max

Fall

Flow

C10P Concrete Apron or as required by S.H.W if situated in carriageway

Flexible joint

500 max

150 min

Grating not shown

NOTES
1. ALL DIMENSIONS ARE IN MILLIMETRES.
2. Catchpit to be constructed in precast concrete to BS 5911 pt 1.
3. For invert details number of branches and type of Grating Cover and frame see the chamber schedule.
4. Mortar to be class 1 to SHW series 2400.
5. Pipes to be built into the catchpit with class 1 mortar are detailed in the pipe schedule.
6. Pipe to be built into catchpit to drain lower portion of trench. Pipe is to be placed above any concrete bed to filter drain.
7. The grating and cover is to be set as dimensioned below the adjacent:-
   a) hardshoulder (for verges)
   b) hardstrips (for dual 2 central reservation)
   c) finished level in other locations.

| DEPARTMENT OF TRANSPORT HIGHWAY CONSTRUCTION DETAILS | DRAINAGE | TYPE 7 CHAMBER (1050 CATCHPIT) | Drawing No. **F11** | Date |

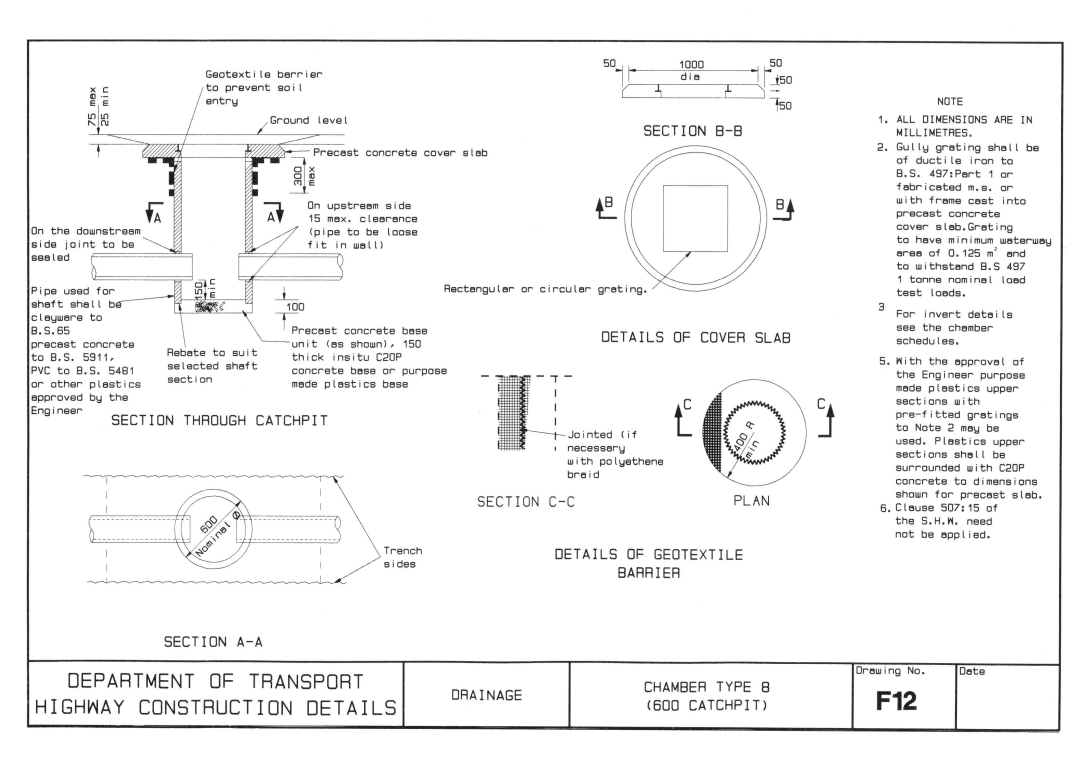

Geotextile barrier to prevent soil entry

Ground level

75 max / 25 min

Precast concrete cover slab

300 max

On upstream side 15 max. clearance (pipe to be loose fit in wall)

On the downstream side joint to be sealed

Pipe used for shaft shall be clayware to B.S.65 precast concrete to B.S. 5911, PVC to B.S. 5481 or other plastics approved by the Engineer

150 min

100

Rebate to suit selected shaft section

Precast concrete base unit (as shown), 150 thick insitu C20P concrete base or purpose made plastics base

SECTION THROUGH CATCHPIT

600 Nominal Ø

Trench sides

SECTION A-A

50 | 1000 dia | 50
50
50

SECTION B-B

Rectangular or circular grating.

DETAILS OF COVER SLAB

Jointed (if necessary with polyethene braid

SECTION C-C

400 R min

PLAN

DETAILS OF GEOTEXTILE BARRIER

NOTE

1. ALL DIMENSIONS ARE IN MILLIMETRES.

2. Gully grating shall be of ductile iron to B.S. 497:Part 1 or fabricated m.s. or with frame cast into precast concrete cover slab. Grating to have minimum waterway area of 0.125 m^2 and to withstand B.S 497 1 tonne nominal load test loads.

3 For invert details see the chamber schedules.

5. With the approval of the Engineer purpose made plastics upper sections with pre-fitted gratings to Note 2 may be used. Plastics upper sections shall be surrounded with C20P concrete to dimensions shown for precast slab.

6. Clause 507:15 of the S.H.W. need not be applied.

| DEPARTMENT OF TRANSPORT HIGHWAY CONSTRUCTION DETAILS | DRAINAGE | CHAMBER TYPE 8 (600 CATCHPIT) | Drawing No. **F12** | Date |

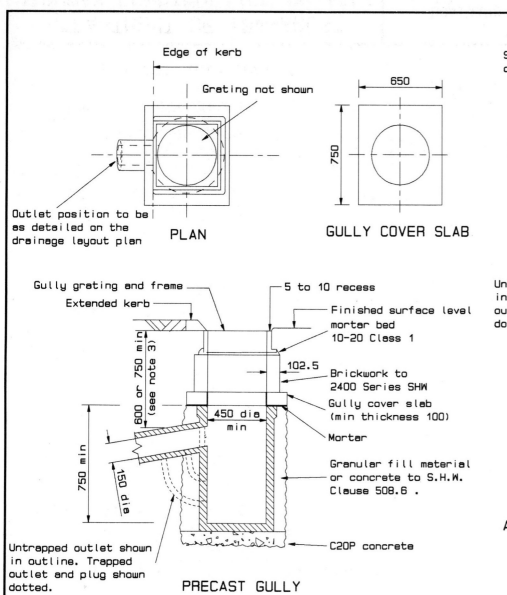

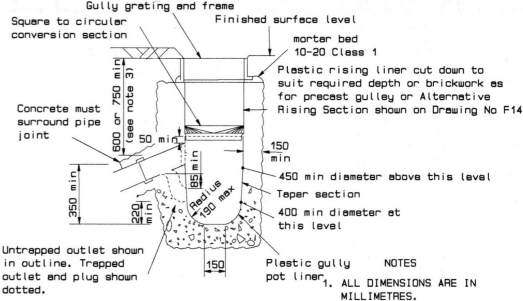

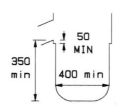

PLAN

Edge of kerb

Grating not shown

Outlet position to be as detailed on the drainage layout plan

GULLY COVER SLAB

650

750

INSITU CAST GULLY

Gully grating and frame

Square to circular conversion section

Finished surface level

mortar bed 10-20 Class 1

Plastic rising liner cut down to suit required depth or brickwork as for precast gulley or Alternative Rising Section shown on Drawing No F14

Concrete must surround pipe joint

600 or 750 min (see note 3)

50 min

85 min

350 min

220 min

Radius 190 max

150

150 min

450 min diameter above this level

Taper section

400 min diameter at this level

Untrapped outlet shown in outline. Trapped outlet and plug shown dotted.

Plastic gully pot liner

PRECAST GULLY

Gully grating and frame

Extended kerb

5 to 10 recess

Finished surface level

mortar bed 10-20 Class 1

102.5

Brickwork to 2400 Series SHW

Gully cover slab (min thickness 100)

Mortar

Granular fill material or concrete to S.H.W. Clause 508.6 .

C20P concrete

600 or 750 min (see note 3)

450 dia min

750 min

150 dia

Untrapped outlet shown in outline. Trapped outlet and plug shown dotted.

ALTERNATIVE INSITU CAST SUMP (PARALLEL SIDES)

50 MIN

350 min

400 min

NOTES

1. ALL DIMENSIONS ARE IN MILLIMETRES.

2. For details of gully grating and frame see the gully schedules.

3. The minimum depth from the top of the grating to the top of the gully outlet is to be 750 when the connecting pipe is under a carriageway or a hardshoulder and 600 elsewhere.

4. Precast concrete gullies and cover slabs shall be to BS.5911 Part 2.

5. When an insitu cast gully has a trap, the stoppers shall comply with the requirements of BS 5911 Pt 2.

6. Alternative rising section shown on Drawing No. F14 may be used.

| DEPARTMENT OF TRANSPORT
HIGHWAY CONSTRUCTION DETAILS | DRAINAGE | PRECAST AND INSITU CAST GULLIES | Drawing No.
F13 | Date |

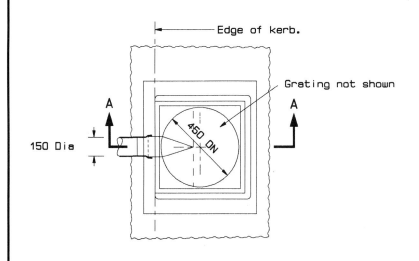

Edge of kerb.

Grating not shown

150 Dia

450 DN

A   A

PLAN

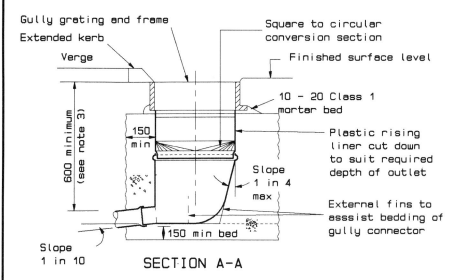

Gully grating and frame
Extended kerb

Verge

Square to circular
conversion section

Finished surface level

10 - 20 Class 1
mortar bed

Plastic rising
liner cut down
to suit required
depth of outlet

External fins to
asssist bedding of
gully connector

600 minimum (see note 3)

150 min

Slope 1 in 4 max

150 min bed

Slope 1 in 10

SECTION A-A

SUMPLESS GULLY CHAMBER

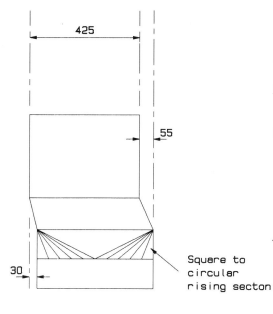

450

425

25

PLAN

425

55

30

Square to circular rising secton

ELEVATION
ALTERNATIVE
RISING SECTION

NOTES

1. ALL DIMENSIONS ARE IN MILLIMETRES.

2. For details of gully grating and frame see the gully schedule.

3. The minimum depth from the top of the grating to the top of the gully connector outlet is to be 750 when the connecting pipe is under a carriageway or hardshoulder and 600 elsewhere.

4. A plastics internal shutter shall be used as shown, bedded on an insitu concrete slab of 150 minimum thickness and surrounded by concrete 150 minimum thickness extending to the sides of the excavation. The insitu concrete shall be C20P.

5. Sumpless gully may also be precast concrete to BS5911.

| DEPARTMENT OF TRANSPORT HIGHWAY CONSTRUCTION DETAILS | DRAINAGE | SUMPLESS GULLY CHAMBER AND ALTERNATIVE RISING SECTION | Drawing No. **F14** | Date |

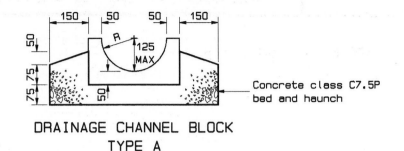

DRAINAGE CHANNEL BLOCK
TYPE A

Concrete class C7.5P
bed and haunch

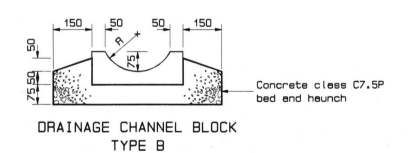

DRAINAGE CHANNEL BLOCK
TYPE B

Concrete class C7.5P
bed and haunch

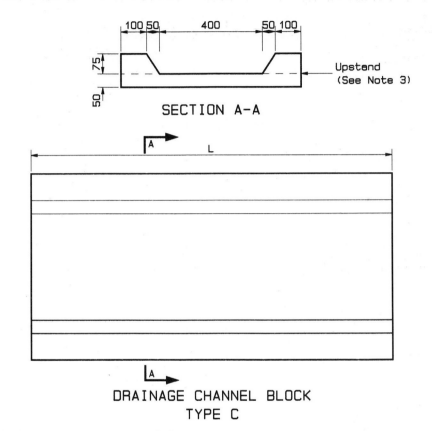

SECTION A-A

Upstand
(See Note 3)

DRAINAGE CHANNEL BLOCK
TYPE C

NOTES

1. ALL DIMENSIONS ARE IN MILLIMETRES.

2. Dimensions R & L shall be as described
   in the contract.

3. Drainage channel blocks to be made of
   pressed concrete to BS340 Grade C30P
   or extruded insitu. For blocks Type C
   the upstand may be insitu concrete or
   the kerb type used for the carriageway.

| DEPARTMENT OF TRANSPORT HIGHWAY CONSTRUCTION DETAILS | DRAINAGE | DRAINAGE CHANNEL BLOCKS TYPES A, B & C | Drawing No. F15 | Date |

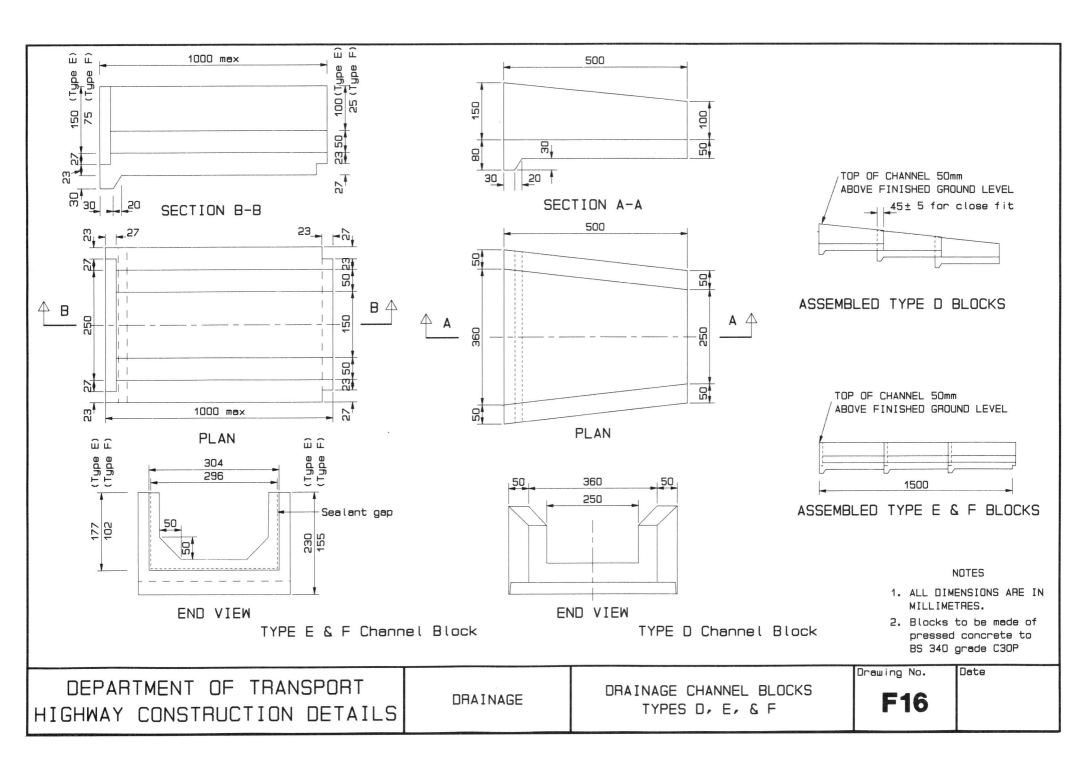

SECTION B-B

SECTION A-A

PLAN

PLAN

END VIEW

TYPE E & F Channel Block

END VIEW

TYPE D Channel Block

TOP OF CHANNEL 50mm
ABOVE FINISHED GROUND LEVEL

45± 5 for close fit

ASSEMBLED TYPE D BLOCKS

TOP OF CHANNEL 50mm
ABOVE FINISHED GROUND LEVEL

ASSEMBLED TYPE E & F BLOCKS

NOTES

1. ALL DIMENSIONS ARE IN
   MILLIMETRES.

2. Blocks to be made of
   pressed concrete to
   BS 340 grade C30P

| DEPARTMENT OF TRANSPORT HIGHWAY CONSTRUCTION DETAILS | DRAINAGE | DRAINAGE CHANNEL BLOCKS TYPES D, E, & F | Drawing No. F16 | Date |

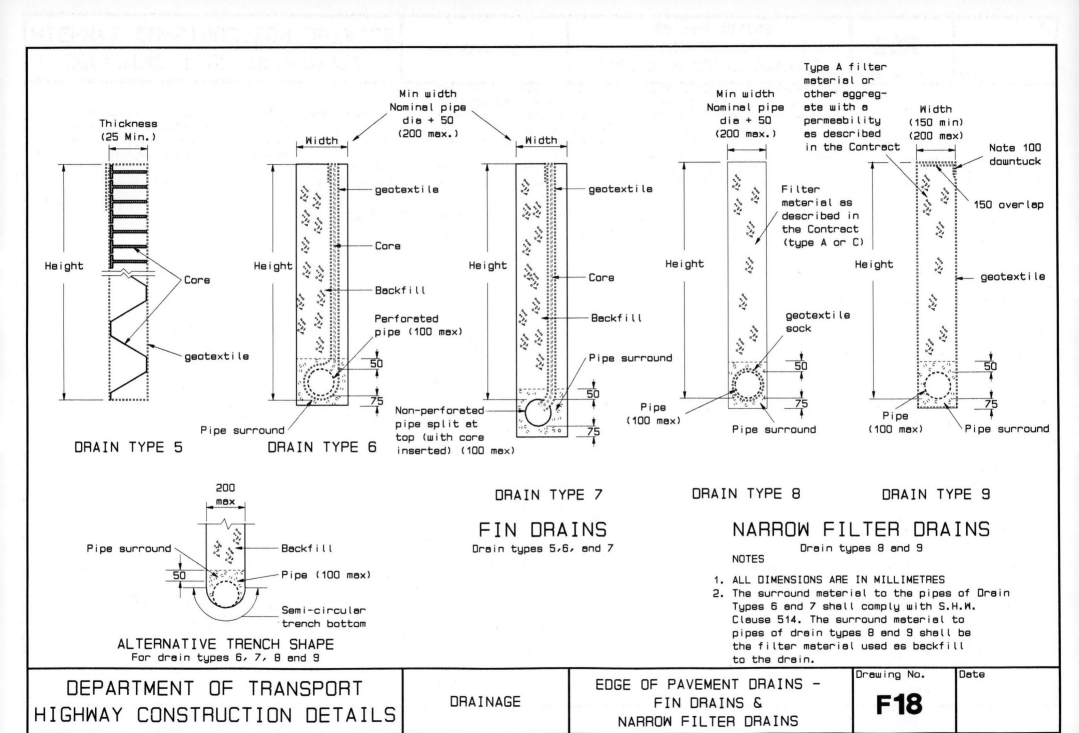

DRAIN TYPE 5

DRAIN TYPE 6

Thickness (25 Min.)

Height

Core

geotextile

Width

Min width
Nominal pipe dia + 50 (200 max.)

Height

geotextile

Core

Backfill

Perforated pipe (100 max)

50

75

Pipe surround

Width

Height

geotextile

Core

Backfill

Pipe surround

Non-perforated pipe split at top (with core inserted) (100 max)

50

50

75

DRAIN TYPE 7

FIN DRAINS
Drain types 5,6, and 7

Min width
Nominal pipe dia + 50 (200 max.)

Type A filter material or other aggregate with a permeability as described in the Contract

Filter material as described in the Contract (type A or C)

Height

geotextile sock

Pipe (100 max)

Pipe surround

50

75

DRAIN TYPE 8

Width (150 min) (200 max)

Note 100 downtuck

150 overlap

Height

geotextile

Pipe (100 max)

Pipe surround

50

75

DRAIN TYPE 9

NARROW FILTER DRAINS
Drain types 8 and 9

NOTES

1. ALL DIMENSIONS ARE IN MILLIMETRES
2. The surround material to the pipes of Drain Types 6 and 7 shall comply with S.H.W. Clause 514. The surround material to pipes of drain types 8 and 9 shall be the filter material used as backfill to the drain.

200 max

Pipe surround

Backfill

50

Pipe (100 max)

Semi-circular trench bottom

ALTERNATIVE TRENCH SHAPE
For drain types 6, 7, 8 and 9

| DEPARTMENT OF TRANSPORT HIGHWAY CONSTRUCTION DETAILS | DRAINAGE | EDGE OF PAVEMENT DRAINS - FIN DRAINS & NARROW FILTER DRAINS | Drawing No. **F18** | Date |

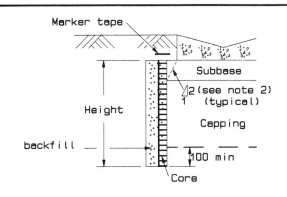

DRAIN TYPE 5

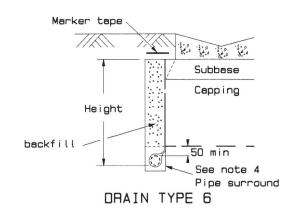

DRAIN TYPE 6

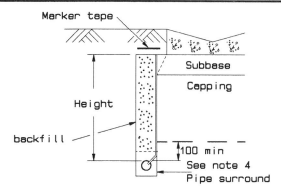

DRAIN TYPE 7

DRAINS LAID IN NARROW TRENCHES

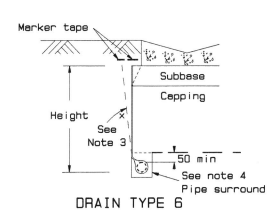

DRAIN TYPE 5

DRAIN TYPE 6

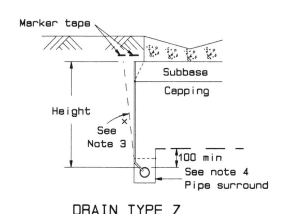

DRAIN TYPE 7

DRAINS LAID IN THE SIDE OF EXCAVATION PRIOR TO
THE PLACEMENT OF PAVEMENT/CAPPING LAYERS

NOTES

1. ALL DIMENSIONS ARE IN MILLIMETRES
2. Fin drains shall be a minimum of 75 from the edge of the surface water channel where appropriate.

3. Marker tapes, surround/ backfill materials and maximum drain slope angle (x) shall be as described in the S.H.W. Clause 514.

4. Pipe surround materials shall be as shown on Drg No. F18
5. Installation of the drains shall be modified accordingly when used in conjunction with the details shown on Drg Nos. B4 & B8 to B10.

6. The drain shall be constructed with one geotextile face in contact with the side of the excavation. The side having the greater permeability shall be facing towards and be in contact with the pavement construction where appropriate.

7. Slots in drain Type 7 shall be not more than 60° from the crown of the pipe.

| DEPARTMENT OF TRANSPORT HIGHWAY CONSTRUCTION DETAILS | DRAINAGE | EDGE OF PAVEMENT DRAINS - INSTALLATION OF FIN DRAINS | Drawing No. **F19** | Date |

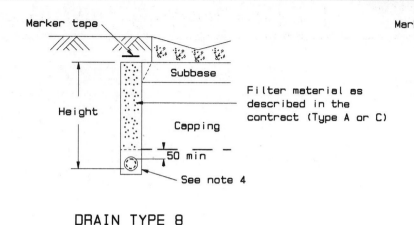

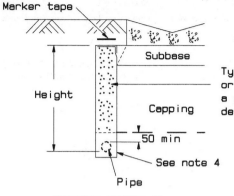

DRAIN TYPE 8

DRAIN TYPE 9

DRAINS LAID IN NARROW TRENCHES

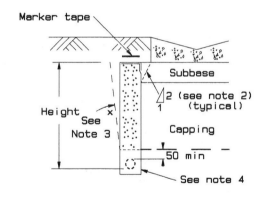

DRAIN TYPE 8

DRAIN TYPE 9

DRAINS LAID IN THE SIDE OF EXCAVATION PRIOR TO
THE PLACEMENT OF PAVEMENT/CAPPING LAYERS

NOTES
1. ALL DIMENSIONS ARE IN MILLIMETRES
2. Narrow filter drains shall be a minimum of 75 from the edge of the surface water channel where appropriate.
3. Marker tapes, and maximum drain slope angle (x) shall be as described in the S.H.W. Clause 514.
4. Pipe surround materials shall be as shown on Drg No. F18
5. Installation of the drains shall be modified accordingly when used in conjunction with the details shown on Drg Nos. B4 & B8 to B10.
6. The drain shall be constructed with one face in contact with the pavement construction.
7. The maximum increased width of filter material shall be 150. In this area either filter material or capping material may be placed.

| DEPARTMENT OF TRANSPORT HIGHWAY CONSTRUCTION DETAILS | DRAINAGE | EDGE OF PAVEMENT DRAINS – APPLICATION OF NARROW FILTER DRAINS | Drawing No. F20 | Date |

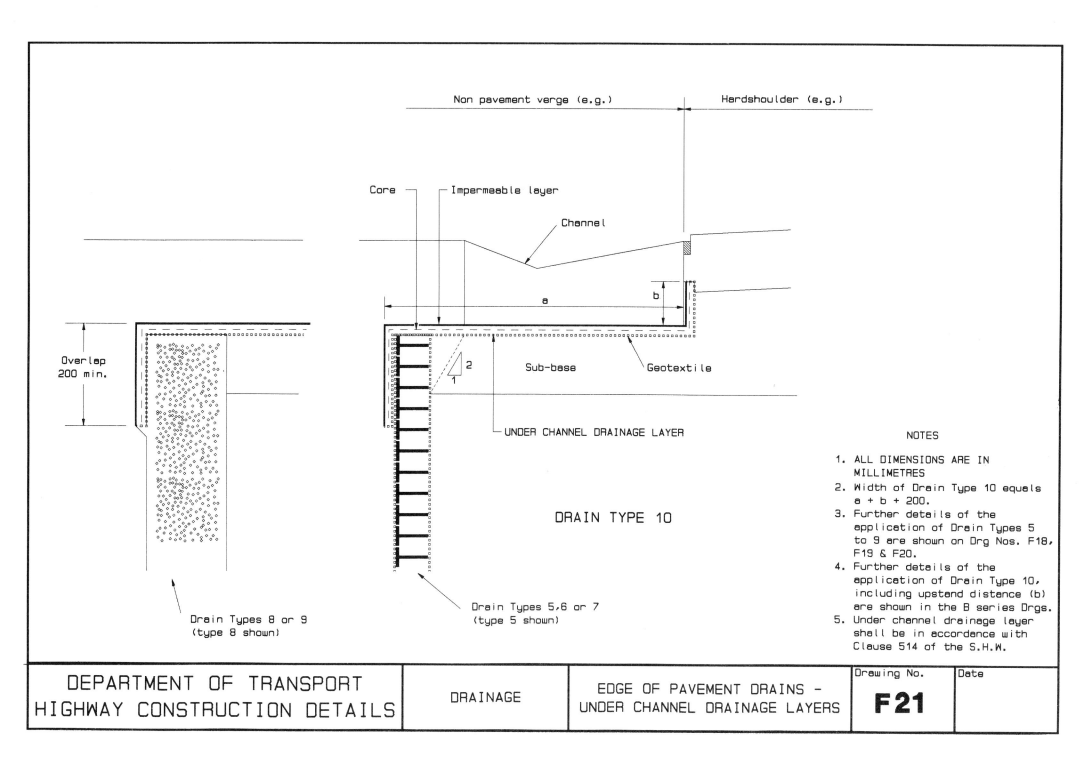

Non pavement verge (e.g.)   Hardshoulder (e.g.)

Core   Impermeable layer

Channel

a   b

Overlap
200 min.

2
1

Sub-base   Geotextile

UNDER CHANNEL DRAINAGE LAYER

DRAIN TYPE 10

Drain Types 8 or 9
(type 8 shown)

Drain Types 5,6 or 7
(type 5 shown)

NOTES

1. ALL DIMENSIONS ARE IN MILLIMETRES
2. Width of Drain Type 10 equals a + b + 200.
3. Further details of the application of Drain Types 5 to 9 are shown on Drg Nos. F18, F19 & F20.
4. Further details of the application of Drain Type 10, including upstand distance (b) are shown in the B series Drgs.
5. Under channel drainage layer shall be in accordance with Clause 514 of the S.H.W.

| DEPARTMENT OF TRANSPORT HIGHWAY CONSTRUCTION DETAILS | DRAINAGE | EDGE OF PAVEMENT DRAINS - UNDER CHANNEL DRAINAGE LAYERS | Drawing No. **F21** | Date |

Series G — Safety Fences

TRRL ITEM NOS.	DESCRIPTION OF ITEMS (As Detailed on TRRL Drawings SG.1040.02/C-Series)	TRRL ITEM NOS.	DESCRIPTION OF ITEMS (As Detailed on TRRL Drawings SG.1040.02/C-Series)
002	Standard Beam	029	Long Post (Driven In Verge)
003	Adjuster Beam	030	Long Post (Driven In Central Reserve)
005	Intermediate Post	031	Anchor Bolt M20
006	Angled Beam Post	032	Cast-In Socket (3 x M20)
007	Bridge Deck Post, Fixed or Adjustable Height (See Also SA1)	033	Washer M8 Special
008	End Post (Double Beam)	034	Angled Beam (Formed)
009	End Post (Single Beam, Approach)	A	Black Washer M8 (Form E) To BS 4320
010	End Post (Single Beam, Departure)	B	Screw M10 x 25 mm Long, Hex, Grade 4.6 To BS 4190
011	Post (Driven In Central Reserve)	C	Bolt M8 x 30 mm Long, Hex, Grade 4.6 To BS 4190
012	Adjuster Bracket	D	Nut M24 Hex, Grade 4 To BS 4190
013	Connecting Strap	E	Nut M16 Hex, Grade 4 To BS 4190
014	Adjuster Bracket Bolt	F	Nut M10 Hex, Grade 4 To BS 4190
015	Anchorage Bolt	G	Nut M8 Hex, Grade 4 To BS 4190
016	Lap Bolt	H	Black Washer M24 (Form E) To BS 4320
018	Taper Washer	J	Black Washer M16 (Form F) To BS 4320
019	Reinforcing Ring	K	Black Washer M10 (Form E) To BS 4320
021	Reinforcing 'U' Bar	M	Screw M16 x 35 mm Long, Stainless Steel Grade A4-80 To BS 6105
023	Bridge Deck Post, Adjustable Height (See Also SA1)	N	Nut M16 Hex, Stainless Steel Grade A4-80 To BS 6150
024	Extension, Bridge Deck Post (See Also SA1)	P	Bolt M12 x 30 mm Long, Hex, Grade 4.6 To BS 4190
025	Anchorage Frame (Approach)	Q	Nut M12 Hex, Grade 4 To BS 4190
026	Anchorage Frame (Departure)	R	Black Washer M12 (Form E) To BS 4320
027	Anchorage Beam (Full Height)	S	Bolt M20 x 50 mm Long, Hex, Grade 4.6 To BS 4190
028	Post (Driven In Verge)	T	Black Washer M20 (Form E) To BS 4320
		U	Washer M16 (Form A) To BS 4320 Stainless Steel To BS 1449: Part 2 304S15

DEPARTMENT OF TRANSPORT HIGHWAY CONSTRUCTION DETAILS	SAFETY FENCING	TENSIONED CORRUGATED BEAM ITEM LIST	Drawing No. G1	Date

TRRL ITEM NOS.	DESCRIPTION OF ITEMS (As Detailed on TRRL Drawings SG.1040.16/B-Series)	TRRL ITEM NOS.	DESCRIPTION OF ITEMS (As Detailed on TRRL Drawings SG.1040.16/B-Series)
003	Standard Beam	031	Spacer, End Post (Double Sided Beam For Lighting Columns)
004	Beam – Half Length	032	Anchorage – Socketed (Approach, Expansion Joint)
005	End Beam	033	Anchorage – Socketed (Departure, Expansion Joint)
006	Transition Piece, Single Sided	034	Anchorage – Bolted (Departure, Expansion Joint)
007	Angled Beam	035	Anchorage – Bolted (Approach, Expansion Joint)
008	End Post (Single Beam, Departure)	036	Connector (Expansion Joint)
009	End Post (Single Beam, Approach)	037	Bridge Deck Post, Adjustable Height (Central Reserve)–(See Also SA1)
010	Bridge Deck Post, Fixed Height (Central Reserve) – (See Also SA1)	038	Extension, Bridge Deck Post (See Also SA1 and SA2)
011	Mounting Bracket (Bridge Pier, Abutment or Retaining Wall)	040	Anchorage, Socketed Double-Sided (Expansion Joint)
012	Fishplate, Standard	041	Anchorage, Bolted Double-Sided (Expansion Joint)
013	Fishplate, Special	042	Anchorage, Socketed For Lighting Columns (Approach, Expansion Joint)
017	Clamp Plate, Standard (Post)	043	Anchorage, Socketed For Lighting Columns (Departure, Expansion Joint)
018	Intermediate Post	044	Anchorage, Bolted For Lighting Columns (Approach, Expansion Joint)
019	Post, (Driven In Central Reserve)	045	Anchorage, Bolted For Lighting Columns (Departure, Expansion Joint)
020	Angled Beam Post	048	Connection Piece, Beam To Steel Parapet
021	Reinforcing Ring	049	Clamp Plate Special (Post)
023	Clamp Plate, Special (Mounting Bracket)	050	Expansion Joint Beam, Long
024	Transition Piece, Double Sided	051	Expansion Joint Beam, Short
025	End Post (Double Sided Beam)	052	Connector (Expansion Beam)
026	End Post (Double Sided Beam for Lighting Columns)	053	Bridge Deck Post, Fixed Height (Verge)–(See Also SA2)
027	Spacer 95 mm (Intermediate Post)	054	Bridge Deck Post, Adjustable Height (Verge)–(See Also SA2)
028	Spacer 95 mm (Angled Beam Post)	055	Long Post (Driven In Central Reserve)
029	Stiffener (Lighting Columns)	056	Long Post (Driven In Verge)
030	Post (Driven In Verge)	057	Parapet Connection Beam, BACO Inclined Alternative 'A' (Approach)

DEPARTMENT OF TRANSPORT HIGHWAY CONSTRUCTION DETAILS	SAFETY FENCING	OPEN BOX BEAM ITEMS LIST	Drawing No. G2	Date

TRRL ITEM NOS.	DESCRIPTION OF ITEMS (As Detailed on TRRL Drawings SG.1040.16/B-Series)	TRRL ITEM NOS.	DESCRIPTION OF ITEMS (As Detailed on TRRL Drawings SG.1040.16/B-Series)
058	Parapet Connection Beam, BACO Inclined Alternative 'A' (Departure)	P	Washer, M12 (Form A) To BS 4320, Stainless Steel Grade A2 to BS 6105
059	Anchor Bolt M10	Q	Nut, M12 Hex, Stainless Steel Grade A4.80 to BS 6105
060	Anchor Bolt M20	R	Nut, M16 Self Locking Stainless Steel With Nylon Insert To BS 4929
061	Connecting Bolt M16 (Expansion Beam)	S	Bolt, M20 × 45 mm Long, Hex, Grade 4.6 To BS 4190
062	Cast-in Socket (3 × M20)	T	Bolt, M20 × 75 mm Long, Hex, Grade 4.6 To BS 4190
063	Cast-in Socket (6 × M20)	W	Bolt, M20 × 50 mm Long, Hex, Grade 4.6 To BS 4190
064	Parapet Connection Beam, BACO and AHDE Vertical Alternative 'A'	X	Bolt, M20 × 100 mm Long, Hex, Grade 4.6 To BS 4190
065	Parapet Connection Beam, BACO Vertical Alternative 'B'	Y	Screw, M12 × 25 mm Long, Hex, Grade 4.6 To BS 4190
066	Parapet Connection Beam, BACO Inclined Alternative 'B' (Approach)	Z	Screw, M12 × 45 mm Long, Hex, Stainless Steel Grade A4.80 To BS 6105
067	Parapet Connection Beam, BACO Inclined Alternative 'B' (Departure)	AA	Screw, M16 × 35 mm Long, Hex, Stainless Steel Grade A4.80 To BS 6105
068	Connecting Bolt M16 Grade 6.9 To BS 4190	AB	Nut, M16 Hex, Stainless Steel Grade A4.80 To BS 6105
069	Reinforcing 'U' Bar	AC	Washer, M16 (Form A) To BS 4320, Stainless Steel Grade A2 To BS 6105
A	Bolt, M16 × 45 mm Long, Hex, Grade 4.6 To BS 4190		
C	Bolt, M16 × 35 mm Long, Hex, Grade 4.6 To BS 4190		
D	Screw, M12 × 40 mm Long, Hex, Grade 4.6 To BS 4190		
E	Screw, M10 × 30 mm Long, Hex, Grade 4.6 To BS 4190		
F	Nut, M20 Hex, Grade 4 To BS 4190		
G	Nut, M16 Hex, Grade 6 To BS 4190		
H	Nut, M12 Hex, Grade 4 To BS 4190		
J	Nut, M10 Hex, Grade 4 To BS 4190		
K	Black Washer, M20 (Form E) To BS 4320		
L	Black Washer, M16 (Form E) To BS 4320		
M	Black Washer, M12 (Form E) To BS 4320		
N	Black Washer, M10 (Form E) To BS 4320		

DEPARTMENT OF TRANSPORT HIGHWAY CONSTRUCTION DETAILS	SAFETY FENCING	OPEN BOX BEAM ITEMS LIST	Drawing No. G3	Date

	CODE	DESCRIPTION
		TENSIONED CORRUGATED BEAM (SINGLE SIDED)
	TS1	Posts at standard 3200 centres
	TS2	Posts at 1600 centres
■	TSA	End Anchorage for TS1
■	TCA	End Anchorage for dual single sided beams
➤	TA1	Adjuster assembly
	TSR	Terminal section
		TENSIONED CORRUGATED BEAM (DOUBLE SIDED)
	TD1	Posts at standard 3200 centres
	TD2	Posts at 1600 centres
■	TDA	End Anchorage for TD1
⇌	TA2	Adjuster assembly
	TDR	Terminal section
		OPEN BOX BEAM (SINGLE SIDED)
	BS1	Posts at standard 2400 centres
	BS2	Posts at 1200 centres
	BSB	With mounting brackets fixed to structures at 1200 centres
■	BSA	End Anchorage for BS1
►	CS1T	Single box beam to single corrugated beam transition piece
►	CD1T	Single box beam to double corrugated beam transition piece
	BSR	Terminal section
		OPEN BOX BEAM (DOUBLE SIDED)
	BD	Posts at standard 2400 centres without spacers
■	BDA	End anchorage for BD
	BDS1	Posts at standard 2400 centres with spacers
	BDS2	Posts at 1200 centres with spacers
■	BDSA	End anchorage for BDS1 and BDS2
	BDR	Terminal section
•		Denotes junction of differently coded sections of safety fencing

GENERAL NOTES:

1. These notes relate to the drawings for tensioned corrugated beam and open box beam safety fencing in the series G1 to G36.

2. All dimensions are in millimetres unless otherwise stated.

3. All dimensions shown thus $\frac{640}{580}$ represent maximum and minimum values respectively.

4. Concrete in post footings, end ramps and anchor blocks shall be Grade C25P to BS 5328.

5. If the dimensions of holes for footings and anchor blocks cannot be maintained before concrete is poured, suitable casings approved by the Engineer shall be provided to retain the earth.

6. All exposed horizontal surfaces of concrete footings and anchor blocks shall have a slope of approximately 1 in 10 unless otherwise stated.

7. Items shown thus 016_8 refer to fabricated components listed on Drg. Nos. G1, G2, and G3. Thus 016_8 or E_8 refers to 8 No. item 16 or 8 No. item E.

DEPARTMENT OF TRANSPORT
HIGHWAY CONSTRUCTION DETAILS

SAFETY FENCING

SCHEDULE OF FENCE TYPE CODES AND GENERAL NOTES

Drawing No. G4

Date

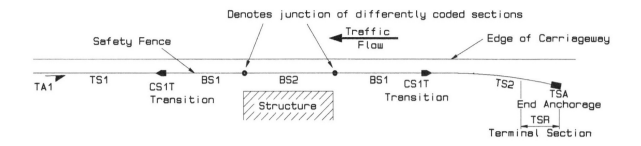

VERGE - SPECIMEN DIAGRAM

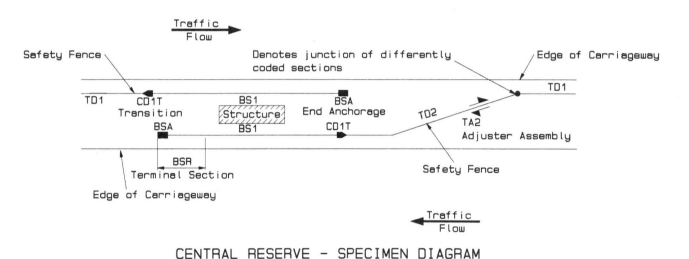

CENTRAL RESERVE - SPECIMEN DIAGRAM

NOTE
1. For description of fence type code see Drg. No. G4.

| DEPARTMENT OF TRANSPORT HIGHWAY CONSTRUCTION DETAILS | SAFETY FENCING | USE OF CODING FOR ALTERNATIVE TYPES OF FENCE ADJACENT TO STRUCTURES | Drawing No. **G5** | Date |

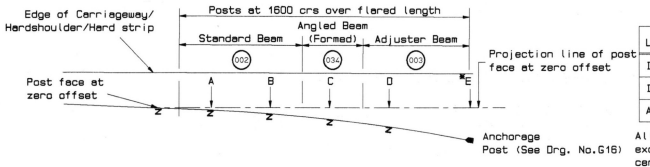

Edge of Carriageway/
Hardshoulder/Hard strip

Posts at 1600 crs over flared length

| Standard Beam | Angled Beam (Formed) | Adjuster Beam |
| 002 | 034 | 003 |

Post face at
zero offset

A B C D *E

Projection line of post
face at zero offset

Anchorage
Post (See Drg. No.G16)

LOCATION OF FLARE	OFFSET				
	A	B	C	D	*E
In Verge	25	50	120	265	570
In Central Reserve	25	55	140	310	660
At Emergency Crossings	25	65	155	335	714

All offsets are measured from projection line to post face
except *E where offset is measured from projection line to
centre of anchorage post.

FLARED END FOR TENSIONED CORRUGATED BEAM

For: Width Of Central Reserve Less Than 4000 mm
Or Width Of Verge Less Than 1500 mm.
Standard Layout Shown On Drg. No. G19.

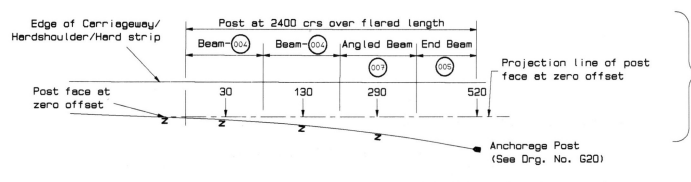

Edge of Carriageway/
Hardshoulder/Hard strip

Post at 2400 crs over flared length

| Beam- 004 | Beam- 004 | Angled Beam 007 | End Beam 005 |

Post face at
zero offset

30   130   290   520

Projection line of post
face at zero offset

Anchorage Post
(See Drg. No. G20)

NOTES:
1. All beam splices in flared
length are made with special
fishplates, item 013.
2. All offsets are measured from
the projection line to post face
including the offset at anchorage
post.

FLARED END FOR OPEN BOX BEAM

For: Width Of Central Reserve Less Than 4000 mm
Or Width Of Verge Less Than 1500 mm.
Standard Layout Shown On Drg. No. G22.

| DEPARTMENT OF TRANSPORT HIGHWAY CONSTRUCTION DETAILS | SAFETY FENCING | TENSIONED CORRUGATED BEAM AND OPEN BOX BEAM - NON-STANDARD FLARED ENDS LAYOUT | Drawing No. G6 | Date |

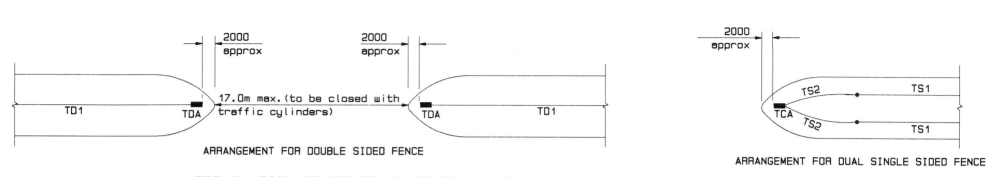

ARRANGEMENT FOR DOUBLE SIDED FENCE

ARRANGEMENT FOR DUAL SINGLE SIDED FENCE

TERMINATION OF FENCE AT CENTRAL RESERVE EMERGENCY CROSSINGS

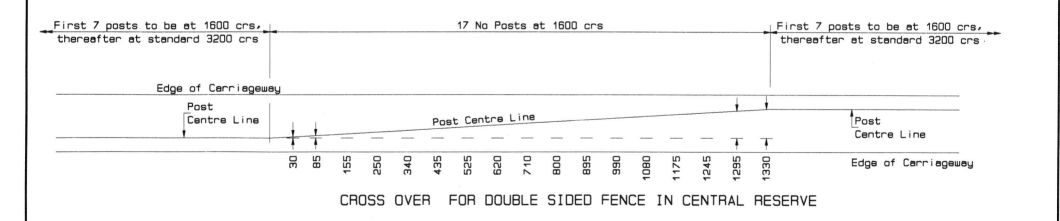

CROSS OVER FOR DOUBLE SIDED FENCE IN CENTRAL RESERVE

| DEPARTMENT OF TRANSPORT HIGHWAY CONSTRUCTION DETAILS | SAFETY FENCING | TENSIONED CORRUGATED BEAM LAYOUT FOR CENTRAL RESERVE EMERGENCY CROSSINGS AND CROSS OVERS | Drawing No. **G7** | Date |

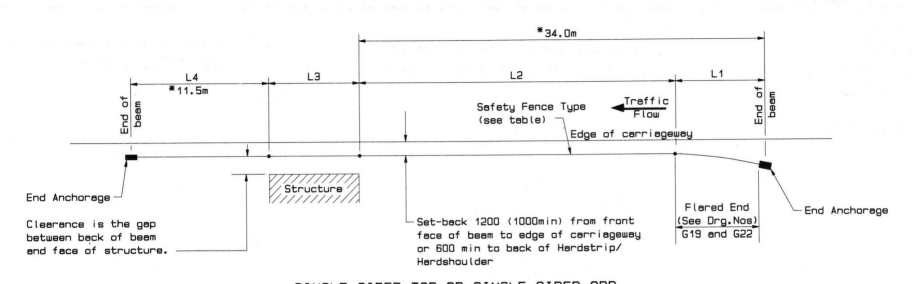

*34.0m

L4   L3   L2   L1
*11.5m

End of beam

Safety Fence Type
(see table)

Traffic
Flow

Edge of carriageway

End of beam

End Anchorage

Clearance is the gap
between back of beam
and face of structure.

Structure

Set-back 1200 (1000min) from front
face of beam to edge of carriageway
or 600 min to back of Hardstrip/
Hardshoulder

Flared End
(See Drg.Nos)
G19 and G22

End Anchorage

SINGLE SIDED TCB OR SINGLE SIDED OBB

TABLE

CLEARANCE (mm)		CODING (See Drg. No. G4)					POST SPACING (mm)
Desirable	Minimum	Fence Length/Type				End Anchorage	
1200	1000 & above	L1	L2	L3	L4	TSA	Posts @ 1600 crs for L1 Posts @ 3200 crs for L2,L3,&L4
		TS2	TS1	TS1	TS1		
1000	600 & above	L1,L2,L3, & L4				BSA	Posts @ 2400 crs for L1,L2,L3 & L4
		BS1					
	460 to 599	L1	L2	L3	L4	BSA	Posts @ 2400 crs for L1 L2 & L4 Posts @ 1200 crs for L3
		BS1	BS1	BS2	BS1		
	300 to 459	L1	L2	L3	L4	BSA	Posts @ 2400 crs for L1,L2 & L4 Brackets @ 1200 crs for L3
		BS1	BS1	BSB	BS1		

NOTES
1. When the structure is less than
   7.5m in length or the length of
   the safety fencing between
   anchorages is less than 45.0m,
   open box beam safety fencing
   shall be used as described in
   the Table.
2. * The sum of these dimensions
   to be increased if necessary
   to suit nearest standard beam
   length.

DEPARTMENT OF TRANSPORT HIGHWAY CONSTRUCTION DETAILS	SAFETY FENCING	VERGE – ALTERNATIVE TYPES OF FENCE ADJACENT TO STRUCTURES	Drawing No. **G8**	Date

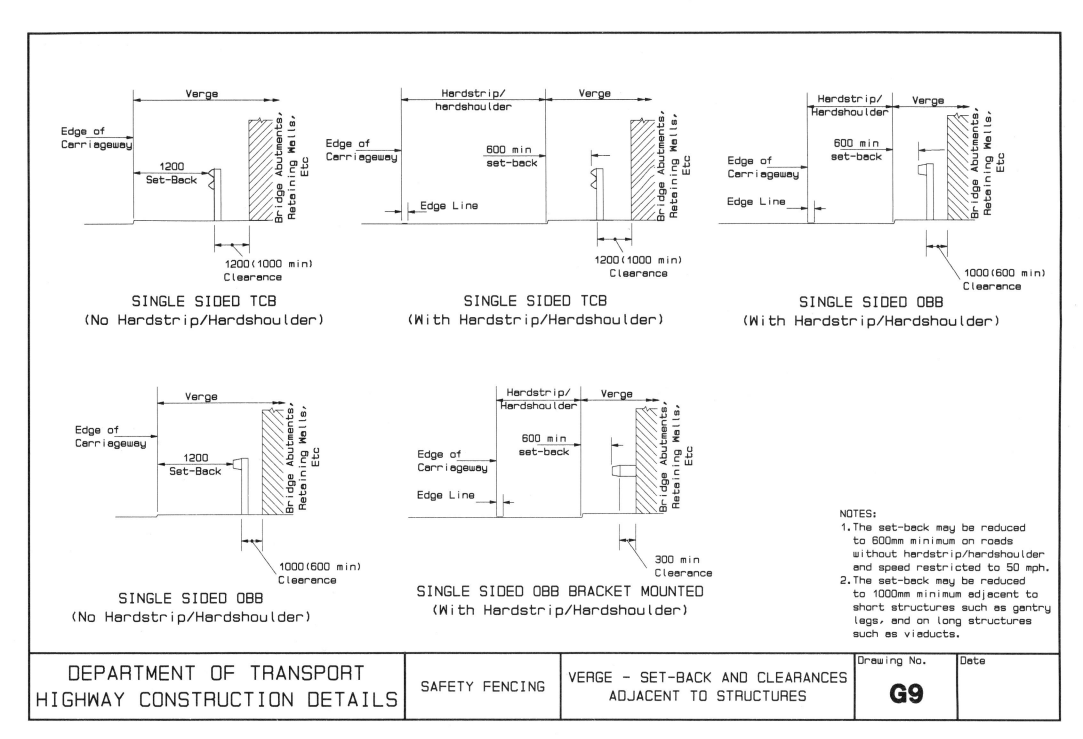

SINGLE SIDED TCB
(No Hardstrip/Hardshoulder)

SINGLE SIDED TCB
(With Hardstrip/Hardshoulder)

SINGLE SIDED OBB
(With Hardstrip/Hardshoulder)

SINGLE SIDED OBB
(No Hardstrip/Hardshoulder)

SINGLE SIDED OBB BRACKET MOUNTED
(With Hardstrip/Hardshoulder)

NOTES:
1. The set-back may be reduced to 600mm minimum on roads without hardstrip/hardshoulder and speed restricted to 50 mph.
2. The set-back may be reduced to 1000mm minimum adjacent to short structures such as gantry legs, and on long structures such as viaducts.

| DEPARTMENT OF TRANSPORT HIGHWAY CONSTRUCTION DETAILS | SAFETY FENCING | VERGE - SET-BACK AND CLEARANCES ADJACENT TO STRUCTURES | Drawing No. G9 | Date |

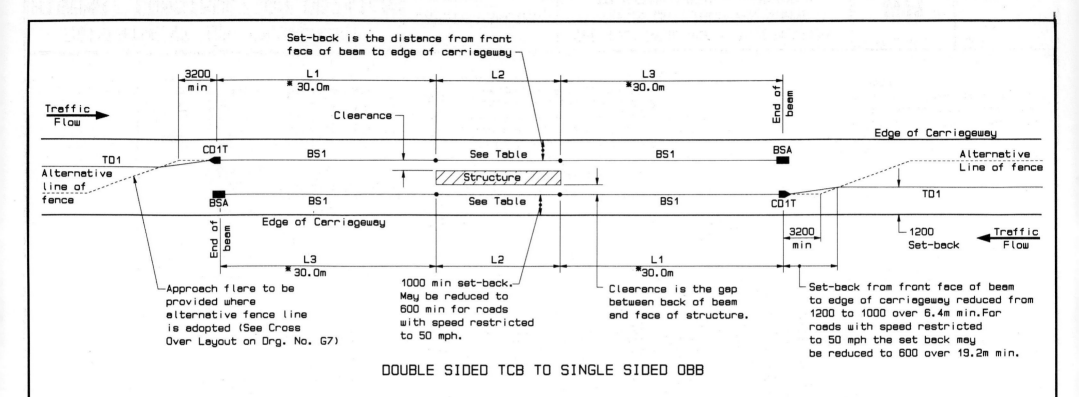

Set-back is the distance from front
face of beam to edge of carriageway

Traffic Flow →

Clearance

Edge of Carriageway

3200 min

L1
* 30.0m

L2

L3
* 30.0m

End of beam

CD1T

TD1
Alternative line of fence

BS1

See Table

Structure

BS1

BSA

Alternative Line of fence

TD1

See Table

End of beam

BSA

BS1

Edge of Carriageway

BS1

CD1T

3200 min

1200 Set-back

Traffic Flow ←

L3
* 30.0m

L2

L1
* 30.0m

Approach flare to be provided where alternative fence line is adopted (See Cross Over Layout on Drg. No. G7)

1000 min set-back. May be reduced to 600 min for roads with speed restricted to 50 mph.

Clearance is the gap between back of beam and face of structure.

Set-back from front face of beam to edge of carriageway reduced from 1200 to 1000 over 6.4m min. For roads with speed restricted to 50 mph the set back may be reduced to 600 over 19.2m min.

DOUBLE SIDED TCB TO SINGLE SIDED OBB

TABLE

CLEARANCE (mm)		CODING (See Drg. No. G4)				POST SPACING (mm)
Desirable	Minimum	Fence Length/Type			Transition	End Anchorage	
1000	600 & above	L1, L2 & L3			CD1T	BSA	Posts @ 2400 crs for L1, L2 & L3
		BS1					
	460 to 599	L1	L2	L3	CD1T	BSA	Posts @ 2400 crs for L1 & L3
		BS1	BS2	BS1			Posts @ 1200 crs for L2
	300 to 459	L1	L2	L3	CD1T	BSA	Posts @ 2400 crs for L1 & L3
		BS1	BSB	BS1			Brackets @ 1200 crs for L2

NOTE:
* The sum of these dimensions to be increased if necessary to suit nearest standard beam length.

DEPARTMENT OF TRANSPORT HIGHWAY CONSTRUCTION DETAILS	SAFETY FENCING	CENTRAL RESERVE - ALTERNATIVE TYPES OF FENCE ADJACENT TO STRUCTURES - LAYOUT 1	Drawing No. G10	Date

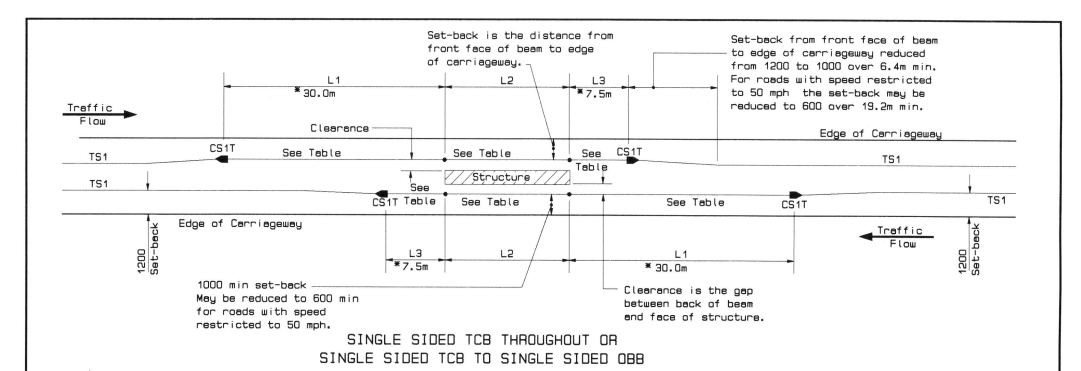

Set-back is the distance from front face of beam to edge of carriageway.

Set-back from front face of beam to edge of carriageway reduced from 1200 to 1000 over 6.4m min. For roads with speed restricted to 50 mph the set-back may be reduced to 600 over 19.2m min.

1000 min set-back
May be reduced to 600 min for roads with speed restricted to 50 mph.

Clearance is the gap between back of beam and face of structure.

SINGLE SIDED TCB THROUGHOUT OR
SINGLE SIDED TCB TO SINGLE SIDED OBB

TABLE

CLEARANCE (mm)		CODING (See Drg. No. G4)				POST SPACING (mm)
Desirable	Minimum	Fence Length/Type			Transition	
1200	1000 & above	L1,L2 & L3			—	Posts @ 3200 crs for L1,L2 & L3
		TS1				
1000	600 & above	L1,L2 & L3			CS1T	Posts @ 2400 crs for L1,L2 & L3
		BS1				
	460 to 599	L1	L2	L3	CS1T	Posts @ 2400 crs for L1 & L3 Posts @ 1200 crs for L2
		BS1	BS2	BS1		
	300 to 459	L1	L2	L3	CS1T	Posts @ 2400 crs for L1 & L3 Brackets @ 1200 crs for L2
		BS1	BSB	BS1		

NOTE:
* The sum of these dimensions to be increased if necessary to suit nearest standard beam length.

DEPARTMENT OF TRANSPORT HIGHWAY CONSTRUCTION DETAILS	SAFETY FENCING	CENTRAL RESERVE - ALTERNATIVE TYPES OF FENCE ADJACENT TO STRUCTURES - LAYOUT 2	Drawing No. **G11**	Date

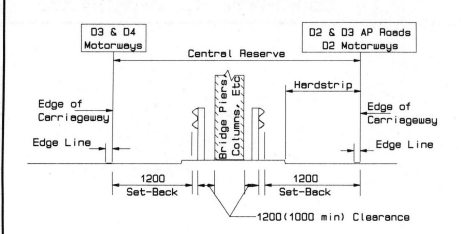

DUAL SINGLE SIDED TCB

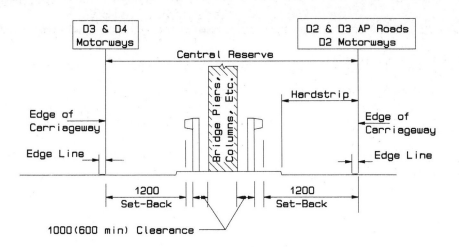

DUAL SINGLE SIDED OBB

NOTE:
The set-back may be reduced to 1000mm minimum adjacent to short structures such as bridge piers, and on long structures.

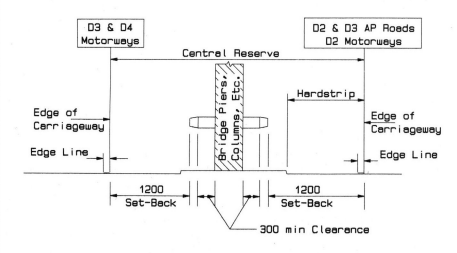

SINGLE SIDED OBB BRACKET MOUNTED

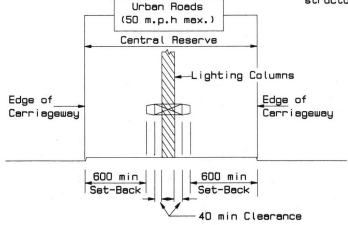

DOUBLE SIDED OBB WITH STIFFENERS BETWEEN BEAMS
(SAFETY FENCING POST AND SPACERS NOT SHOWN)

| DEPARTMENT OF TRANSPORT HIGHWAY CONSTRUCTION DETAILS | SAFETY FENCING | CENTRAL RESERVE - SET-BACK AND CLEARENCES ADJACENT TO STRUCTURES | Drawing No. G12 | Date |

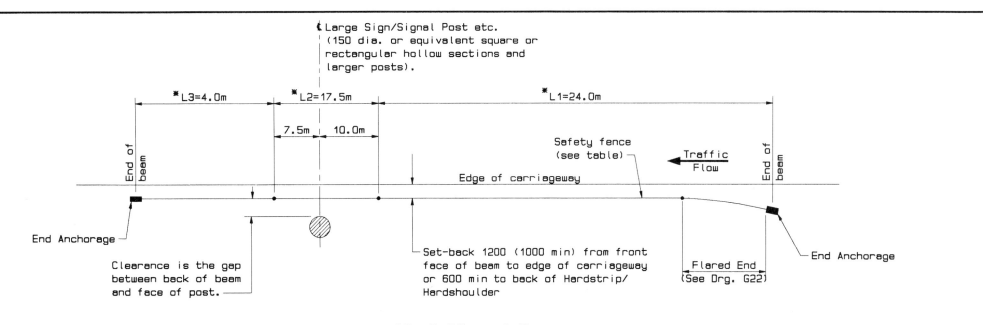

Large Sign/Signal Post etc.
(150 dia. or equivalent square or rectangular hollow sections and larger posts).

*L3=4.0m   *L2=17.5m   *L1=24.0m

7.5m   10.0m

End of beam

Safety fence (see table)

Traffic Flow

Edge of carriageway

End of beam

End Anchorage

Clearance is the gap between back of beam and face of post.

Set-back 1200 (1000 min) from front face of beam to edge of carriageway or 600 min to back of Hardstrip/ Hardshoulder

Flared End (See Drg. G22)

End Anchorage

STANDARD LAYOUT
SINGLE SIDED OBB

TABLE

CLEARANCE (mm)		CODING (See Drg. No. G4)				POST SPACING (mm)
Desirable	Minimum	Fence Length/Type			End Anchorage	
1000	600 & above	L1,L2, & L3			BSA	Posts @ 2400 crs for L1,L2, & L3
		BS1				
	**460 to 599	L1	L2	L3	BSA	Posts @ 2400 crs for L1 & L3
		BS1	BS2	BS1		Posts @ 1200 crs for L2

NOTES:

1. * The sum of these dimensions to be increased if necessary to suit the nearest standard beam length.

2. ** This clearance may be reduced to 330mm minimum adjacent to lighting columns on 50 mph or less speed restricted roads.

3. Signs/Signal posts less than 150mm dia. or equivalent do not require protection.

DEPARTMENT OF TRANSPORT HIGHWAY CONSTRUCTION DETAILS	SAFETY FENCING	VERGE – ALTERNATIVE TYPES OF FENCE ADJACENT TO LARGE SIGN/SIGNAL POSTS ETC	Drawing No. **G13**	Date

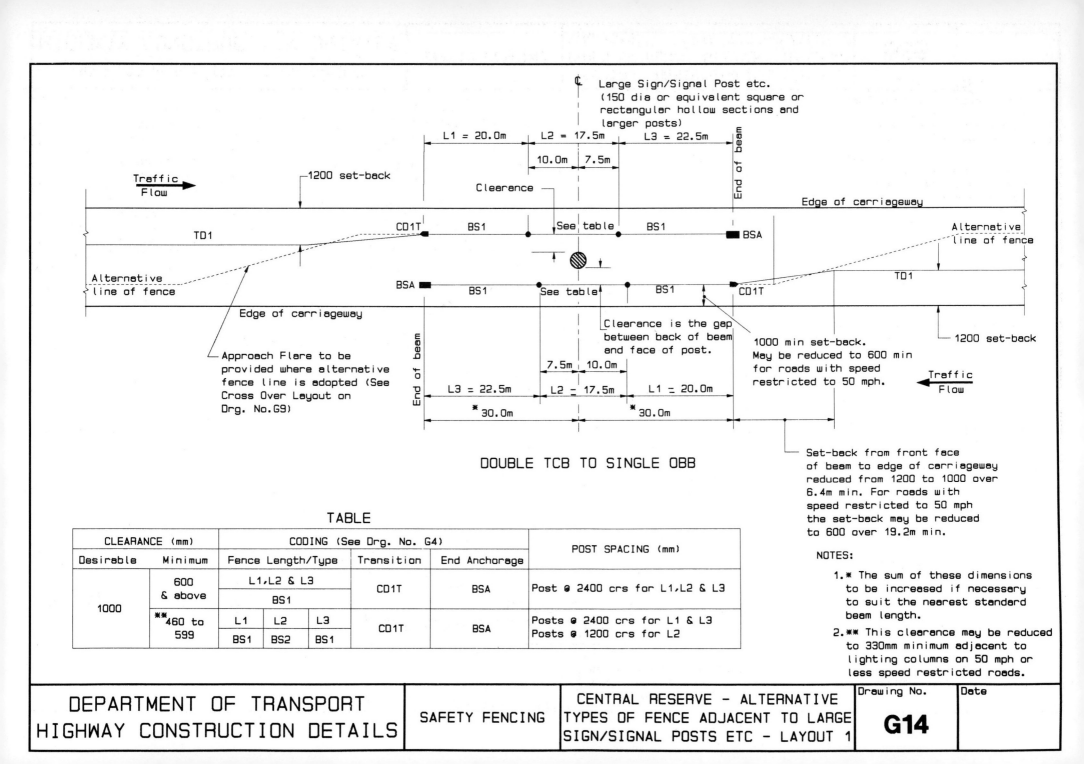

DOUBLE TCB TO SINGLE OBB

Large Sign/Signal Post etc.
(150 dia or equivalent square or
rectangular hollow sections and
larger posts)

Traffic Flow

1200 set-back

Clearance

Edge of carriageway

TD1

CD1T   BS1   See table   BS1   BSA

BSA   BS1   See table   BS1   CD1T

Alternative line of fence

Edge of carriageway

L1 = 20.0m   L2 = 17.5m   L3 = 22.5m

10.0m   7.5m

End of beam

Alternative line of fence

TD1

1200 set-back

Clearance is the gap
between back of beam
and face of post.

1000 min set-back.
May be reduced to 600 min
for roads with speed
restricted to 50 mph.

Traffic Flow

Approach Flare to be
provided where alternative
fence line is adopted (See
Cross Over Layout on
Drg. No.G9)

End of beam

7.5m   10.0m

L3 = 22.5m   L2 = 17.5m   L1 = 20.0m

* 30.0m   * 30.0m

Set-back from front face
of beam to edge of carriageway
reduced from 1200 to 1000 over
6.4m min. For roads with
speed restricted to 50 mph
the set-back may be reduced
to 600 over 19.2m min.

TABLE

CLEARANCE (mm)		CODING (See Drg. No. G4)			POST SPACING (mm)
Desirable	Minimum	Fence Length/Type	Transition	End Anchorage	
1000	600 & above	L1, L2 & L3	CD1T	BSA	Post @ 2400 crs for L1,L2 & L3
		BS1			
	** 460 to 599	L1 / L2 / L3	CD1T	BSA	Posts @ 2400 crs for L1 & L3
		BS1 / BS2 / BS1			Posts @ 1200 crs for L2

NOTES:

1. * The sum of these dimensions
   to be increased if necessary
   to suit the nearest standard
   beam length.

2. ** This clearance may be reduced
   to 330mm minimum adjacent to
   lighting columns on 50 mph or
   less speed restricted roads.

DEPARTMENT OF TRANSPORT
HIGHWAY CONSTRUCTION DETAILS

SAFETY FENCING

CENTRAL RESERVE - ALTERNATIVE
TYPES OF FENCE ADJACENT TO LARGE
SIGN/SIGNAL POSTS ETC - LAYOUT 1

Drawing No.
G14

Date

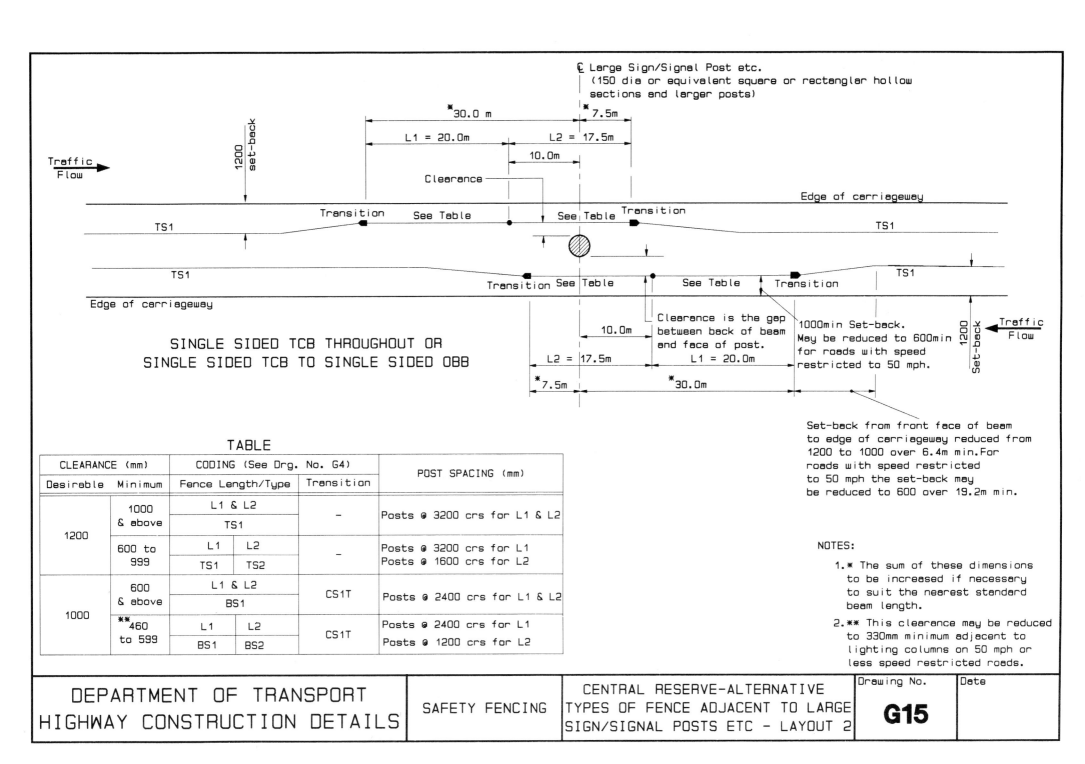

C Large Sign/Signal Post etc.
(150 dia or equivalent square or rectanglar hollow sections and larger posts)

Traffic Flow →

1200 set-back

* 30.0 m   * 7.5m

L1 = 20.0m   L2 = 17.5m

10.0m

Clearance

Edge of carriageway

Transition   See Table   See Table   Transition

TS1   TS1

TS1   TS1

Transition See Table   See Table   Transition

Edge of carriageway

SINGLE SIDED TCB THROUGHOUT OR
SINGLE SIDED TCB TO SINGLE SIDED OBB

10.0m

Clearance is the gap between back of beam and face of post.

L2 = 17.5m   L1 = 20.0m

* 7.5m   * 30.0m

1000min Set-back. May be reduced to 600min for roads with speed restricted to 50 mph.

1200 Set-back

← Traffic Flow

Set-back from front face of beam to edge of carriageway reduced from 1200 to 1000 over 6.4m min. For roads with speed restricted to 50 mph the set-back may be reduced to 600 over 19.2m min.

TABLE

CLEARANCE (mm)		CODING (See Drg. No. G4)			POST SPACING (mm)
Desirable	Minimum	Fence Length/Type		Transition	
1200	1000 & above	L1 & L2		–	Posts @ 3200 crs for L1 & L2
		TS1			
	600 to 999	L1	L2	–	Posts @ 3200 crs for L1
		TS1	TS2		Posts @ 1600 crs for L2
1000	600 & above	L1 & L2		CS1T	Posts @ 2400 crs for L1 & L2
		BS1			
	**460 to 599	L1	L2	CS1T	Posts @ 2400 crs for L1
		BS1	BS2		Posts @ 1200 crs for L2

NOTES:

1. * The sum of these dimensions to be increased if necessary to suit the nearest standard beam length.

2. ** This clearance may be reduced to 330mm minimum adjacent to lighting columns on 50 mph or less speed restricted roads.

| DEPARTMENT OF TRANSPORT HIGHWAY CONSTRUCTION DETAILS | SAFETY FENCING | CENTRAL RESERVE-ALTERNATIVE TYPES OF FENCE ADJACENT TO LARGE SIGN/SIGNAL POSTS ETC - LAYOUT 2 | Drawing No. **G15** | Date |

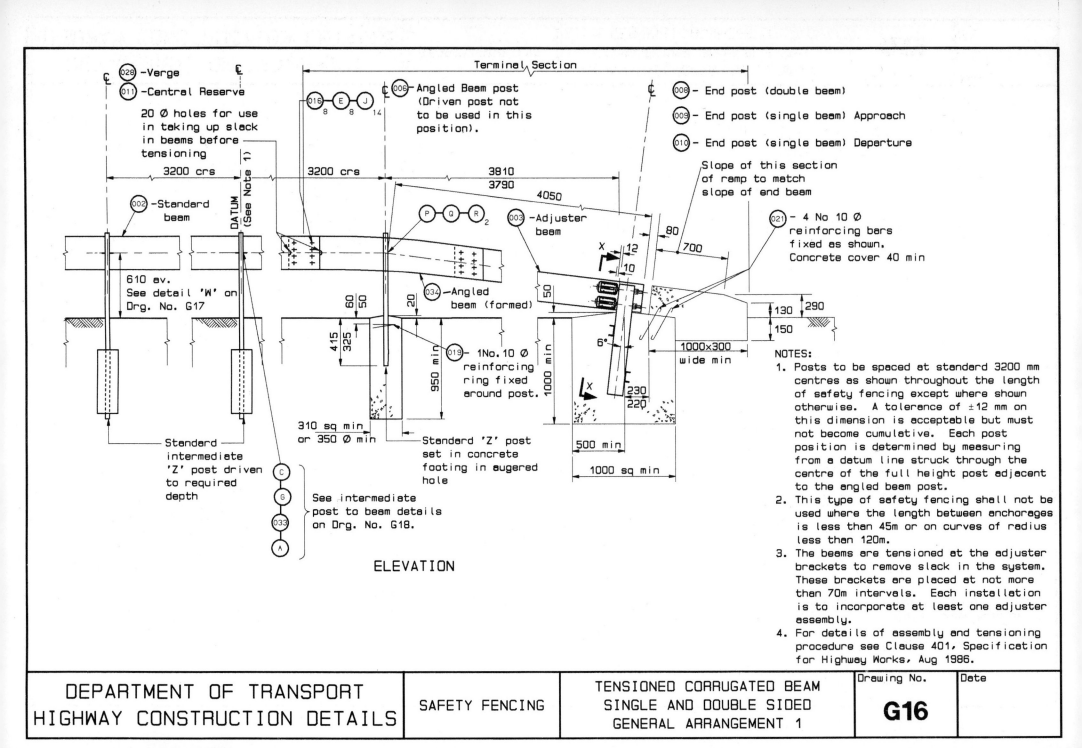

ELEVATION

Terminal Section

028 – Verge
011 – Central Reserve

20 Ø holes for use in taking up slack in beams before tensioning

3200 crs
3200 crs
3810
3790
4050

DATUM (See Note 1)

016 E J
8 8 14

006 – Angled Beam post (Driven post not to be used in this position).

008 – End post (double beam)
009 – End post (single beam) Approach
010 – End post (single beam) Departure

Slope of this section of ramp to match slope of end beam

002 – Standard beam

P Q R₂
003 – Adjuster beam

021 – 4 No 10 Ø reinforcing bars fixed as shown. Concrete cover 40 min

610 av. See detail 'W' on Drg. No. G17

034 – Angled beam (formed)

80
700
12
10
50
X
130 290
150

60 50
415 325
20
950 min
1000 min

019 – 1No. 10 Ø reinforcing ring fixed around post.

X
6°

230
220

1000×300 wide min

Standard intermediate 'Z' post driven to required depth

310 sq min or 350 Ø min

Standard 'Z' post set in concrete footing in augered hole

500 min
1000 sq min

C
G
033
A

See intermediate post to beam details on Drg. No. G18.

NOTES:
1. Posts to be spaced at standard 3200 mm centres as shown throughout the length of safety fencing except where shown otherwise. A tolerance of ±12 mm on this dimension is acceptable but must not become cumulative. Each post position is determined by measuring from a datum line struck through the centre of the full height post adjacent to the angled beam post.
2. This type of safety fencing shall not be used where the length between anchorages is less than 45m or on curves of radius less than 120m.
3. The beams are tensioned at the adjuster brackets to remove slack in the system. These brackets are placed at not more than 70m intervals. Each installation is to incorporate at least one adjuster assembly.
4. For details of assembly and tensioning procedure see Clause 401, Specification for Highway Works, Aug 1986.

| DEPARTMENT OF TRANSPORT HIGHWAY CONSTRUCTION DETAILS | SAFETY FENCING | TENSIONED CORRUGATED BEAM SINGLE AND DOUBLE SIDED GENERAL ARRANGEMENT 1 | Drawing No. G16 | Date |

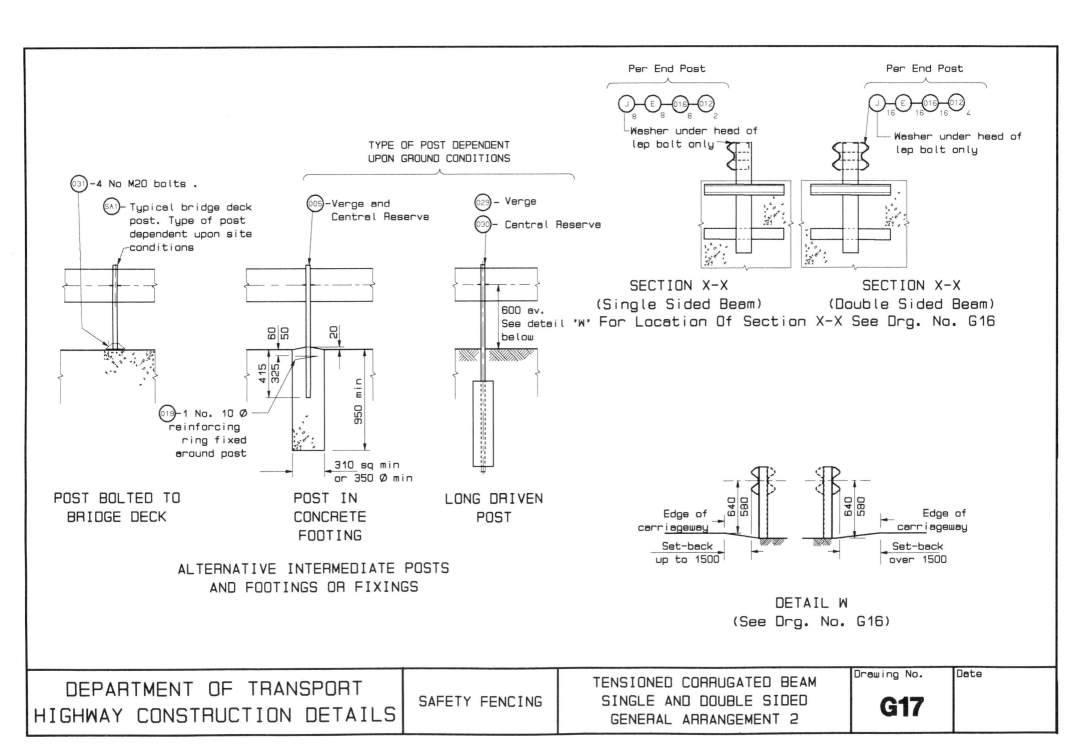

031 -4 No M20 bolts .

SA1 - Typical bridge deck post. Type of post dependent upon site conditions

019 -1 No. 10 Ø reinforcing ring fixed around post

TYPE OF POST DEPENDENT UPON GROUND CONDITIONS

005 -Verge and Central Reserve

029 - Verge

030 - Central Reserve

60
50
20
415
325
950 min

600 av.
See detail 'W' below

310 sq min
or 350 Ø min

POST BOLTED TO BRIDGE DECK

POST IN CONCRETE FOOTING

LONG DRIVEN POST

ALTERNATIVE INTERMEDIATE POSTS
AND FOOTINGS OR FIXINGS

Per End Post

J 8 — E 8 — 016 8 — 012 2

Washer under head of lap bolt only

Per End Post

J 16 — E 16 — 016 16 — 012 4

Washer under head of lap bolt only

SECTION X-X
(Single Sided Beam)

SECTION X-X
(Double Sided Beam)

See detail 'W' For Location Of Section X-X See Drg. No. G16

Edge of carriageway
640
580
Set-back up to 1500

640
580
Edge of carriageway
Set-back over 1500

DETAIL W
(See Drg. No. G16)

| DEPARTMENT OF TRANSPORT HIGHWAY CONSTRUCTION DETAILS | SAFETY FENCING | TENSIONED CORRUGATED BEAM SINGLE AND DOUBLE SIDED GENERAL ARRANGEMENT 2 | Drawing No. **G17** | Date |

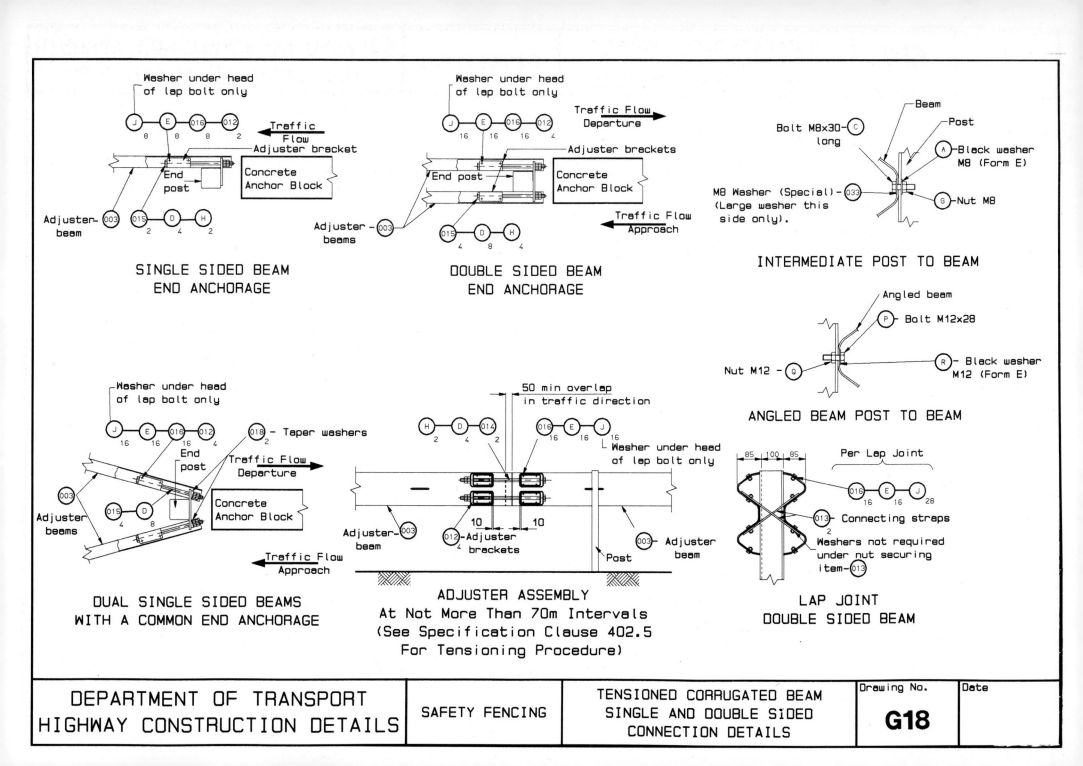

SINGLE SIDED BEAM
END ANCHORAGE

DOUBLE SIDED BEAM
END ANCHORAGE

INTERMEDIATE POST TO BEAM

ANGLED BEAM POST TO BEAM

DUAL SINGLE SIDED BEAMS
WITH A COMMON END ANCHORAGE

ADJUSTER ASSEMBLY
At Not More Than 70m Intervals
(See Specification Clause 402.5
For Tensioning Procedure)

LAP JOINT
DOUBLE SIDED BEAM

| DEPARTMENT OF TRANSPORT HIGHWAY CONSTRUCTION DETAILS | SAFETY FENCING | TENSIONED CORRUGATED BEAM SINGLE AND DOUBLE SIDED CONNECTION DETAILS | Drawing No. G18 | Date |

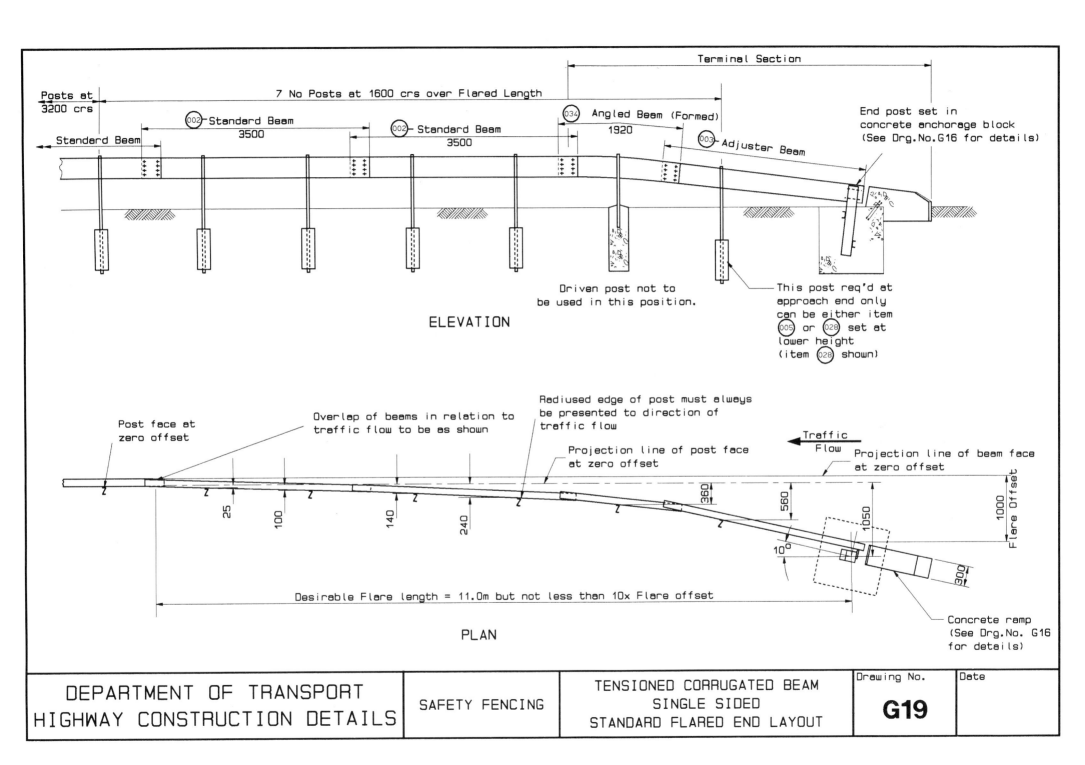

ELEVATION

PLAN

Posts at 3200 crs

7 No Posts at 1600 crs over Flared Length

Terminal Section

Standard Beam

002 Standard Beam 3500

002 Standard Beam 3500

034 Angled Beam (Formed) 1920

003 Adjuster Beam

End post set in concrete anchorage block (See Drg.No.G16 for details)

Driven post not to be used in this position.

This post req'd at approach end only can be either item 005 or 028 set at lower height (item 028 shown)

Post face at zero offset

Overlap of beams in relation to traffic flow to be as shown

Radiused edge of post must always be presented to direction of traffic flow

Projection line of post face at zero offset

Traffic Flow

Projection line of beam face at zero offset

25

100

140

240

360

560

1050

1000 Flare Offset

10°

300

Desirable Flare length = 11.0m but not less than 10x Flare offset

Concrete ramp (See Drg.No. G16 for details)

| DEPARTMENT OF TRANSPORT HIGHWAY CONSTRUCTION DETAILS | SAFETY FENCING | TENSIONED CORRUGATED BEAM SINGLE SIDED STANDARD FLARED END LAYOUT | Drawing No. G19 | Date |

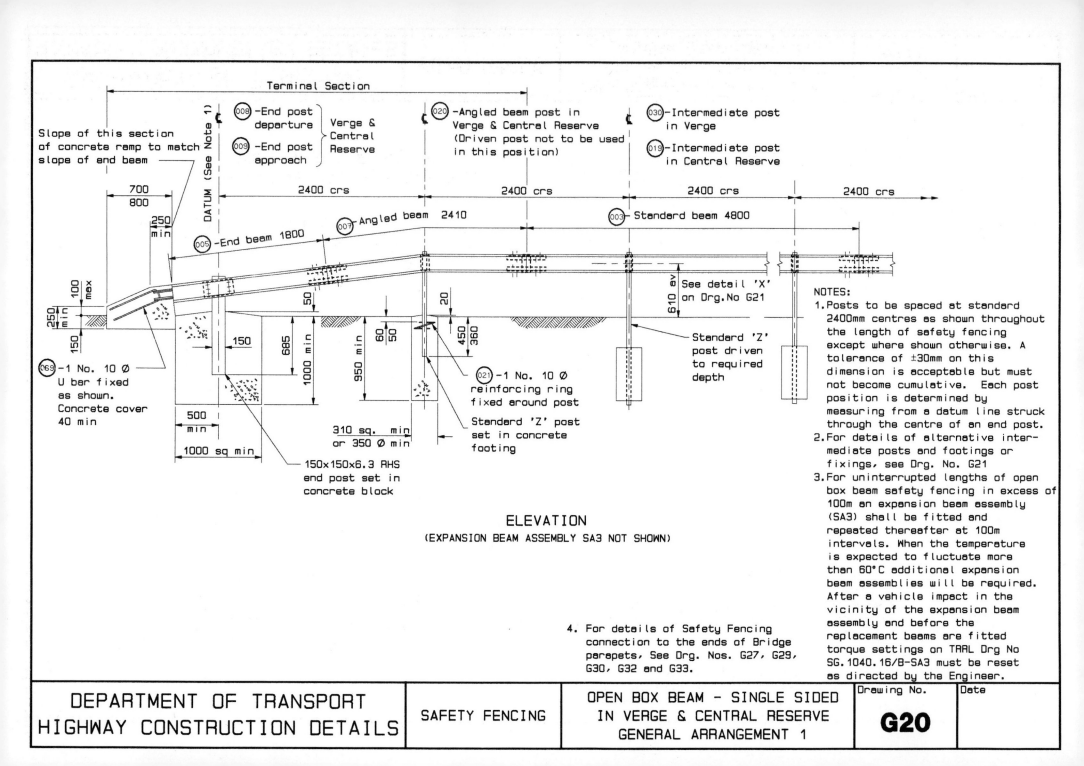

ELEVATION

(EXPANSION BEAM ASSEMBLY SA3 NOT SHOWN)

NOTES:

1. Posts to be spaced at standard 2400mm centres as shown throughout the length of safety fencing except where shown otherwise. A tolerance of ±30mm on this dimension is acceptable but must not become cumulative. Each post position is determined by measuring from a datum line struck through the centre of an end post.

2. For details of alternative intermediate posts and footings or fixings, see Drg. No. G21

3. For uninterrupted lengths of open box beam safety fencing in excess of 100m an expansion beam assembly (SA3) shall be fitted and repeated thereafter at 100m intervals. When the temperature is expected to fluctuate more than 60°C additional expansion beam assemblies will be required. After a vehicle impact in the vicinity of the expansion beam assembly and before the replacement beams are fitted torque settings on TRRL Drg No SG.1040.16/B-SA3 must be reset as directed by the Engineer.

4. For details of Safety Fencing connection to the ends of Bridge parapets, See Drg. Nos. G27, G29, G30, G32 and G33.

| DEPARTMENT OF TRANSPORT HIGHWAY CONSTRUCTION DETAILS | SAFETY FENCING | OPEN BOX BEAM - SINGLE SIDED IN VERGE & CENTRAL RESERVE GENERAL ARRANGEMENT 1 | Drawing No. **G20** | Date |

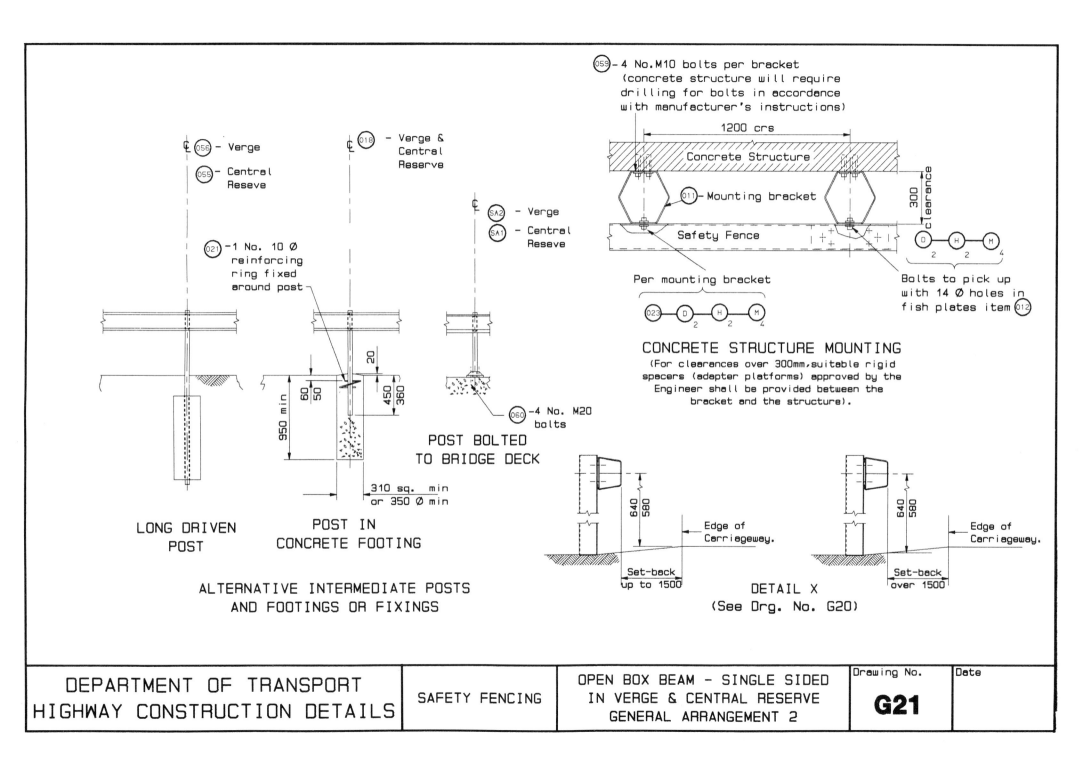

(056) - Verge

(055) - Central Reseve

(018) - Verge & Central Reseve

(SA2) - Verge

(SA1) - Central Reseve

(021) - 1 No. 10 Ø reinforcing ring fixed around post

(059) - 4 No. M10 bolts per bracket (concrete structure will require drilling for bolts in accordance with manufacturer's instructions)

1200 crs

Concrete Structure

(011) - Mounting bracket

Safety Fence

300 clearance

Per mounting bracket

(023) — D₂ — H₂ — M₄

D₂ — H₂ — M₄

Bolts to pick up with 14 Ø holes in fish plates item (012)

CONCRETE STRUCTURE MOUNTING
(For clearances over 300mm, suitable rigid spacers (adapter platforms) approved by the Engineer shall be provided between the bracket and the structure).

60
50
20
950 min
450
360

310 sq. min or 350 Ø min

(060) - 4 No. M20 bolts

POST BOLTED TO BRIDGE DECK

LONG DRIVEN POST

POST IN CONCRETE FOOTING

ALTERNATIVE INTERMEDIATE POSTS AND FOOTINGS OR FIXINGS

640
580

Edge of Carriageway.

Set-back up to 1500

640
580

Edge of Carriageway.

Set-back over 1500

DETAIL X
(See Drg. No. G20)

| DEPARTMENT OF TRANSPORT HIGHWAY CONSTRUCTION DETAILS | SAFETY FENCING | OPEN BOX BEAM - SINGLE SIDED IN VERGE & CENTRAL RESERVE GENERAL ARRANGEMENT 2 | Drawing No. G21 | Date |

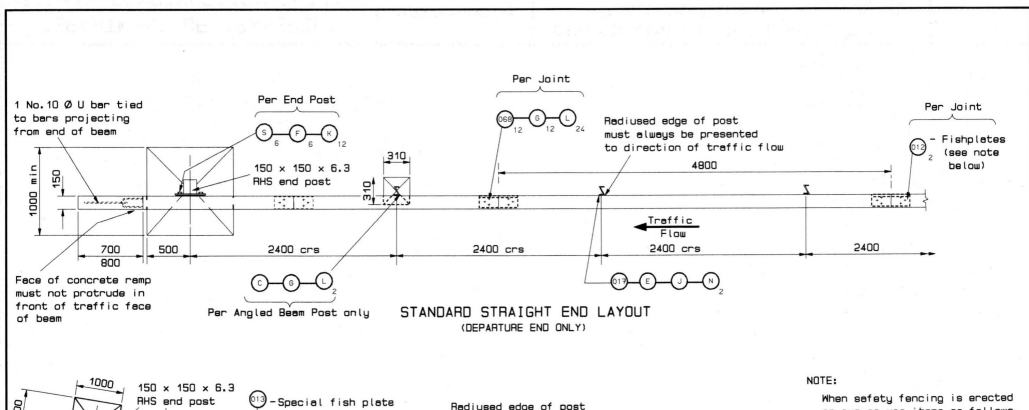

Per End Post
S⁶ — F⁶ — K¹²

Per Joint
068¹² — G¹² — L²⁴

Per Joint
012² — Fishplates (see note below)

1 No.10 Ø U bar tied to bars projecting from end of beam

150 x 150 x 6.3 RHS end post

310

310

150

1000 min

Radiused edge of post must always be presented to direction of traffic flow

4800

Traffic Flow

700
800
500
2400 crs
2400 crs
2400 crs
2400

Face of concrete ramp must not protrude in front of traffic face of beam

C — G — L²

017² — E — J — N²

Per Angled Beam Post only

STANDARD STRAIGHT END LAYOUT
(DEPARTURE END ONLY)

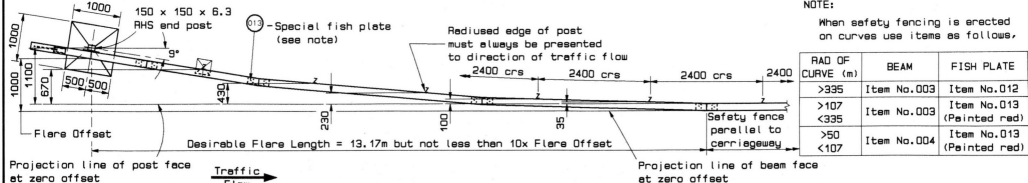

1000

1000
1100
670
500 500
430
230
100
35

9°

150 x 150 x 6.3 RHS end post

013 — Special fish plate (see note)

Radiused edge of post must always be presented to direction of traffic flow

2400 crs
2400 crs
2400 crs
2400

Safety fence parallel to carriageway

Flare Offset

Traffic Flow

Desirable Flare Length = 13.17m but not less than 10x Flare Offset

Projection line of post face at zero offset

Projection line of beam face at zero offset

STANDARD FLARED END LAYOUT
(APPROACH END ONLY)

NOTE:

When safety fencing is erected on curves use items as follows,

RAD OF CURVE (m)	BEAM	FISH PLATE
>335	Item No.003	Item No.012
>107 <335	Item No.003	Item No.013 (Painted red)
>50 <107	Item No.004	Item No.013 (Painted red)

DEPARTMENT OF TRANSPORT HIGHWAY CONSTRUCTION DETAILS	SAFETY FENCING	OPEN BOX BEAM - SINGLE SIDED IN VERGE AND CENTRAL RESERVE GENERAL ARRANGEMENT 3	Drawing No. **G22**	Date

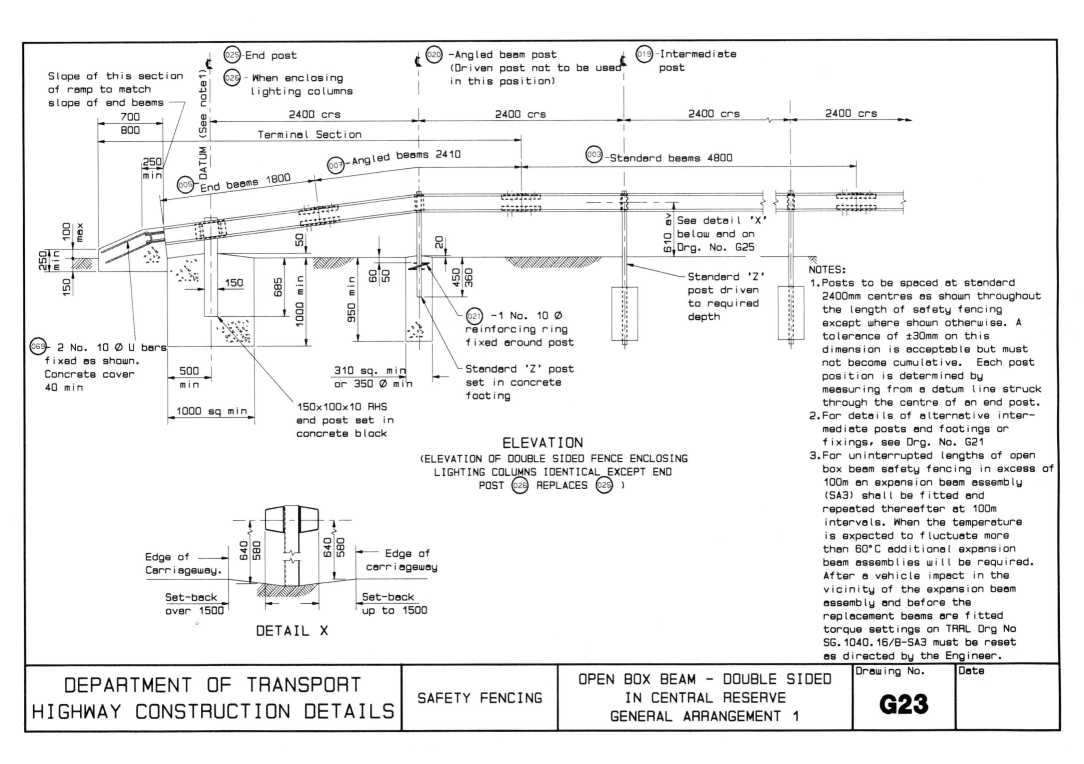

Slope of this section of ramp to match slope of end beams

(025)—End post

(026)— When enclosing lighting columns

(020) —Angled beam post (Driven post not to be used in this position)

(019)—Intermediate post

700
800

2400 crs
2400 crs
2400 crs
2400 crs

Terminal Section

DATUM (See note1)

(007)—Angled beams 2410

(003)—Standard beams 4800

250 min

(005) End beams 1800

See detail 'X' below and on Drg. No. G25

100 max

50

20

610 av

250 min

150

685

1000 min

950 min

60
50

450
360

Standard 'Z' post driven to required depth

(069)— 2 No. 10 Ø U bars fixed as shown. Concrete cover 40 min

150

500 min

310 sq. min or 350 Ø min

(021) —1 No. 10 Ø reinforcing ring fixed around post

Standard 'Z' post set in concrete footing

1000 sq min

150x100x10 RHS end post set in concrete block

ELEVATION

(ELEVATION OF DOUBLE SIDED FENCE ENCLOSING LIGHTING COLUMNS IDENTICAL EXCEPT END POST (026) REPLACES (025))

NOTES:
1. Posts to be spaced at standard 2400mm centres as shown throughout the length of safety fencing except where shown otherwise. A tolerance of ±30mm on this dimension is acceptable but must not become cumulative. Each post position is determined by measuring from a datum line struck through the centre of an end post.
2. For details of alternative inter- mediate posts and footings or fixings, see Drg. No. G21
3. For uninterrupted lengths of open box beam safety fencing in excess of 100m an expansion beam assembly (SA3) shall be fitted and repeated thereafter at 100m intervals. When the temperature is expected to fluctuate more than 60°C additional expansion beam assemblies will be required. After a vehicle impact in the vicinity of the expansion beam assembly and before the replacement beams are fitted torque settings on TRRL Drg No SG.1040.16/B-SA3 must be reset as directed by the Engineer.

640
580
640
580

Edge of Carriageway.

Edge of carriageway

Set-back over 1500

Set-back up to 1500

DETAIL X

| DEPARTMENT OF TRANSPORT HIGHWAY CONSTRUCTION DETAILS | SAFETY FENCING | OPEN BOX BEAM - DOUBLE SIDED IN CENTRAL RESERVE GENERAL ARRANGEMENT 1 | Drawing No. G23 | Date |

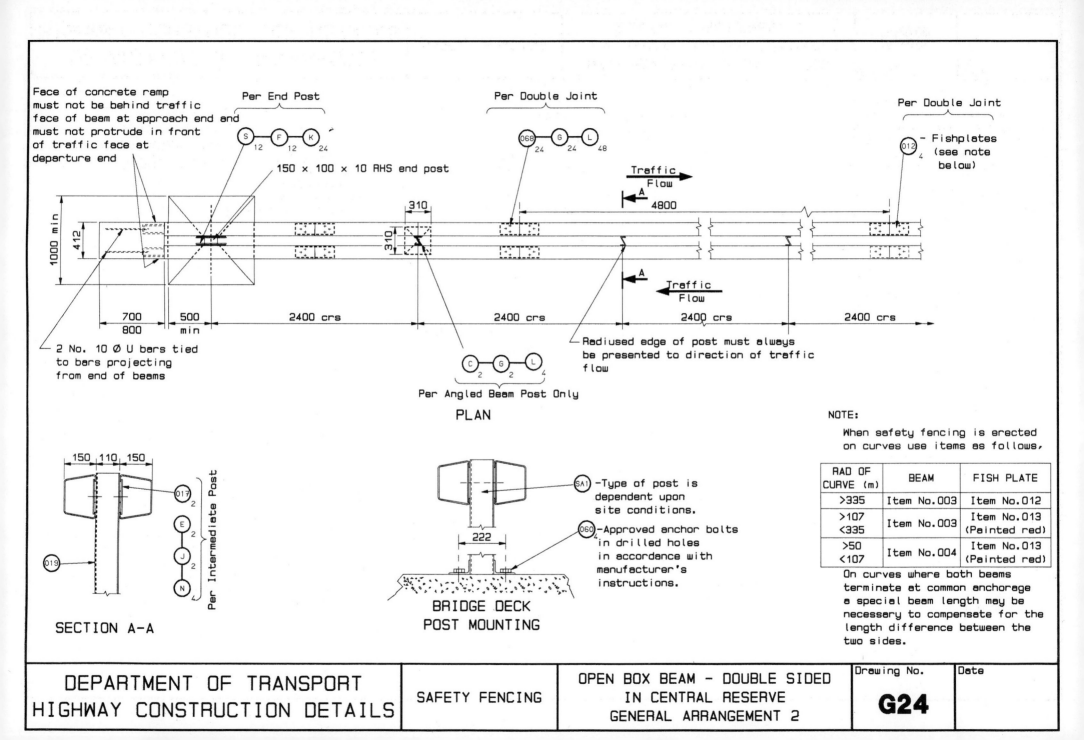

Face of concrete ramp must not be behind traffic face of beam at approach end and must not protrude in front of traffic face at departure end

Per End Post

Per Double Joint

Per Double Joint

S 12 — F 12 — K 24

068 24 — G 24 — L 48

012 4 — Fishplates (see note below)

150 × 100 × 10 RHS end post

Traffic Flow

A

4800

1000 min

412

310

310

A

Traffic Flow

700
800

500 min

2400 crs

2400 crs

2400 crs

2400 crs

2 No. 10 Ø U bars tied to bars projecting from end of beams

C 2 — G 2 — L 4

Radiused edge of post must always be presented to direction of traffic flow

Per Angled Beam Post Only

PLAN

SECTION A-A

150 | 110 | 150

017 2
019

E 2
J 2
N 4

Per Intermediate Post

BRIDGE DECK POST MOUNTING

222

SA1 -Type of post is dependent upon site conditions.

060 4 -Approved anchor bolts in drilled holes in accordance with manufacturer's instructions.

NOTE:

When safety fencing is erected on curves use items as follows,

RAD OF CURVE (m)	BEAM	FISH PLATE
>335	Item No.003	Item No.012
>107 <335	Item No.003	Item No.013 (Painted red)
>50 <107	Item No.004	Item No.013 (Painted red)

On curves where both beams terminate at common anchorage a special beam length may be necessary to compensate for the length difference between the two sides.

DEPARTMENT OF TRANSPORT HIGHWAY CONSTRUCTION DETAILS	SAFETY FENCING	OPEN BOX BEAM - DOUBLE SIDED IN CENTRAL RESERVE GENERAL ARRANGEMENT 2	Drawing No. G24	Date

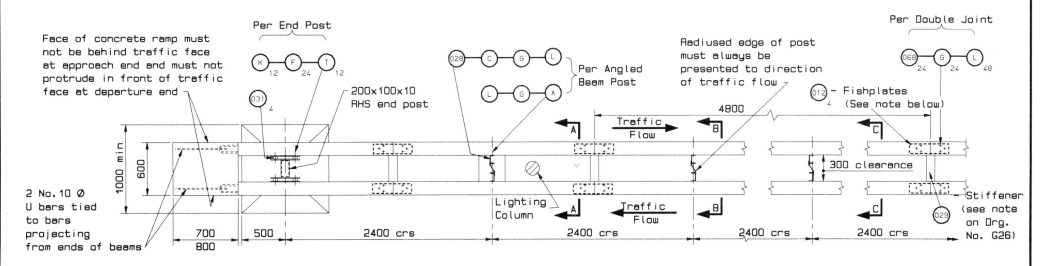

Face of concrete ramp must
not be behind traffic face
at approach end and must not
protrude in front of traffic
face at departure end

Per End Post

Per Angled
Beam Post

Radiused edge of post
must always be
presented to direction
of traffic flow

Per Double Joint

200x100x10
RHS end post

Traffic
Flow

4800

012 - Fishplates
(See note below)

300 clearance

2 No. 10 Ø
U bars tied
to bars
projecting
from ends of beams

Lighting
Column

Traffic
Flow

Stiffener
(see note
on Drg.
No. G26)

700   500   2400 crs   2400 crs   2400 crs   2400 crs
800

PLAN
(See G20 For Elevation)

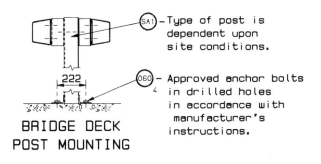

SA1 - Type of post is
dependent upon
site conditions.

222

060 - Approved anchor bolts
in drilled holes
in accordance with
manufacturer's
instructions.

**BRIDGE DECK
POST MOUNTING**

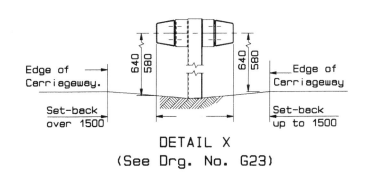

Edge of
Carriageway.

640 580

640 580

Edge of
Carriageway

Set-back
over 1500

Set-back
up to 1500

DETAIL X
(See Drg. No. G23)

NOTE:

When safety fencing is erected
on curves use items as follows,

RAD OF CURVE (m)	BEAM	FISH PLATE
>335	Item No. 003	Item No. 012
>107 <335	Item No. 003	Item No. 013 (Painted red)
>50 <107	Item No. 004	Item No. 013 (Painted red)

On curves where both beams
terminate at common anchorage
a special beam length may be
necessary to compensate for the
length difference between the
two sides.

DEPARTMENT OF TRANSPORT HIGHWAY CONSTRUCTION DETAILS	SAFETY FENCING	OPEN BOX BEAM -DOUBLE SIDED ENCLOSING LIGHTING COLUMNS GENERAL ARRANGEMENT 1	Drawing No. **G25**	Date

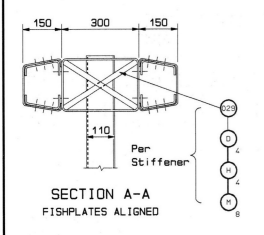

SECTION A-A
FISHPLATES ALIGNED

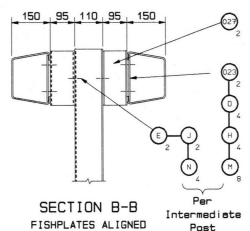

SECTION B-B
FISHPLATES ALIGNED

Per Intermediate Post

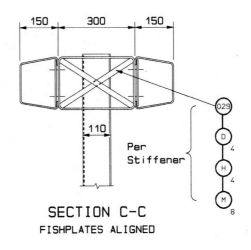

SECTION C-C
FISHPLATES ALIGNED

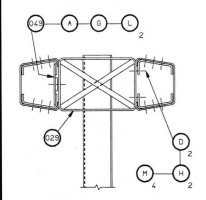

SECTION A-A
WHEN FISHPLATES ARE OUT OF ALIGNMENT eg ON A CURVE

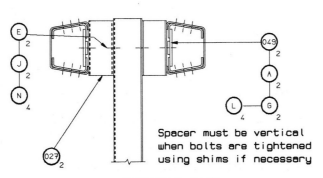

Spacer must be vertical when bolts are tightened using shims if necessary

SECTION B-B
ALTERNATIVE ASSEMBLY WHEN POSTS ARE MOUNTED ADJACENT TO FISHPLATES

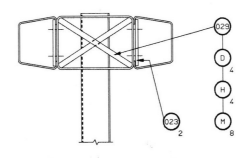

SECTION C-C
ALTERNATIVE ASSEMBLY USING CLAMP PLATE (023) WHEN BOLT HOLES IN STIFFENER DO NOT ALIGN WITH HOLES IN BEAM

NOTE:

If large dia. lighting columns are required to be installed item (029) may be increased in width by up to 100mm (items (027) and (028) increased to suit) and spacer, (031) with larger bolts, inserted between the post (026) and the beams (005).

| DEPARTMENT OF TRANSPORT HIGHWAY CONSTRUCTION DETAILS | SAFETY FENCING | OPEN BOX BEAM - DOUBLE SIDED ENCLOSING LIGHTING COLUMNS GENERAL ARRANGEMENT 2 | Drawing No. G26 | Date |

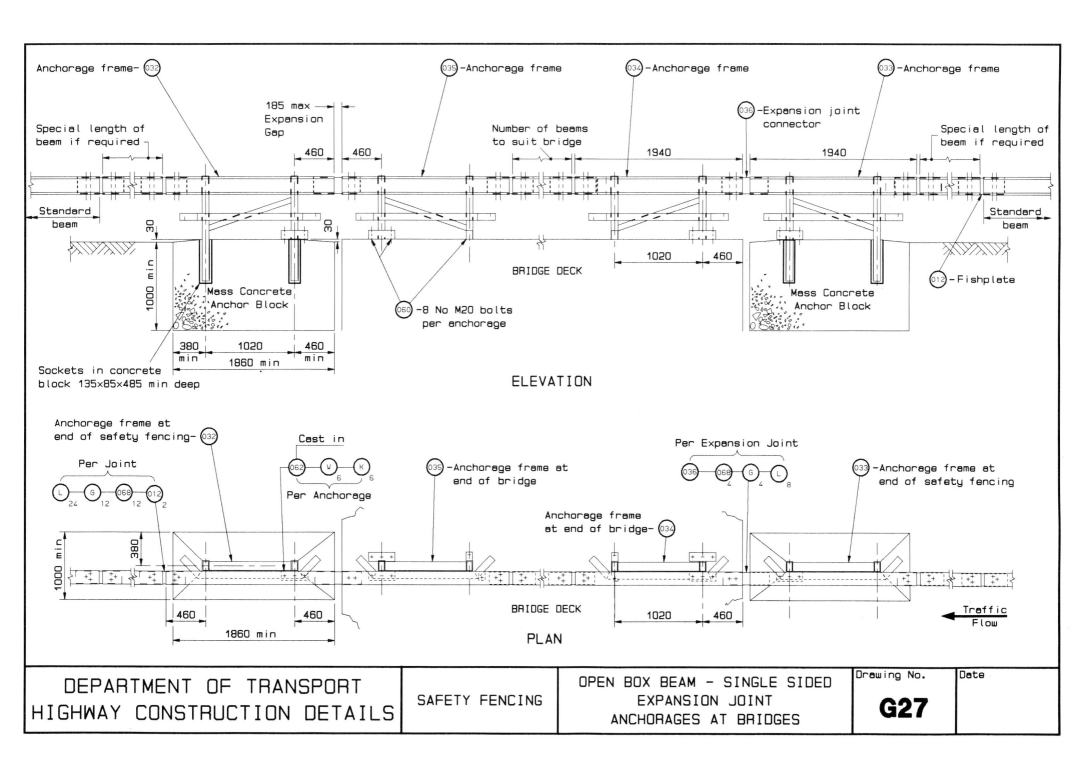

ELEVATION

PLAN

| DEPARTMENT OF TRANSPORT HIGHWAY CONSTRUCTION DETAILS | SAFETY FENCING | OPEN BOX BEAM - SINGLE SIDED EXPANSION JOINT ANCHORAGES AT BRIDGES | Drawing No. **G27** | Date |

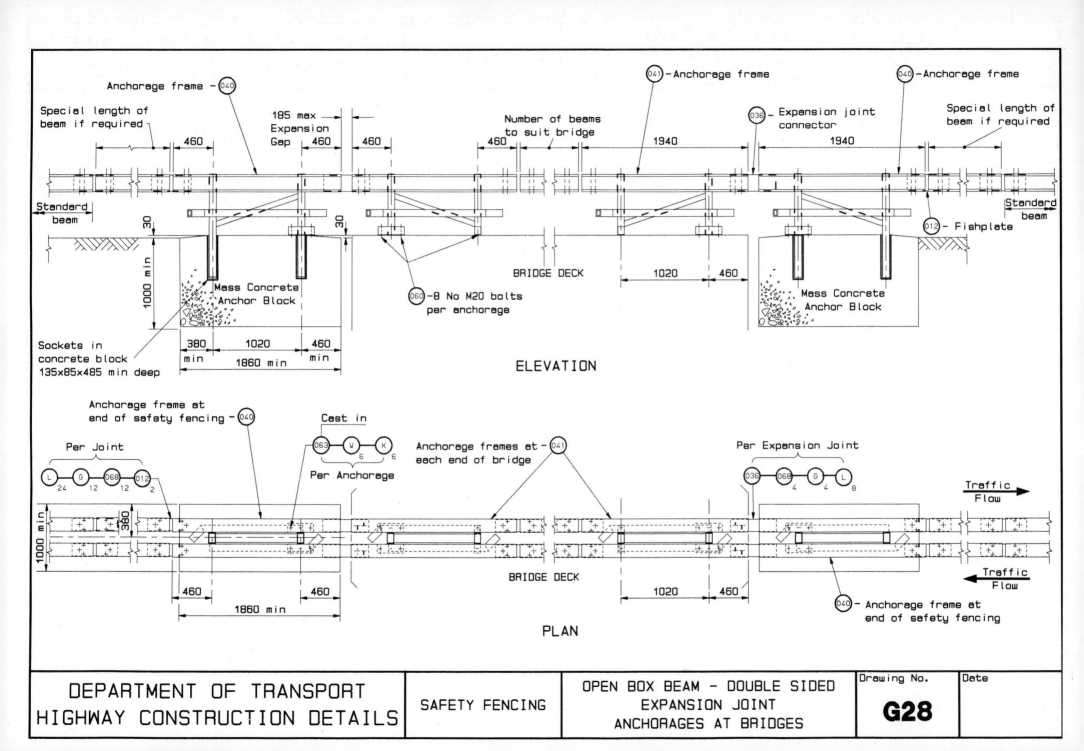

ELEVATION

PLAN

DEPARTMENT OF TRANSPORT HIGHWAY CONSTRUCTION DETAILS	SAFETY FENCING	OPEN BOX BEAM - DOUBLE SIDED EXPANSION JOINT ANCHORAGES AT BRIDGES	Drawing No. G28	Date

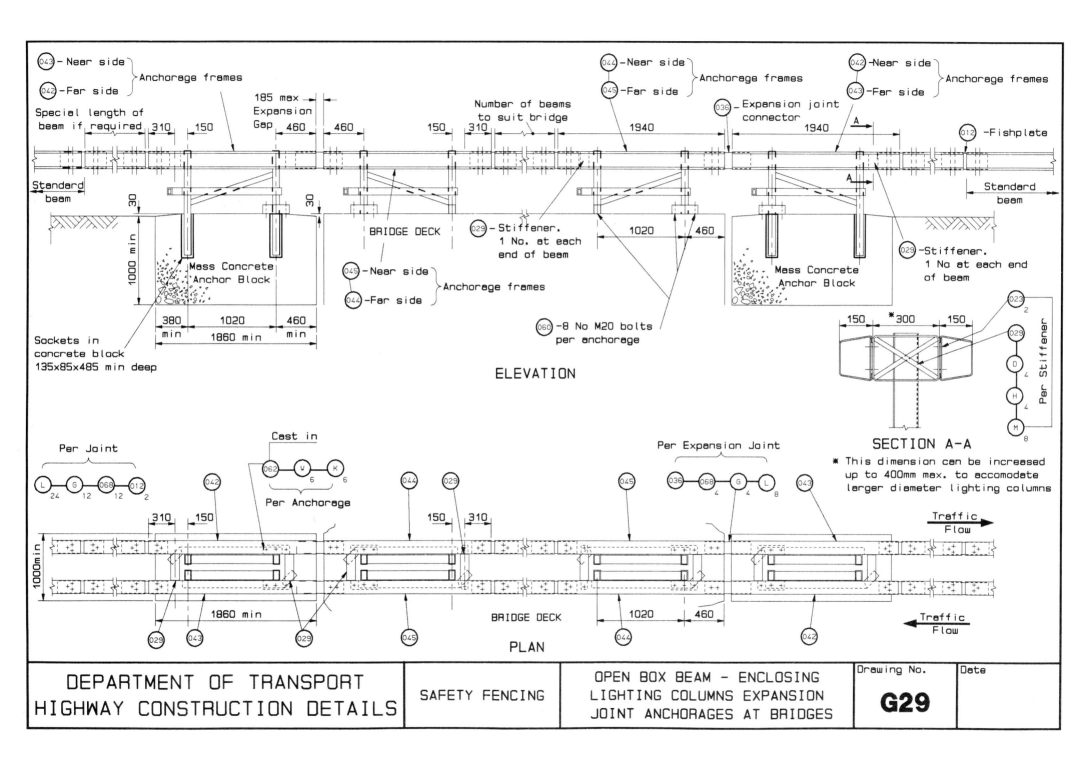

ELEVATION

SECTION A-A

* This dimension can be increased
up to 400mm max. to accomodate
larger diameter lighting columns

PLAN

DEPARTMENT OF TRANSPORT HIGHWAY CONSTRUCTION DETAILS	SAFETY FENCING	OPEN BOX BEAM - ENCLOSING LIGHTING COLUMNS EXPANSION JOINT ANCHORAGES AT BRIDGES	Drawing No. **G29**	Date

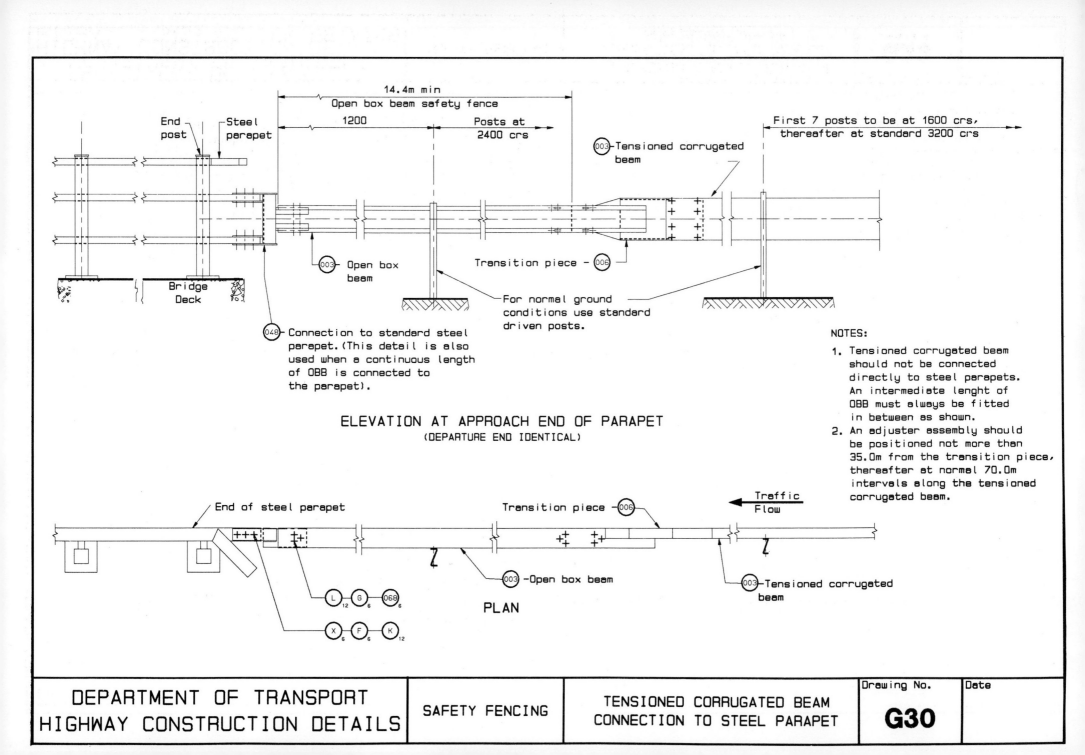

14.4m min
Open box beam safety fence

1200

Posts at 2400 crs

First 7 posts to be at 1600 crs, thereafter at standard 3200 crs

End post

Steel parapet

(003)-Tensioned corrugated beam

(003)-Open box beam

Transition piece - (006)

Bridge Deck

For normal ground conditions use standard driven posts.

(048)-Connection to standard steel parapet. (This detail is also used when a continuous length of OBB is connected to the parapet).

ELEVATION AT APPROACH END OF PARAPET
(DEPARTURE END IDENTICAL)

NOTES:

1. Tensioned corrugated beam should not be connected directly to steel parapets. An intermediate lenght of OBB must always be fitted in between as shown.

2. An adjuster assembly should be positioned not more than 35.0m from the transition piece, thereafter at normal 70.0m intervals along the tensioned corrugated beam.

End of steel parapet

Transition piece - (006)

Traffic Flow

(003) -Open box beam

(003)-Tensioned corrugated beam

(L)₁₂ (G)₆ (068)₆

(X)₆ (F)₆ (K)₁₂

PLAN

DEPARTMENT OF TRANSPORT
HIGHWAY CONSTRUCTION DETAILS

SAFETY FENCING

TENSIONED CORRUGATED BEAM CONNECTION TO STEEL PARAPET

Drawing No.
G30

Date

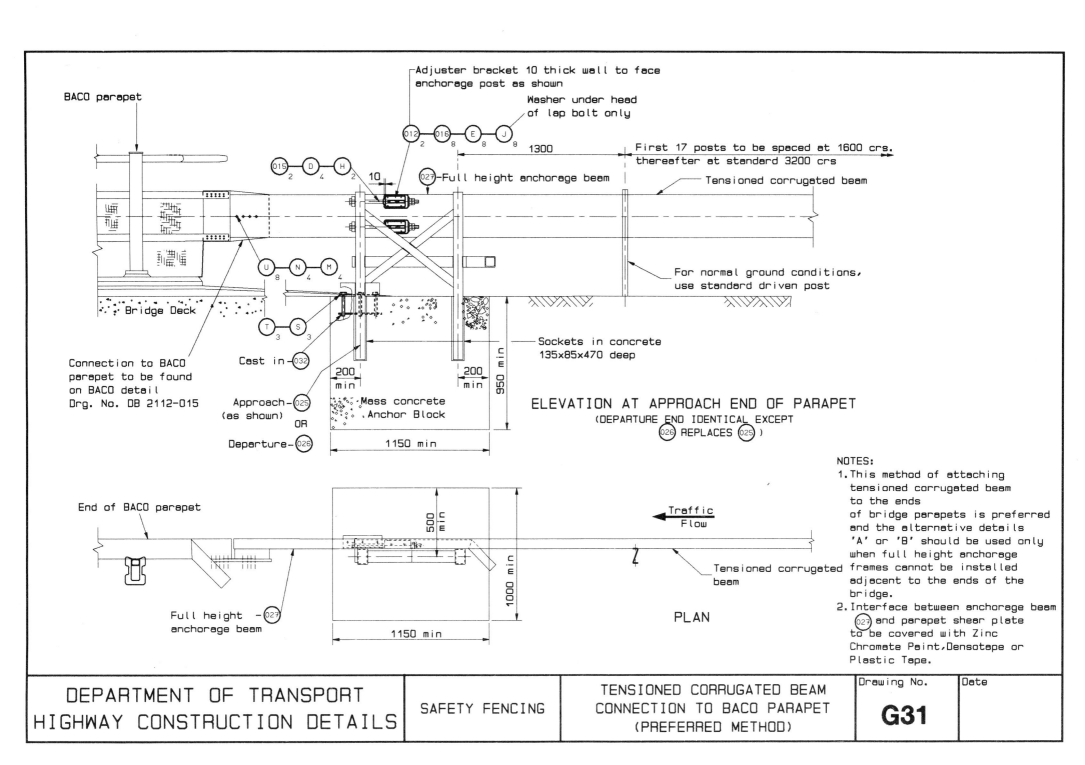

BACO parapet

Adjuster bracket 10 thick wall to face
anchorage post as shown

Washer under head
of lap bolt only

(012)2 —(016)8 —(E)8 —(J)8

(015)2 —(D)4 —(H)2

10

(027)-Full height anchorage beam

1300

First 17 posts to be spaced at 1600 crs.
thereafter at standard 3200 crs

Tensioned corrugated beam

(U)8 —(N)4 —(M)4

Bridge Deck

For normal ground conditions,
use standard driven post

Connection to BACO
parapet to be found
on BACO detail
Drg. No. DB 2112-015

Cast in -(032)

(T)3 —(S)3

Sockets in concrete
135x85x470 deep

950 min

200 min

200 min

Approach -(025)
(as shown)
OR

Departure -(026)

Mass concrete
Anchor Block

1150 min

ELEVATION AT APPROACH END OF PARAPET
(DEPARTURE END IDENTICAL EXCEPT
(026) REPLACES (025))

End of BACO parapet

500 min

1000 min

Traffic
Flow

Tensioned corrugated
beam

Full height -(027)
anchorage beam

1150 min

PLAN

NOTES:
1. This method of attaching
   tensioned corrugated beam
   to the ends
   of bridge parapets is preferred
   and the alternative details
   'A' or 'B' should be used only
   when full height anchorage
   frames cannot be installed
   adjacent to the ends of the
   bridge.
2. Interface between anchorage beam
   (027) and parapet shear plate
   to be covered with Zinc
   Chromate Paint,Densotape or
   Plastic Tape.

| DEPARTMENT OF TRANSPORT HIGHWAY CONSTRUCTION DETAILS | SAFETY FENCING | TENSIONED CORRUGATED BEAM CONNECTION TO BACO PARAPET (PREFERRED METHOD) | Drawing No. G31 | Date |

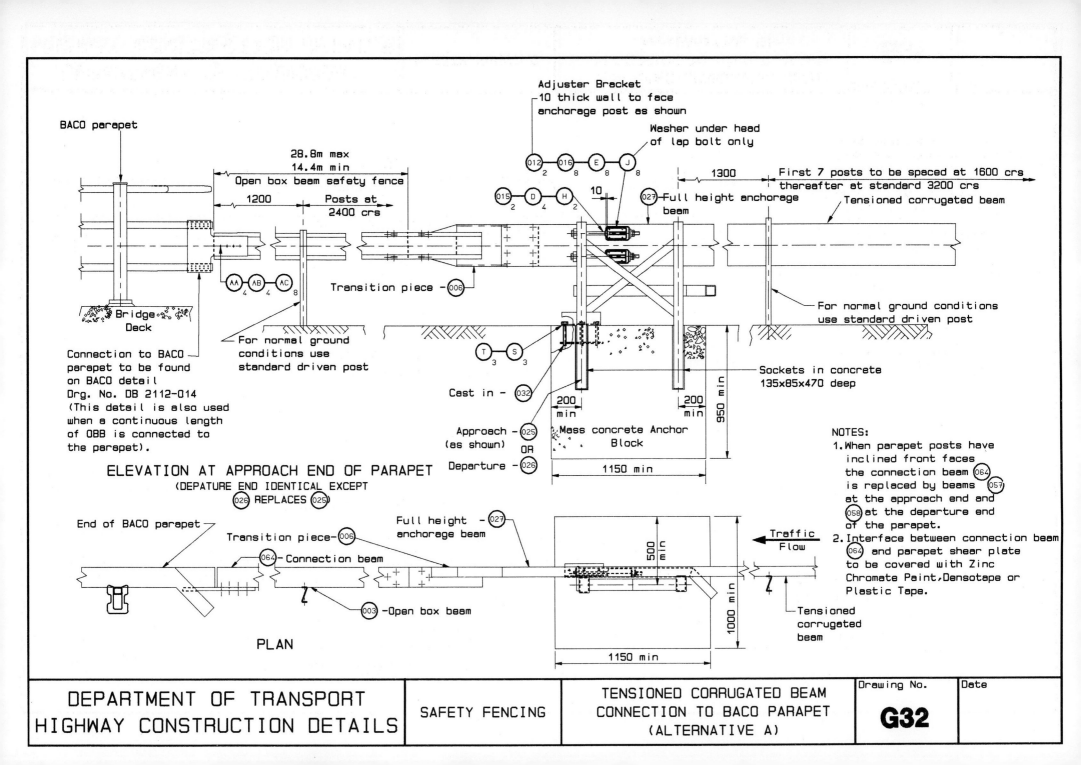

BACO parapet

Adjuster Bracket
-10 thick wall to face
anchorage post as shown

Washer under head
of lap bolt only

28.8m max
14.4m min
Open box beam safety fence

1300

First 7 posts to be spaced at 1600 crs
thereafter at standard 3200 crs

Tensioned corrugated beam

1200

Posts at
2400 crs

(012)₂ (016)₈ (E)₈ (J)₈

(015)₂ (D)₄ (H)₂

10

(027) Full height anchorage
beam

(AA)₄ (AB)₄ (AC)₈

Transition piece - (006)

For normal ground conditions
use standard driven post

Bridge
Deck

For normal ground
conditions use
standard driven post

(T)₃ (S)₃

Sockets in concrete
135x85x470 deep

Connection to BACO
parapet to be found
on BACO detail
Drg. No. DB 2112-014
(This detail is also used
when a continuous length
of OBB is connected to
the parapet).

Cast in - (032)

Approach - (025)
(as shown)
OR
Departure - (026)

200
min

Mass concrete Anchor
Block

200
min

950
min

1150 min

NOTES:
1. When parapet posts have
   inclined front faces
   the connection beam (064)
   is replaced by beams (057)
   at the approach end and
   (058) at the departure end
   of the parapet.
2. Interface between connection beam
   (064) and parapet shear plate
   to be covered with Zinc
   Chromate Paint, Densotape or
   Plastic Tape.

ELEVATION AT APPROACH END OF PARAPET
(DEPATURE END IDENTICAL EXCEPT
(026) REPLACES (025))

End of BACO parapet

Transition piece- (006)

Full height - (027)
anchorage beam

(064) -Connection beam

Traffic
Flow

500
min

1000
min

(003) -Open box beam

Tensioned
corrugated
beam

PLAN

1150 min

DEPARTMENT OF TRANSPORT
HIGHWAY CONSTRUCTION DETAILS

SAFETY FENCING

TENSIONED CORRUGATED BEAM
CONNECTION TO BACO PARAPET
(ALTERNATIVE A)

Drawing No.

G32

Date

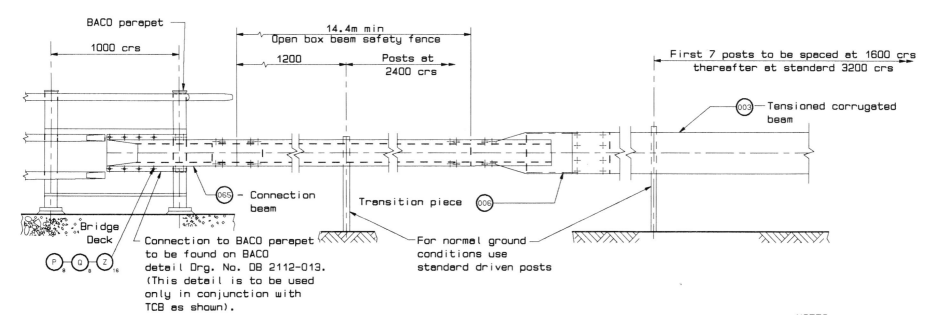

BACO parapet

1000 crs

14.4m min
Open box beam safety fence

1200   Posts at
              2400 crs

First 7 posts to be spaced at 1600 crs
thereafter at standard 3200 crs

003 – Tensioned corrugated
      beam

065 – Connection
      beam

Bridge
Deck

Connection to BACO parapet
to be found on BACO
detail Drg. No. DB 2112-013.
(This detail is to be used
only in conjunction with
TCB as shown).

P   Q   Z
 8   8   16

Transition piece 006

For normal ground
conditions use
standard driven posts

ELEVATION AT APPROACH END OF PARAPET
(DEPARTURE END IDENTICAL)

NOTES:

1. When parapet posts have
   inclined front faces the
   connection beam 065
   is replaced by beams 066
   at approach end and 067
   at the departure end of
   the parapet.

2. Interface between connection beam
   065 and parapet shear plate
   to be covered with Zinc
   Chromate Paint, Densotape or
   Plastic Tape.

3. An adjuster assembly should
   be positioned not more than
   35.0m from the transition piece,
   thereafter at normal 70.0m
   intervals along the tensioned
   corrugated beam.

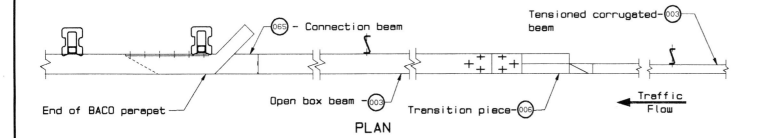

065 – Connection beam

Tensioned corrugated- 003
beam

End of BACO parapet

Open box beam – 003

Transition piece- 006

Traffic
Flow

PLAN

| DEPARTMENT OF TRANSPORT HIGHWAY CONSTRUCTION DETAILS | SAFETY FENCING | TENSIONED CORRUGATED BEAM CONNECTION TO BACO PARAPET (ALTERNATIVE B) | Drawing No. **G33** | Date |

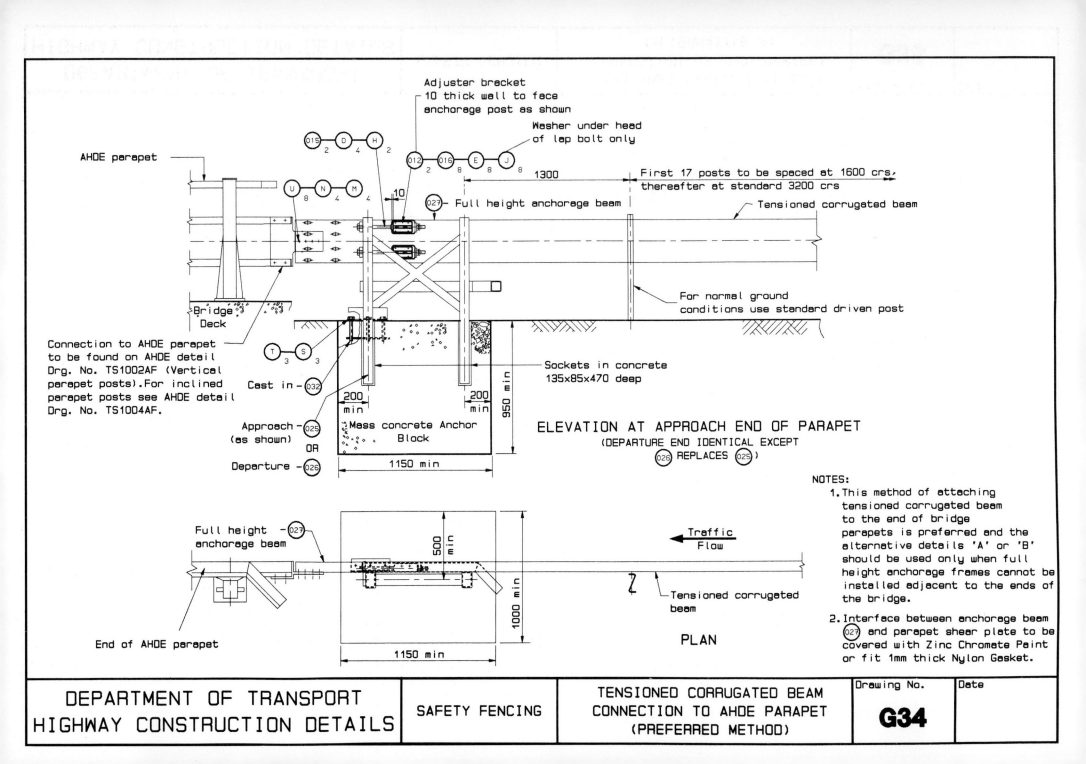

Adjuster bracket
10 thick wall to face
anchorage post as shown

Washer under head
of lap bolt only

AHDE parapet

⊙015 — D — H
   2   4   2

⊙012 — ⊙016 — E — J
   2   8   8   8

U — N — M
8   4   4

1300

First 17 posts to be spaced at 1600 crs,
thereafter at standard 3200 crs

10

⊙027 — Full height anchorage beam

Tensioned corrugated beam

Bridge
Deck

T — S
3   3

Connection to AHDE parapet
to be found on AHDE detail
Drg. No. TS1002AF (Vertical
parapet posts). For inclined
parapet posts see AHDE detail
Drg. No. TS1004AF.

Cast in — ⊙032

200
min

200
min

950 min

For normal ground
conditions use standard driven post

Sockets in concrete
135x85x470 deep

ELEVATION AT APPROACH END OF PARAPET
(DEPARTURE END IDENTICAL EXCEPT
⊙026 REPLACES ⊙025)

Approach — ⊙025
(as shown)

OR

Departure — ⊙026

Mass concrete Anchor
Block

1150 min

NOTES:

1. This method of attaching
tensioned corrugated beam
to the end of bridge
parapets is preferred and the
alternative details 'A' or 'B'
should be used only when full
height anchorage frames cannot be
installed adjacent to the ends of
the bridge.

Full height — ⊙027
anchorage beam

500 min

Traffic
Flow

1000 min

Tensioned corrugated
beam

End of AHDE parapet

1150 min

PLAN

2. Interface between anchorage beam
⊙027 and parapet shear plate to be
covered with Zinc Chromate Paint
or fit 1mm thick Nylon Gasket.

| DEPARTMENT OF TRANSPORT HIGHWAY CONSTRUCTION DETAILS | SAFETY FENCING | TENSIONED CORRUGATED BEAM CONNECTION TO AHDE PARAPET (PREFERRED METHOD) | Drawing No. **G34** | Date |

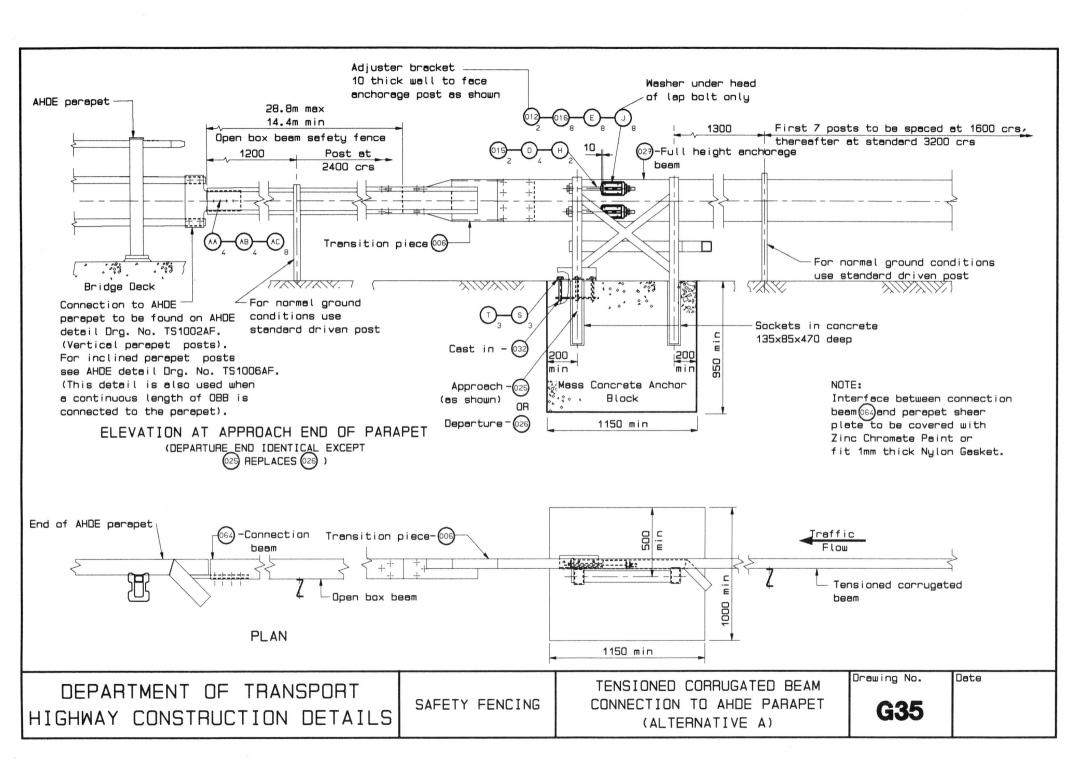

AHDE parapet

Adjuster bracket
10 thick wall to face
anchorage post as shown

Washer under head
of lap bolt only

28.8m max
14.4m min

Open box beam safety fence

1200

Post at
2400 crs

(012)₂ (016)₈ (E)₈ (J)₈

1300

First 7 posts to be spaced at 1600 crs,
thereafter at standard 3200 crs

(015)₂ (D)₄ (H)₂

10

(027)—Full height anchorage
beam

Transition piece (006)

For normal ground conditions
use standard driven post

(AA)₄ (AB)₄ (AC)₈

Bridge Deck

Connection to AHDE
parapet to be found on AHDE
detail Drg. No. TS1002AF.
(Vertical parapet posts).
For inclined parapet posts
see AHDE detail Drg. No. TS1006AF.
(This detail is also used when
a continuous length of OBB is
connected to the parapet).

For normal ground
conditions use
standard driven post

(T)₃ (S)₃

Cast in — (032)

Approach — (025)
(as shown)
OR
Departure — (026)

200
min

Mass Concrete Anchor
Block

200
min

950 min

Sockets in concrete
135x85x470 deep

NOTE:
Interface between connection
beam (064) and parapet shear
plate to be covered with
Zinc Chromate Paint or
fit 1mm thick Nylon Gasket.

1150 min

ELEVATION AT APPROACH END OF PARAPET
(DEPARTURE END IDENTICAL EXCEPT
(025) REPLACES (026))

End of AHDE parapet

(064)—Connection
beam

Transition piece—(006)

Traffic
Flow

Open box beam

500 min

1000 min

Tensioned corrugated
beam

PLAN

1150 min

DEPARTMENT OF TRANSPORT
HIGHWAY CONSTRUCTION DETAILS

SAFETY FENCING

TENSIONED CORRUGATED BEAM
CONNECTION TO AHDE PARAPET
(ALTERNATIVE A)

Drawing No.
G35

Date

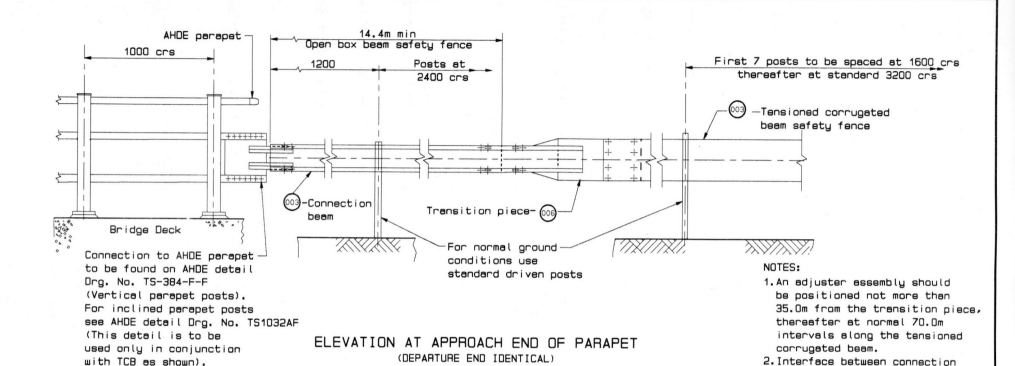

AHDE parapet

1000 crs

14.4m min
Open box beam safety fence

1200

Posts at
2400 crs

First 7 posts to be spaced at 1600 crs
thereafter at standard 3200 crs

(003) —Tensioned corrugated
beam safety fence

(003)—Connection
beam

Transition piece—(006)

For normal ground
conditions use
standard driven posts

Bridge Deck

Connection to AHDE parapet
to be found on AHDE detail
Drg. No. TS-384-F-F
(Vertical parapet posts).
For inclined parapet posts
see AHDE detail Drg. No. TS1032AF
(This detail is to be
used only in conjunction
with TCB as shown).

ELEVATION AT APPROACH END OF PARAPET
(DEPARTURE END IDENTICAL)

NOTES:

1. An adjuster assembly should
   be positioned not more than
   35.0m from the transition piece,
   thereafter at normal 70.0m
   intervals along the tensioned
   corrugated beam.
2. Interface between connection
   beam (003) and parapet shear plate
   to be covered in Zinc Chromate
   Paint or fit 1mm thick
   Nylon Gasket.

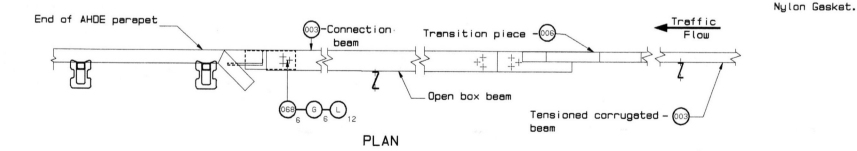

End of AHDE parapet

(003)—Connection
beam

Transition piece —(006)

Traffic
Flow

Open box beam

(068)—(G)—(L)
  6   6   12

Tensioned corrugated —(003)
beam

PLAN

DEPARTMENT OF TRANSPORT HIGHWAY CONSTRUCTION DETAILS	SAFETY FENCING	TENSIONED CORRUGATED BEAM CONNECTION TO AHDE PARAPET (ALTERNATIVE B)	Drawing No. G36	Date

Series H—
Fences, Stiles and Gates

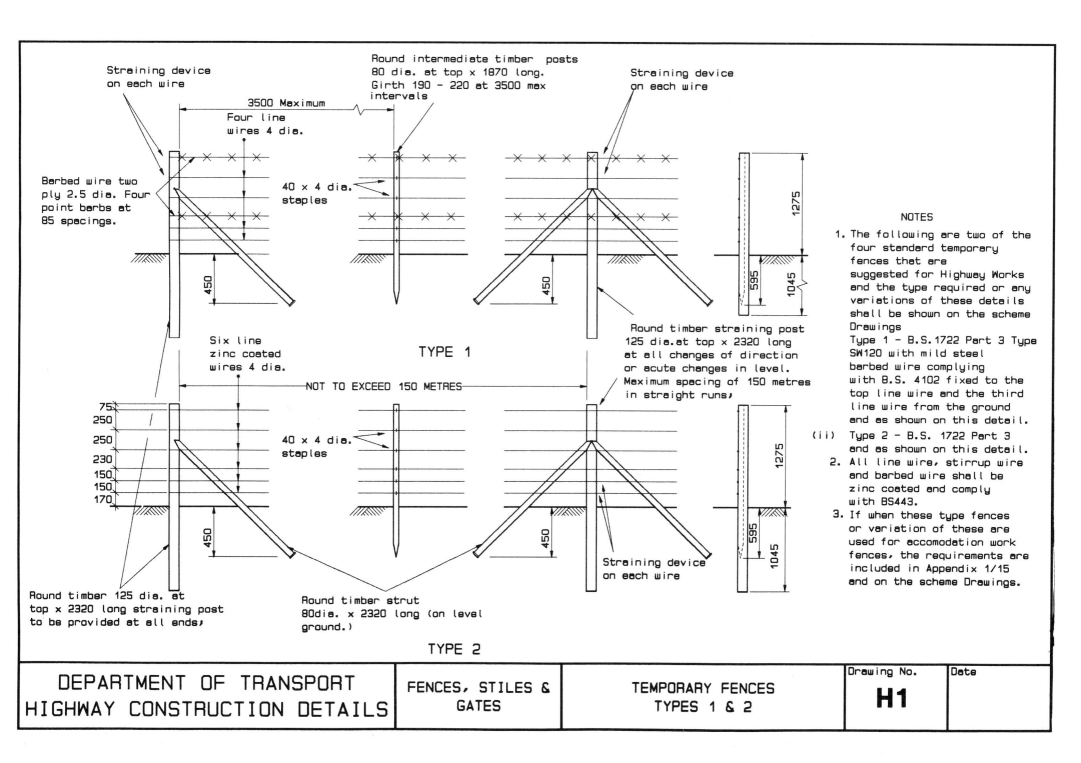

Straining device on each wire

Round intermediate timber posts 80 dia. at top x 1870 long. Girth 190 – 220 at 3500 max intervals

Straining device on each wire

3500 Maximum

Four line wires 4 dia.

Barbed wire two ply 2.5 dia. Four point barbs at 85 spacings.

40 x 4 dia. staples

450

450

1275

595

1045

TYPE 1

Six line zinc coated wires 4 dia.

Round timber straining post 125 dia. at top x 2320 long at all changes of direction or acute changes in level. Maximum spacing of 150 metres in straight runs;

NOT TO EXCEED 150 METRES

75
250
250
230
150
150
170

40 x 4 dia. staples

450

450

1275

595

1045

Round timber 125 dia. at top x 2320 long straining post to be provided at all ends;

Round timber strut 80dia. x 2320 long (on level ground.)

Straining device on each wire

TYPE 2

NOTES

1. The following are two of the four standard temporary fences that are suggested for Highway Works and the type required or any variations of these details shall be shown on the scheme Drawings
Type 1 – B.S. 1722 Part 3 Type SW120 with mild steel barbed wire complying with B.S. 4102 fixed to the top line wire and the third line wire from the ground and as shown on this detail.

(ii) Type 2 – B.S. 1722 Part 3 and as shown on this detail.

2. All line wire, stirrup wire and barbed wire shall be zinc coated and comply with BS443.

3. If when these type fences or variation of these are used for accomodation work fences, the requirements are included in Appendix 1/15 and on the scheme Drawings.

| DEPARTMENT OF TRANSPORT HIGHWAY CONSTRUCTION DETAILS | FENCES, STILES & GATES | TEMPORARY FENCES TYPES 1 & 2 | Drawing No. H1 | Date |

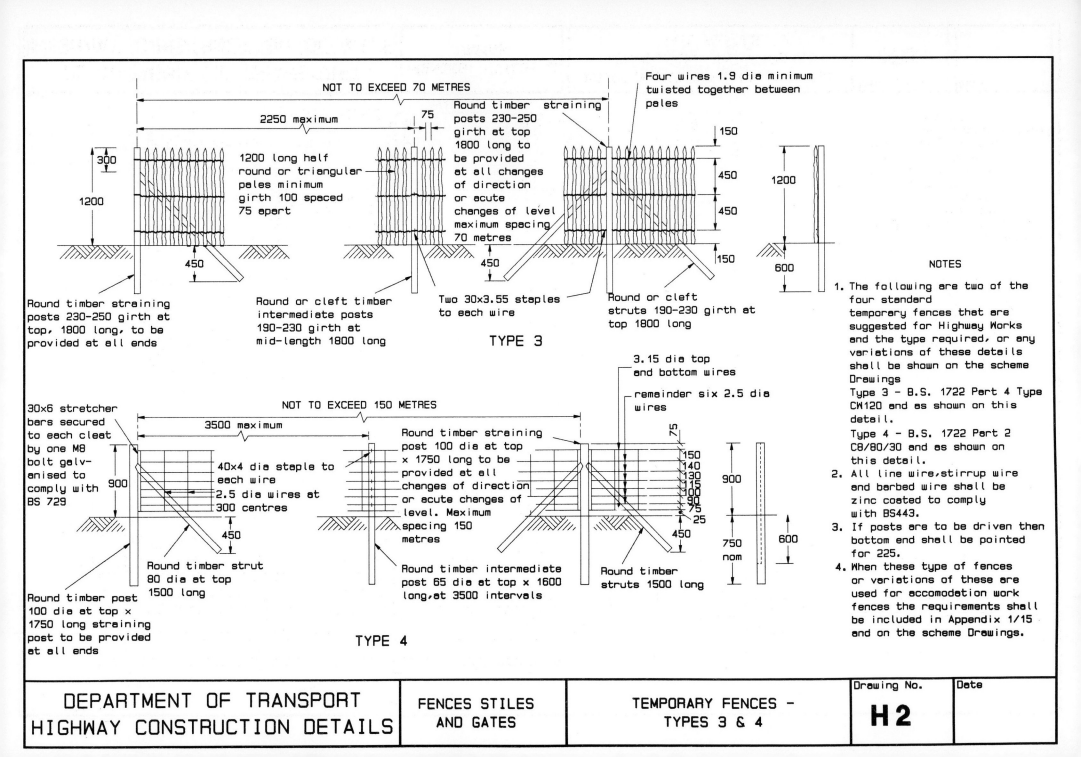

NOT TO EXCEED 70 METRES

2250 maximum

75

300

1200

450

1200 long half round or triangular pales minimum girth 100 spaced 75 apart

Round timber straining posts 230-250 girth at top 1800 long to be provided at all changes of direction or acute changes of level maximum spacing 70 metres

Four wires 1.9 dia minimum twisted together between pales

150

450

450

1200

150

600

450

Round timber straining posts 230-250 girth at top, 1800 long, to be provided at all ends

Round or cleft timber intermediate posts 190-230 girth at mid-length 1800 long

Two 30x3.55 staples to each wire

Round or cleft struts 190-230 girth at top 1800 long

TYPE 3

NOTES

1. The following are two of the four standard temporary fences that are suggested for Highway Works and the type required, or any variations of these details shall be shown on the scheme Drawings
   Type 3 - B.S. 1722 Part 4 Type CW120 and as shown on this detail.
   Type 4 - B.S. 1722 Part 2 C8/80/30 and as shown on this detail.
2. All line wire, stirrup wire and barbed wire shall be zinc coated to comply with BS443.
3. If posts are to be driven then bottom end shall be pointed for 225.
4. When these type of fences or variations of these are used for accomodation work fences the requirements shall be included in Appendix 1/15 and on the scheme Drawings.

30x6 stretcher bars secured to each cleat by one M8 bolt galvanised to comply with BS 729

NOT TO EXCEED 150 METRES

3500 maximum

900

40x4 dia staple to each wire
2.5 dia wires at 300 centres

Round timber straining post 100 dia at top x 1750 long to be provided at all changes of direction or acute changes of level. Maximum spacing 150 metres

3.15 dia top and bottom wires

remainder six 2.5 dia wires

75

150
140
130
115
100
90
75
25

900

450

750 nom

600

450

Round timber strut 80 dia at top 1500 long

Round timber post 100 dia at top x 1750 long straining post to be provided at all ends

Round timber intermediate post 65 dia at top x 1600 long, at 3500 intervals

Round timber struts 1500 long

TYPE 4

DEPARTMENT OF TRANSPORT
HIGHWAY CONSTRUCTION DETAILS

FENCES STILES AND GATES

TEMPORARY FENCES - TYPES 3 & 4

Drawing No.
H2

Date

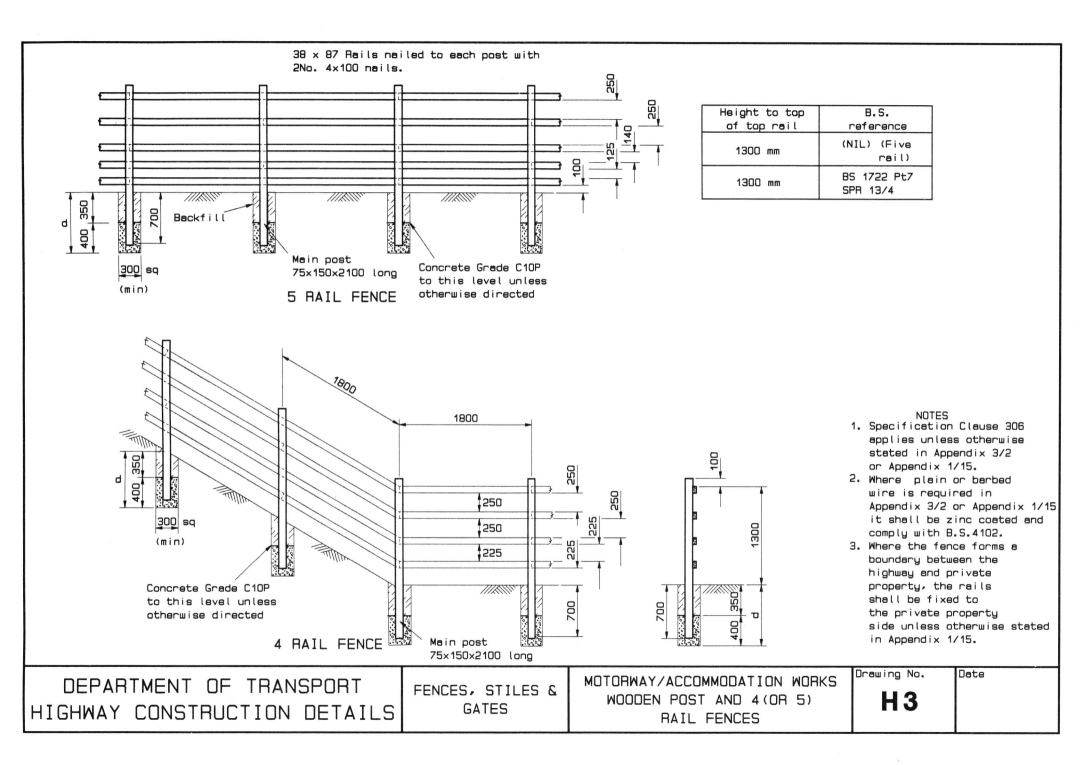

38 x 87 Rails nailed to each post with 2No. 4x100 nails.

5 RAIL FENCE

250
250
140
125
100

Backfill
Main post
75x150x2100 long
Concrete Grade C10P
to this level unless
otherwise directed

d 350 400 700
300 sq (min)

Height to top of top rail	B.S. reference
1300 mm	(NIL) (Five rail)
1300 mm	BS 1722 Pt7 SPR 13/4

4 RAIL FENCE

1800
1800

250
250
250
225
225
225
250
1300
100
700
700
350
400
d

d 350 400
300 sq (min)

Concrete Grade C10P
to this level unless
otherwise directed

Main post
75x150x2100 long

NOTES
1. Specification Clause 306 applies unless otherwise stated in Appendix 3/2 or Appendix 1/15.
2. Where plain or barbed wire is required in Appendix 3/2 or Appendix 1/15 it shall be zinc coated and comply with B.S.4102.
3. Where the fence forms a boundary between the highway and private property, the rails shall be fixed to the private property side unless otherwise stated in Appendix 1/15.

DEPARTMENT OF TRANSPORT HIGHWAY CONSTRUCTION DETAILS	FENCES, STILES & GATES	MOTORWAY/ACCOMMODATION WORKS WOODEN POST AND 4(OR 5) RAIL FENCES	Drawing No. **H3**	Date

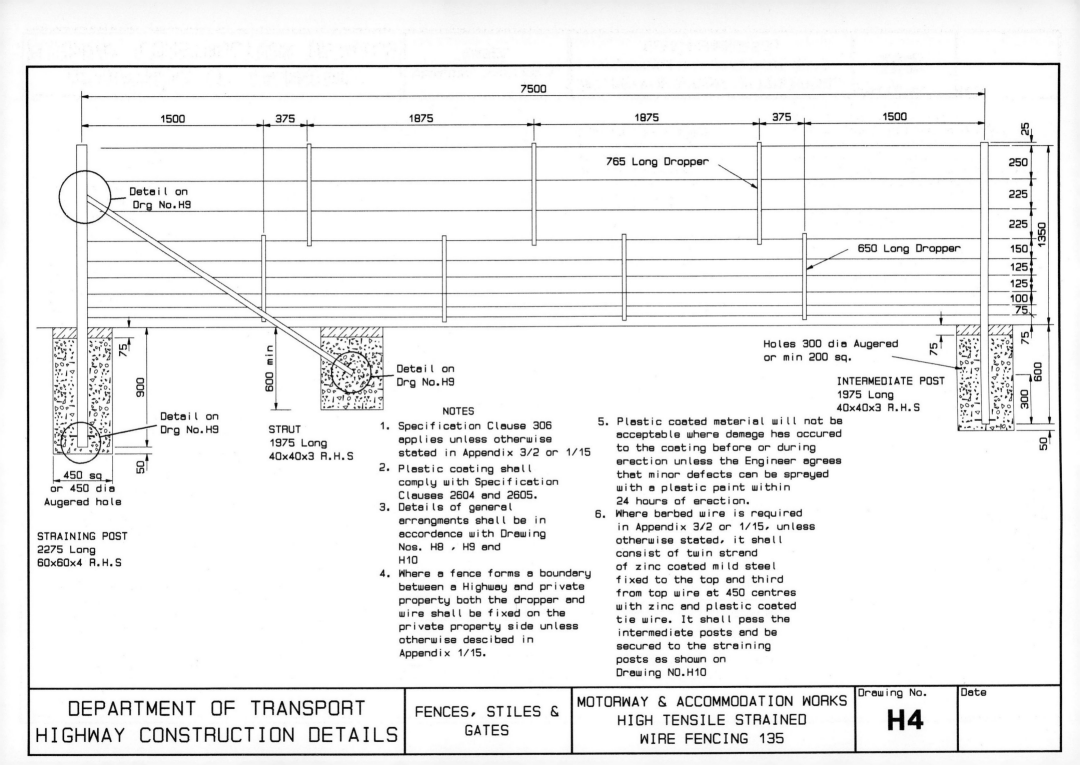

7500

1500 | 375 | 1875 | 1875 | 375 | 1500

765 Long Dropper

25
250
225
225 — 1350
150
125
125
100
75

Detail on Drg No.H9

650 Long Dropper

Holes 300 dia Augered or min 200 sq.

75

600

300

50

INTERMEDIATE POST
1975 Long
40x40x3 R.H.S

Detail on Drg No.H9

600 min

Detail on Drg No.H9

STRUT
1975 Long
40x40x3 R.H.S

75

900

50

450 sq
or 450 dia
Augered hole

STRAINING POST
2275 Long
60x60x4 R.H.S

NOTES

1. Specification Clause 306 applies unless otherwise stated in Appendix 3/2 or 1/15

2. Plastic coating shall comply with Specification Clauses 2604 and 2605.

3. Details of general arrangments shall be in accordance with Drawing Nos. H8 , H9 and H10

4. Where a fence forms a boundary between a Highway and private property both the dropper and wire shall be fixed on the private property side unless otherwise descibed in Appendix 1/15.

5. Plastic coated material will not be acceptable where damage has occured to the coating before or during erection unless the Engineer agrees that minor defects can be sprayed with a plastic paint within 24 hours of erection.

6. Where barbed wire is required in Appendix 3/2 or 1/15, unless otherwise stated, it shall consist of twin strand of zinc coated mild steel fixed to the top and third from top wire at 450 centres with zinc and plastic coated tie wire. It shall pass the intermediate posts and be secured to the straining posts as shown on Drawing NO.H10

| DEPARTMENT OF TRANSPORT HIGHWAY CONSTRUCTION DETAILS | FENCES, STILES & GATES | MOTORWAY & ACCOMMODATION WORKS HIGH TENSILE STRAINED WIRE FENCING 135 | Drawing No. **H4** | Date |

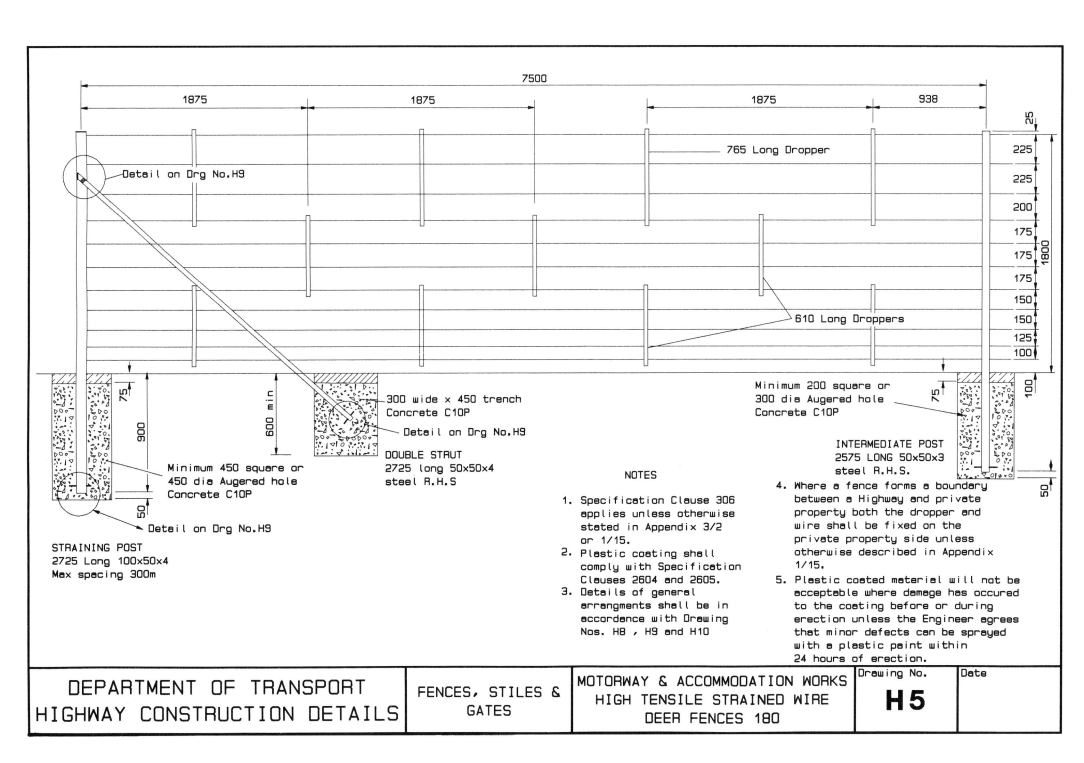

7500

1875   1875   1875   938

25
225
225
200
175
175
175
150
150
125
100

1800

765 Long Dropper

Detail on Drg No.H9

610 Long Droppers

Minimum 200 square or
300 dia Augered hole
Concrete C10P

75
100
50

INTERMEDIATE POST
2575 LONG 50x50x3
steel R.H.S.

75
900
50
600 min

300 wide x 450 trench
Concrete C10P

Detail on Drg No.H9

DOUBLE STRUT
2725 long 50x50x4
steel R.H.S

Minimum 450 square or
450 dia Augered hole
Concrete C10P

Detail on Drg No.H9

STRAINING POST
2725 Long 100x50x4
Max spacing 300m

NOTES

1. Specification Clause 306
   applies unless otherwise
   stated in Appendix 3/2
   or 1/15.
2. Plastic coating shall
   comply with Specification
   Clauses 2604 and 2605.
3. Details of general
   arrangments shall be in
   accordance with Drawing
   Nos. H8 , H9 and H10

4. Where a fence forms a boundary
   between a Highway and private
   property both the dropper and
   wire shall be fixed on the
   private property side unless
   otherwise described in Appendix
   1/15.
5. Plastic coated material will not be
   acceptable where damage has occured
   to the coating before or during
   erection unless the Engineer agrees
   that minor defects can be sprayed
   with a plastic paint within
   24 hours of erection.

| DEPARTMENT OF TRANSPORT HIGHWAY CONSTRUCTION DETAILS | FENCES, STILES & GATES | MOTORWAY & ACCOMMODATION WORKS HIGH TENSILE STRAINED WIRE DEER FENCES 180 | Drawing No. H5 | Date |

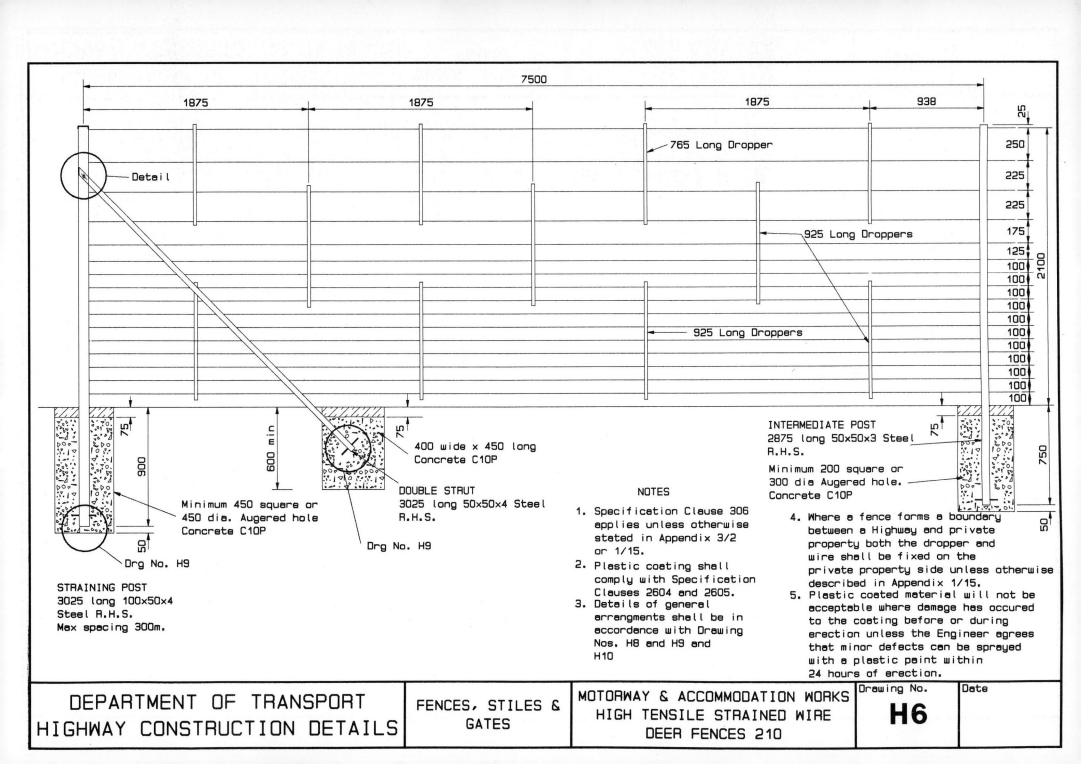

7500

1875   1875   1875   938

25
250
225
225
175
125
100
100
100
100
100
100
100
100
100
100
100
100

2100

765 Long Dropper

Detail

925 Long Droppers

925 Long Droppers

75

900

600 min

75

Minimum 450 square or
450 dia. Augered hole
Concrete C10P

400 wide x 450 long
Concrete C10P

DOUBLE STRUT
3025 long 50x50x4 Steel
R.H.S.

Drg No. H9

50

Drg No. H9

STRAINING POST
3025 long 100x50x4
Steel R.H.S.
Max spacing 300m.

INTERMEDIATE POST
2875 long 50x50x3 Steel
R.H.S.

Minimum 200 square or
300 dia Augered hole.
Concrete C10P

75

750

50

NOTES

1. Specification Clause 306
applies unless otherwise
stated in Appendix 3/2
or 1/15.
2. Plastic coating shall
comply with Specification
Clauses 2604 and 2605.
3. Details of general
arrangments shall be in
accordance with Drawing
Nos. H8 and H9 and
H10

4. Where a fence forms a boundary
between a Highway and private
property both the dropper and
wire shall be fixed on the
private property side unless otherwise
described in Appendix 1/15.
5. Plastic coated material will not be
acceptable where damage has occured
to the coating before or during
erection unless the Engineer agrees
that minor defects can be sprayed
with a plastic paint within
24 hours of erection.

| DEPARTMENT OF TRANSPORT HIGHWAY CONSTRUCTION DETAILS | FENCES, STILES & GATES | MOTORWAY & ACCOMMODATION WORKS HIGH TENSILE STRAINED WIRE DEER FENCES 210 | Drawing No. H6 | Date |

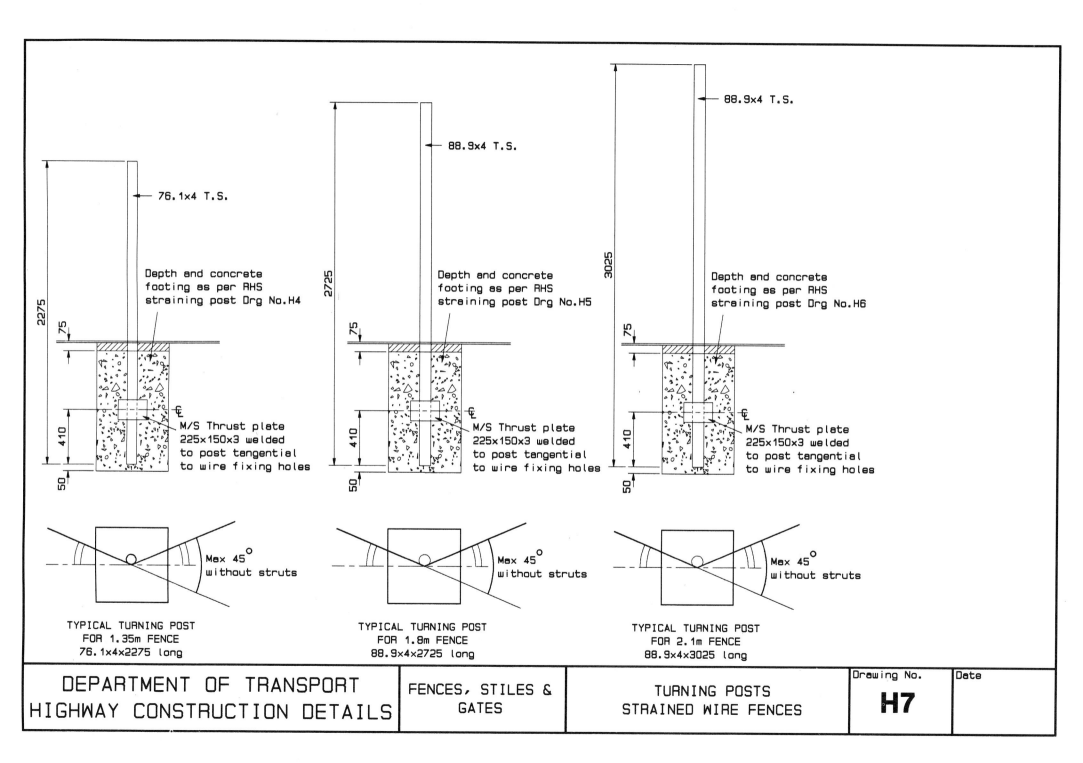

76.1x4 T.S.

88.9x4 T.S.

88.9x4 T.S.

2275

2725

3025

75

75

75

Depth and concrete
footing as per RHS
straining post Drg No.H4

Depth and concrete
footing as per RHS
straining post Drg No.H5

Depth and concrete
footing as per RHS
straining post Drg No.H6

410

410

410

50

50

50

M/S Thrust plate
225x150x3 welded
to post tangential
to wire fixing holes

M/S Thrust plate
225x150x3 welded
to post tangential
to wire fixing holes

M/S Thrust plate
225x150x3 welded
to post tangential
to wire fixing holes

Max 45° without struts

Max 45° without struts

Max 45° without struts

TYPICAL TURNING POST
FOR 1.35m FENCE
76.1x4x2275 long

TYPICAL TURNING POST
FOR 1.8m FENCE
88.9x4x2725 long

TYPICAL TURNING POST
FOR 2.1m FENCE
88.9x4x3025 long

| DEPARTMENT OF TRANSPORT HIGHWAY CONSTRUCTION DETAILS | FENCES, STILES & GATES | TURNING POSTS STRAINED WIRE FENCES | Drawing No. **H7** | Date |

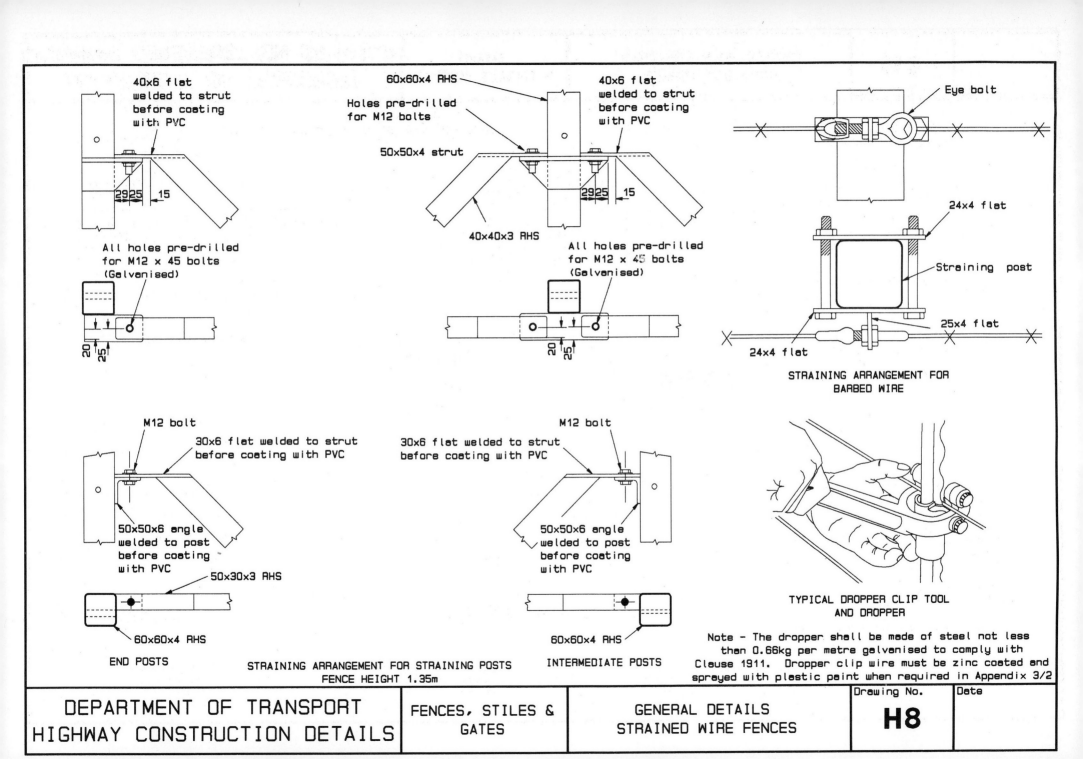

40x6 flat welded to strut before coating with PVC

All holes pre-drilled for M12 x 45 bolts (Galvanised)

29 25 15

20 25

60x60x4 RHS

Holes pre-drilled for M12 bolts

50x50x4 strut

40x6 flat welded to strut before coating with PVC

40x40x3 RHS

All holes pre-drilled for M12 x 45 bolts (Galvanised)

29 25 15

20 25

Eye bolt

24x4 flat

Straining post

25x4 flat

24x4 flat

STRAINING ARRANGEMENT FOR BARBED WIRE

M12 bolt

30x6 flat welded to strut before coating with PVC

50x50x6 angle welded to post before coating with PVC

50x30x3 RHS

60x60x4 RHS

END POSTS

STRAINING ARRANGEMENT FOR STRAINING POSTS FENCE HEIGHT 1.35m

M12 bolt

30x6 flat welded to strut before coating with PVC

50x50x6 angle welded to post before coating with PVC

60x60x4 RHS

INTERMEDIATE POSTS

TYPICAL DROPPER CLIP TOOL AND DROPPER

Note - The dropper shall be made of steel not less than 0.66kg per metre galvanised to comply with Clause 1911. Dropper clip wire must be zinc coated and sprayed with plastic paint when required in Appendix 3/2

| DEPARTMENT OF TRANSPORT HIGHWAY CONSTRUCTION DETAILS | FENCES, STILES & GATES | GENERAL DETAILS STRAINED WIRE FENCES | Drawing No. **H8** | Date |

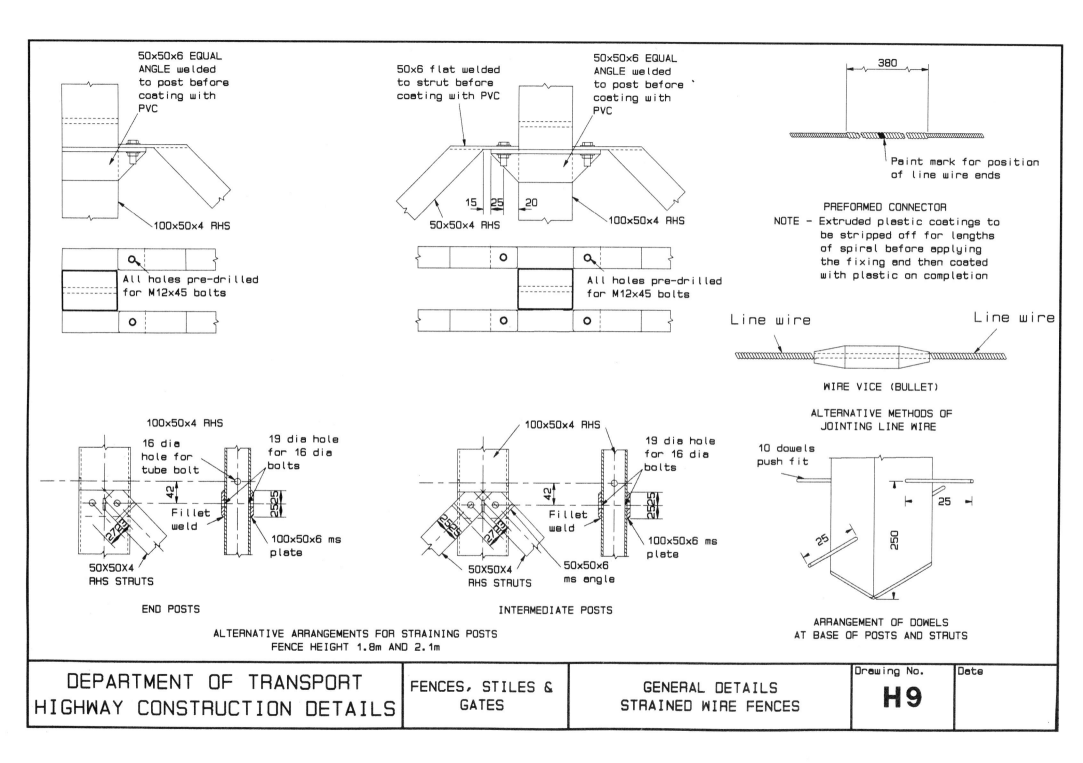

50x50x6 EQUAL ANGLE welded to post before coating with PVC

100x50x4 RHS

All holes pre-drilled for M12x45 bolts

50x6 flat welded to strut before coating with PVC

50x50x4 RHS

15 25 20

50x50x6 EQUAL ANGLE welded to post before coating with PVC

100x50x4 RHS

All holes pre-drilled for M12x45 bolts

380

Paint mark for position of line wire ends

PREFORMED CONNECTOR

NOTE - Extruded plastic coatings to be stripped off for lengths of spiral before applying the fixing and then coated with plastic on completion

Line wire   Line wire

WIRE VICE (BULLET)

ALTERNATIVE METHODS OF JOINTING LINE WIRE

100x50x4 RHS

16 dia hole for tube bolt

19 dia hole for 16 dia bolts

42

25 25

Fillet weld

100x50x6 ms plate

50X50X4 RHS STRUTS

END POSTS

100x50x4 RHS

19 dia hole for 16 dia bolts

42

25 25

Fillet weld

100x50x6 ms plate

50X50X4 RHS STRUTS

50x50x6 ms angle

INTERMEDIATE POSTS

ALTERNATIVE ARRANGEMENTS FOR STRAINING POSTS
FENCE HEIGHT 1.8m AND 2.1m

10 dowels push fit

25

25

250

ARRANGEMENT OF DOWELS AT BASE OF POSTS AND STRUTS

| DEPARTMENT OF TRANSPORT HIGHWAY CONSTRUCTION DETAILS | FENCES, STILES & GATES | GENERAL DETAILS STRAINED WIRE FENCES | Drawing No. H9 | Date |

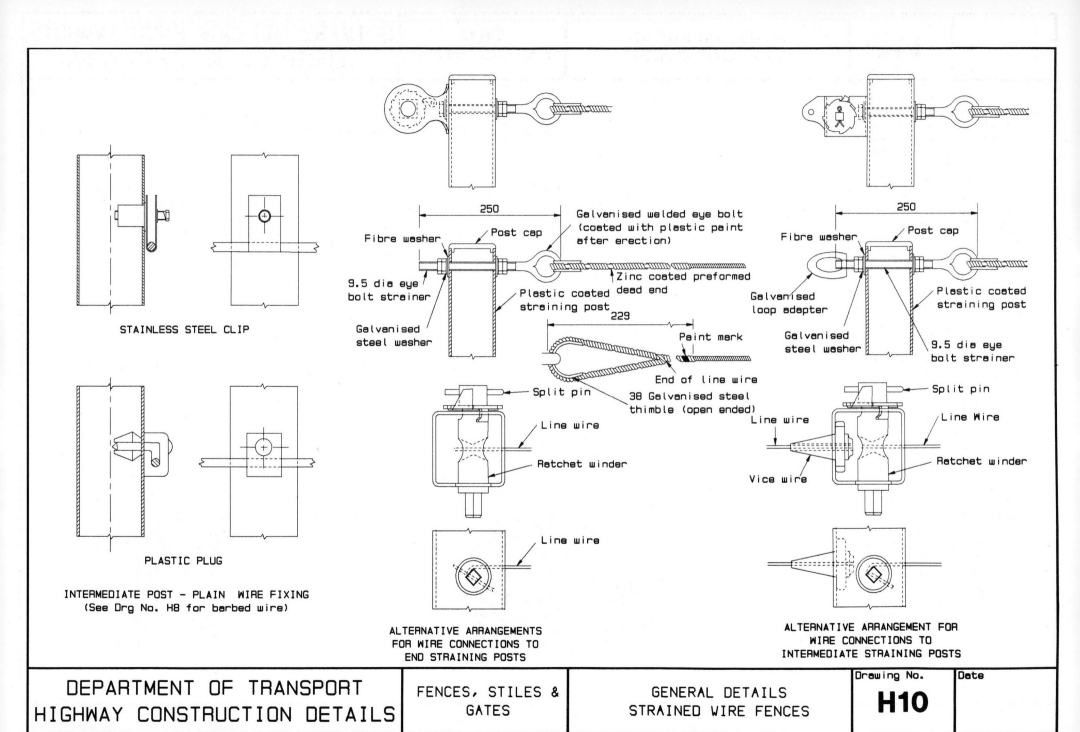

STAINLESS STEEL CLIP

PLASTIC PLUG

INTERMEDIATE POST – PLAIN WIRE FIXING
(See Drg No. H8 for barbed wire)

250

Fibre washer

Post cap

Galvanised welded eye bolt
(coated with plastic paint
after erection)

9.5 dia eye
bolt strainer

Zinc coated preformed
dead end

Plastic coated
straining post

Galvanised
steel washer

229

Paint mark

End of line wire

38 Galvanised steel
thimble (open ended)

Split pin

Line wire

Ratchet winder

Line wire

ALTERNATIVE ARRANGEMENTS
FOR WIRE CONNECTIONS TO
END STRAINING POSTS

250

Fibre washer

Post cap

Galvanised
loop adapter

Plastic coated
straining post

Galvanised
steel washer

9.5 dia eye
bolt strainer

Split pin

Line wire

Line Wire

Ratchet winder

Vice wire

ALTERNATIVE ARRANGEMENT FOR
WIRE CONNECTIONS TO
INTERMEDIATE STRAINING POSTS

| DEPARTMENT OF TRANSPORT HIGHWAY CONSTRUCTION DETAILS | FENCES, STILES & GATES | GENERAL DETAILS STRAINED WIRE FENCES | Drawing No. **H10** | Date |

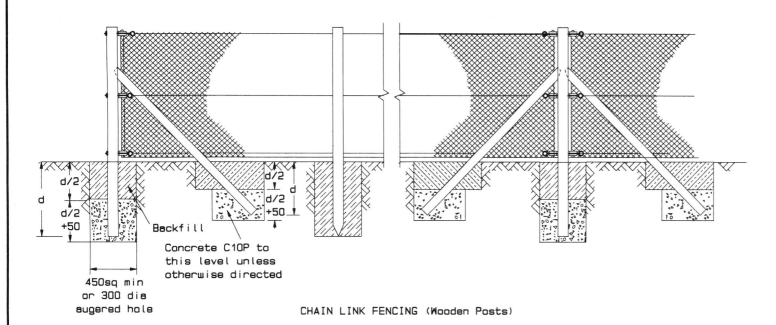

CHAIN LINK FENCING (Wooden Posts)

d/2

d

d/2 +50

Backfill

Concrete C10P to this level unless otherwise directed

450sq min or 300 dia augered hole

d/2

d

d/2 +50

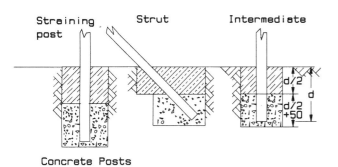

Straining post   Strut   Intermediate

Concrete Posts

d/2

d

d/2 +50

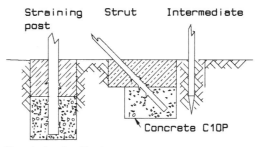

Straining post   Strut   Intermediate

Steel Angle Post

Concrete C10P

VARIATIONS FOR POSTS OF DIFFERENT MATERIALS

NOTES

1. B.S. 1722 Part 1 applies unless otherwise stated.

2. Dimensions of foundation, type and size of posts, struts mesh, etc. shall be taken from B.S. 1722 Part 1 appropriate to the height and with any other requirement described in Appendix 1/15 and on the scheme Drawings.

3. Plastic coated when required in Appendix 1/15 shall comply with Specification Clauses 2604 and 2605.

4. Plastic coating material will not be acceptable where damage has occured to the coating before or during erection unless the Engineer agrees that minor defects can be sprayed with an approved plastic paint within 24 hours of erection.

5. All timber shall comply with Specification Clause 304 unless otherwise stated in Appendix 1/15.

6. Where a fence forms a boundary between the Highway and private property the wire shall be fixed to the Highway side unless otherwise stated in Appendix 1/15.

| DEPARTMENT OF TRANSPORT HIGHWAY CONSTRUCTION DETAILS | FENCES, STILES & GATES | ACCOMMODATION WORK. CHAIN LINK FENCES | Drawing No. **H 11** | Date |

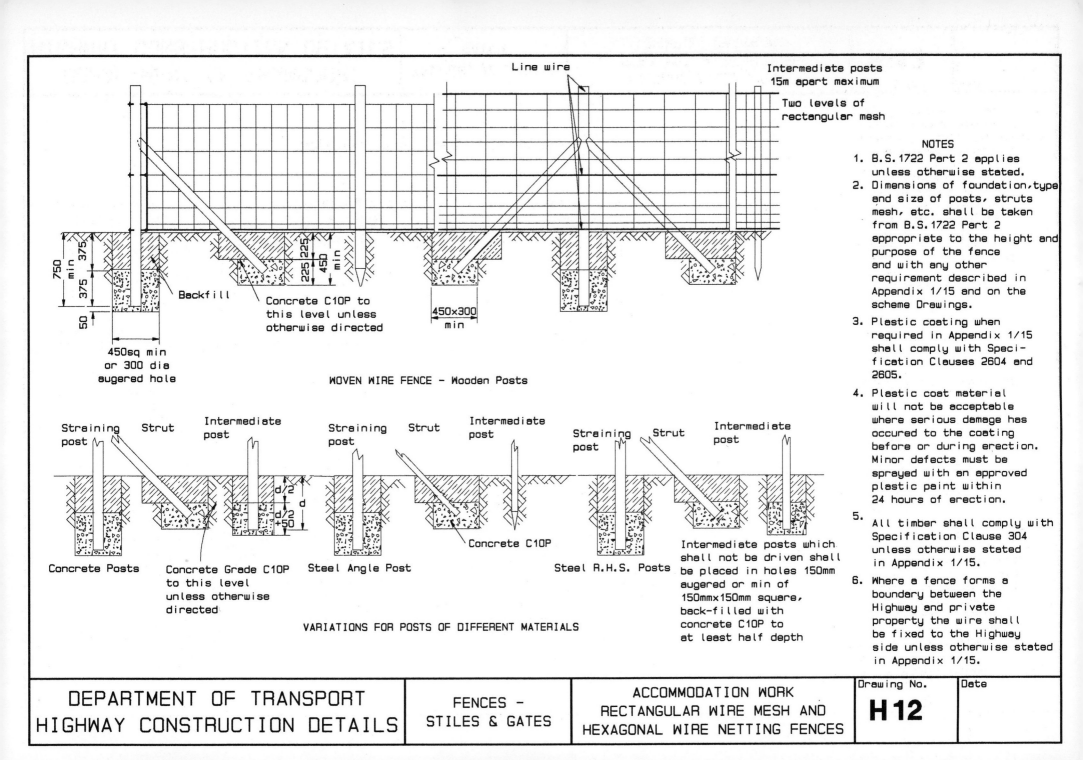

Line wire

Intermediate posts
15m apart maximum

Two levels of
rectangular mesh

750 min
375
375
50
225 225
450 min

Backfill

Concrete C10P to
this level unless
otherwise directed

450×300
min

450sq min
or 300 dia
augered hole

WOVEN WIRE FENCE - Wooden Posts

Straining post   Strut   Intermediate post

Straining post   Strut   Intermediate post

Straining post   Strut   Intermediate post

d/2
d
d/2
+50

Concrete Posts

Concrete Grade C10P
to this level
unless otherwise
directed

Steel Angle Post

Concrete C10P

Steel R.H.S. Posts

Intermediate posts which
shall not be driven shall
be placed in holes 150mm
augered or min of
150mm×150mm square,
back-filled with
concrete C10P to
at least half depth

VARIATIONS FOR POSTS OF DIFFERENT MATERIALS

NOTES

1. B.S. 1722 Part 2 applies
   unless otherwise stated.

2. Dimensions of foundation, type
   and size of posts, struts
   mesh, etc. shall be taken
   from B.S. 1722 Part 2
   appropriate to the height and
   purpose of the fence
   and with any other
   requirement described in
   Appendix 1/15 and on the
   scheme Drawings.

3. Plastic coating when
   required in Appendix 1/15
   shall comply with Specification Clauses 2604 and
   2605.

4. Plastic coat material
   will not be acceptable
   where serious damage has
   occured to the coating
   before or during erection.
   Minor defects must be
   sprayed with an approved
   plastic paint within
   24 hours of erection.

5. All timber shall comply with
   Specification Clause 304
   unless otherwise stated
   in Appendix 1/15.

6. Where a fence forms a
   boundary between the
   Highway and private
   property the wire shall
   be fixed to the Highway
   side unless otherwise stated
   in Appendix 1/15.

| DEPARTMENT OF TRANSPORT HIGHWAY CONSTRUCTION DETAILS | FENCES - STILES & GATES | ACCOMMODATION WORK RECTANGULAR WIRE MESH AND HEXAGONAL WIRE NETTING FENCES | Drawing No. H12 | Date |

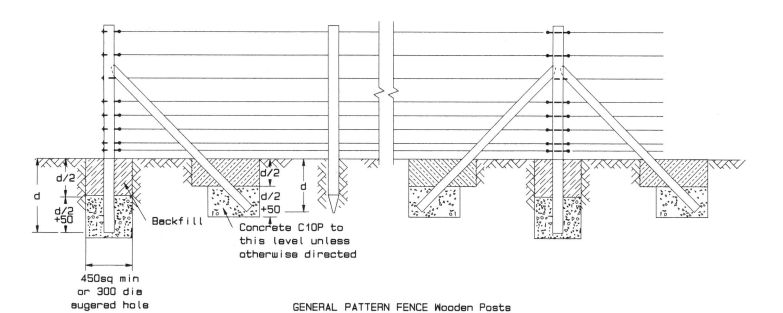

d/2

d

d/2
+50

Backfill

d/2

d/2
+50

d

Concrete C10P to
this level unless
otherwise directed

450sq min
or 300 dia
augered hole

GENERAL PATTERN FENCE Wooden Posts

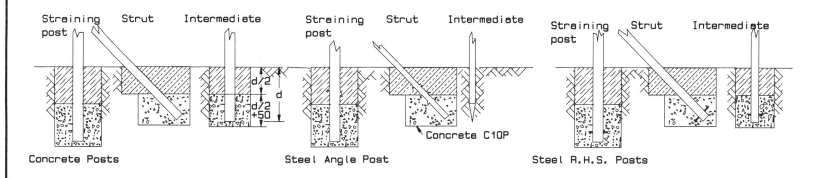

Straining
post

Strut

Intermediate

Concrete Posts

d/2

d/2
+50

d

Straining
post

Strut

Intermediate

Concrete C10P

Steel Angle Post

Straining
post

Strut

Intermediate

Steel R.H.S. Posts

VARIATIONS FOR POSTS OF DIFFERENT MATERIALS

NOTES

1. B.S.1722 Part 3 Section
   1,2 & 3 apply unless
   otherwise stated.

2. Dimension of foundation,
   type and sizes of posts,
   struts and wire etc.
   shall be taken from
   B.S.1722 Part 3 as appropriate
   to the height and purpose
   of the fence and with any
   other requirements described
   in Appendix 1/15
   and on the scheme
   Drawings.

3. All timber shall
   comply with Specif-
   ication Clause 304
   unless otherwise stated
   in Appendix 1/15.

4. When plastic coating is
   required in Appendix 1/15
   it shall comply with
   Specification Clause 2604
   and 2605.

5. Details of general
   arrangements shall be in
   accordance with Drawing
   Nos. H7 to H10 .

6. Where the fence forms a
   boundary between the Highway
   and private property, the
   wire shall be fixed on the
   Highway side unless otherwise
   stated in Appendix 1/15.

7. Plastic coated material
   will not be acceptable
   when damage has occured
   to the coating before or
   after erection unless the
   Engineer agrees that minor
   defects can be during erection
   sprayed with an approved
   paint within 24 hours.

| DEPARTMENT OF TRANSPORT HIGHWAY CONSTRUCTION DETAILS | FENCES, STILES & GATES | ACCOMMODATION WORK. STRAINED WIRE FENCES (GENERAL PATTERN) | Drawing No. H13 | Date |

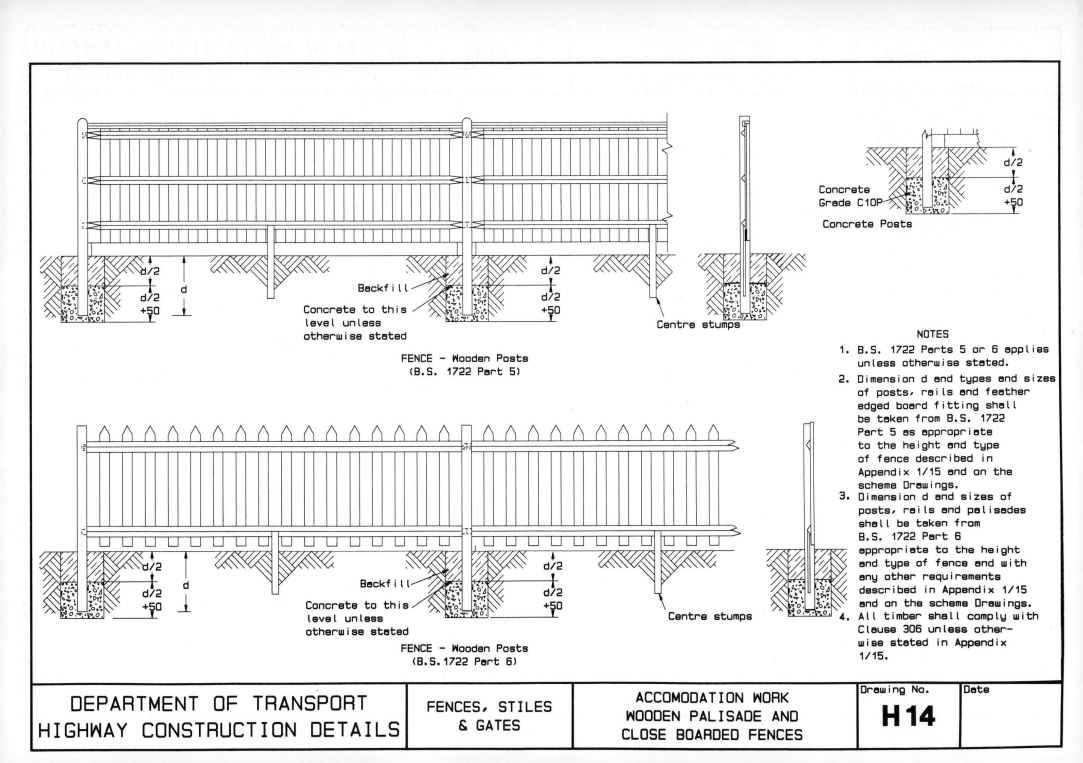

Concrete
Grade C10P

Concrete Posts

FENCE – Wooden Posts
(B.S. 1722 Part 5)

Backfill

Concrete to this
level unless
otherwise stated

Centre stumps

d/2
d/2
+50

d/2
d/2
+50

d

FENCE – Wooden Posts
(B.S. 1722 Part 6)

Backfill

Concrete to this
level unless
otherwise stated

Centre stumps

d/2
d/2
+50

d/2
d/2
+50

d

NOTES

1. B.S. 1722 Parts 5 or 6 applies
   unless otherwise stated.

2. Dimension d and types and sizes
   of posts, rails and feather
   edged board fitting shall
   be taken from B.S. 1722
   Part 5 as appropriate
   to the height and type
   of fence described in
   Appendix 1/15 and on the
   scheme Drawings.

3. Dimension d and sizes of
   posts, rails and palisades
   shall be taken from
   B.S. 1722 Part 6
   appropriate to the height
   and type of fence and with
   any other requirements
   described in Appendix 1/15
   and on the scheme Drawings.

4. All timber shall comply with
   Clause 306 unless otherwise stated in Appendix
   1/15.

| DEPARTMENT OF TRANSPORT HIGHWAY CONSTRUCTION DETAILS | FENCES, STILES & GATES | ACCOMODATION WORK WOODEN PALISADE AND CLOSE BOARDED FENCES | Drawing No. **H14** | Date |

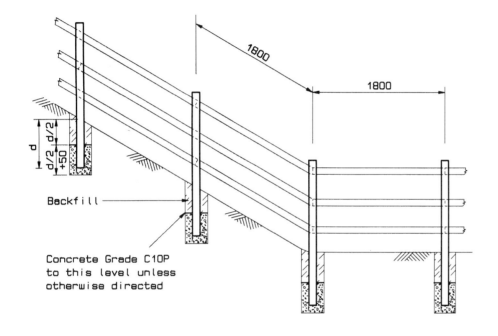

1800

1800

100

325

275

240

1100

d

d/2
+50

d/2

d

d/2

d/2
+50

Backfill

Concrete Grade C10P
to this level unless
otherwise directed

3 RAIL FENCE

NOTES

1. B.S.1722 Part 7 applies
   unless otherwise stated.
2. Where plain or barbed
   wire is required in
   Appendix 1/15 it shall
   be zinc coated and
   comply with B.S.4102
3. Where the fence forms a
   boundary between the
   highway and private
   property, the rails
   shall be fixed to
   the private property
   side unless otherwise stated
   in Appendix 1/15.

| DEPARTMENT OF TRANSPORT HIGHWAY CONSTRUCTION DETAILS | FENCES, STILES & GATES | ACCOMMODATION WORKS WOODEN POST AND 3 RAIL FENCES | Drawing No. **H15** | Date |

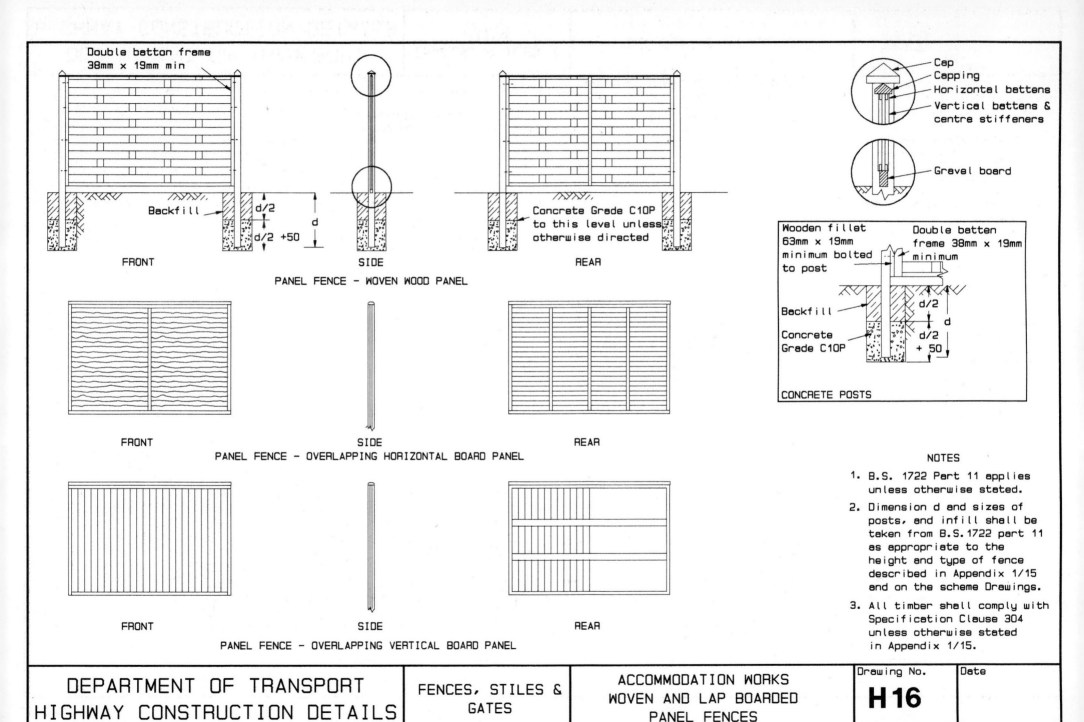

Double batton frame
38mm x 19mm min

Backfill

d/2
d
d/2 +50

FRONT

SIDE

Concrete Grade C10P
to this level unless
otherwise directed

REAR

PANEL FENCE - WOVEN WOOD PANEL

FRONT

SIDE

REAR

PANEL FENCE - OVERLAPPING HORIZONTAL BOARD PANEL

FRONT

SIDE

REAR

PANEL FENCE - OVERLAPPING VERTICAL BOARD PANEL

Cap
Capping
Horizontal battens
Vertical battens &
centre stiffeners

Gravel board

Wooden fillet
63mm x 19mm
minimum bolted
to post

Double batten
frame 38mm x 19mm
minimum

Backfill

Concrete
Grade C10P

d/2
d
d/2
+ 50

CONCRETE POSTS

NOTES

1. B.S. 1722 Part 11 applies
   unless otherwise stated.

2. Dimension d and sizes of
   posts, and infill shall be
   taken from B.S. 1722 part 11
   as appropriate to the
   height and type of fence
   described in Appendix 1/15
   and on the scheme Drawings.

3. All timber shall comply with
   Specification Clause 304
   unless otherwise stated
   in Appendix 1/15.

| DEPARTMENT OF TRANSPORT HIGHWAY CONSTRUCTION DETAILS | FENCES, STILES & GATES | ACCOMMODATION WORKS WOVEN AND LAP BOARDED PANEL FENCES | Drawing No. **H16** | Date |

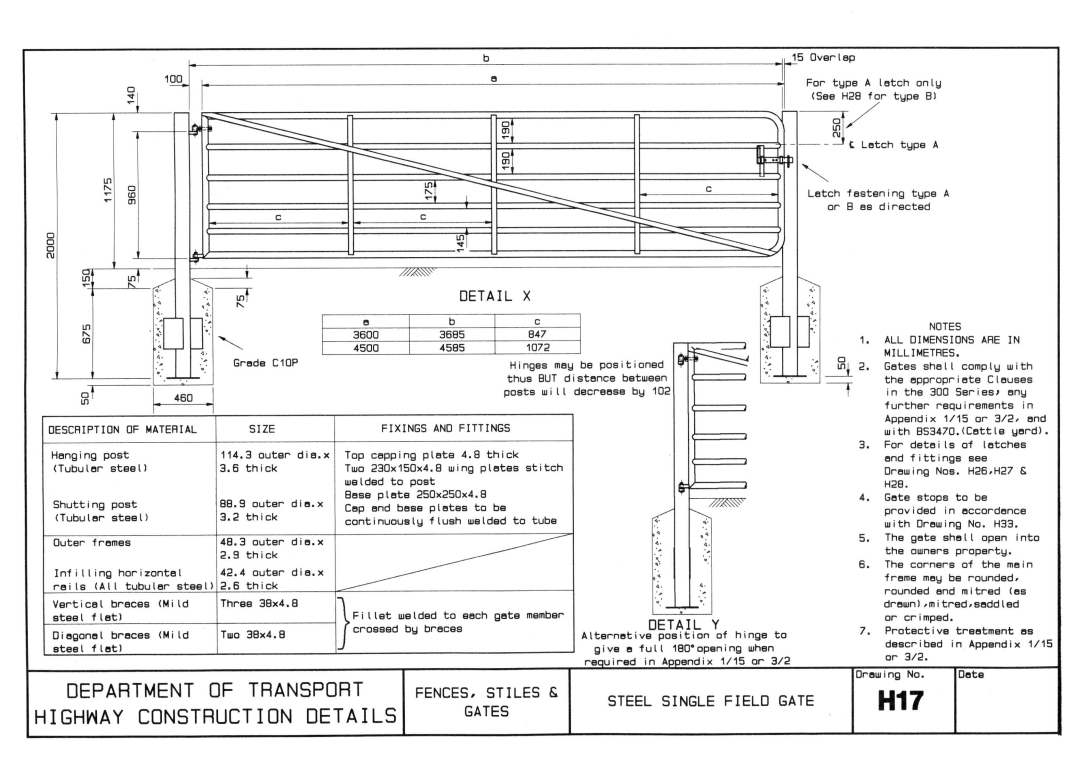

b

a

15 Overlap

For type A latch only
(See H28 for type B)

100

140

190

190

175

145

1175

960

2000

150

75

75

675

50

460

Grade C10P

DETAIL X

	a	b	c
	3600	3685	847
	4500	4585	1072

Hinges may be positioned
thus BUT distance between
posts will decrease by 102

250

£ Latch type A

Latch fastening type A
or B as directed

50

c

DETAIL Y
Alternative position of hinge to
give a full 180° opening when
required in Appendix 1/15 or 3/2

DESCRIPTION OF MATERIAL	SIZE	FIXINGS AND FITTINGS
Hanging post (Tubular steel)	114.3 outer dia.x 3.6 thick	Top capping plate 4.8 thick Two 230x150x4.8 wing plates stitch welded to post Base plate 250x250x4.8 Cap and base plates to be continuously flush welded to tube
Shutting post (Tubular steel)	88.9 outer dia.x 3.2 thick	
Outer frames	48.3 outer dia.x 2.9 thick	
Infilling horizontal rails (All tubular steel)	42.4 outer dia.x 2.6 thick	
Vertical braces (Mild steel flat)	Three 38x4.8	Fillet welded to each gate member crossed by braces
Diagonal braces (Mild steel flat)	Two 38x4.8	

NOTES

1. ALL DIMENSIONS ARE IN MILLIMETRES.
2. Gates shall comply with the appropriate Clauses in the 300 Series, any further requirements in Appendix 1/15 or 3/2, and with BS3470.(Cattle yard).
3. For details of latches and fittings see Drawing Nos. H26,H27 & H28.
4. Gate stops to be provided in accordance with Drawing No. H33.
5. The gate shall open into the owners property.
6. The corners of the main frame may be rounded, rounded and mitred (as drawn),mitred,saddled or crimped.
7. Protective treatment as described in Appendix 1/15 or 3/2.

DEPARTMENT OF TRANSPORT HIGHWAY CONSTRUCTION DETAILS	FENCES, STILES & GATES	STEEL SINGLE FIELD GATE	Drawing No. H17	Date

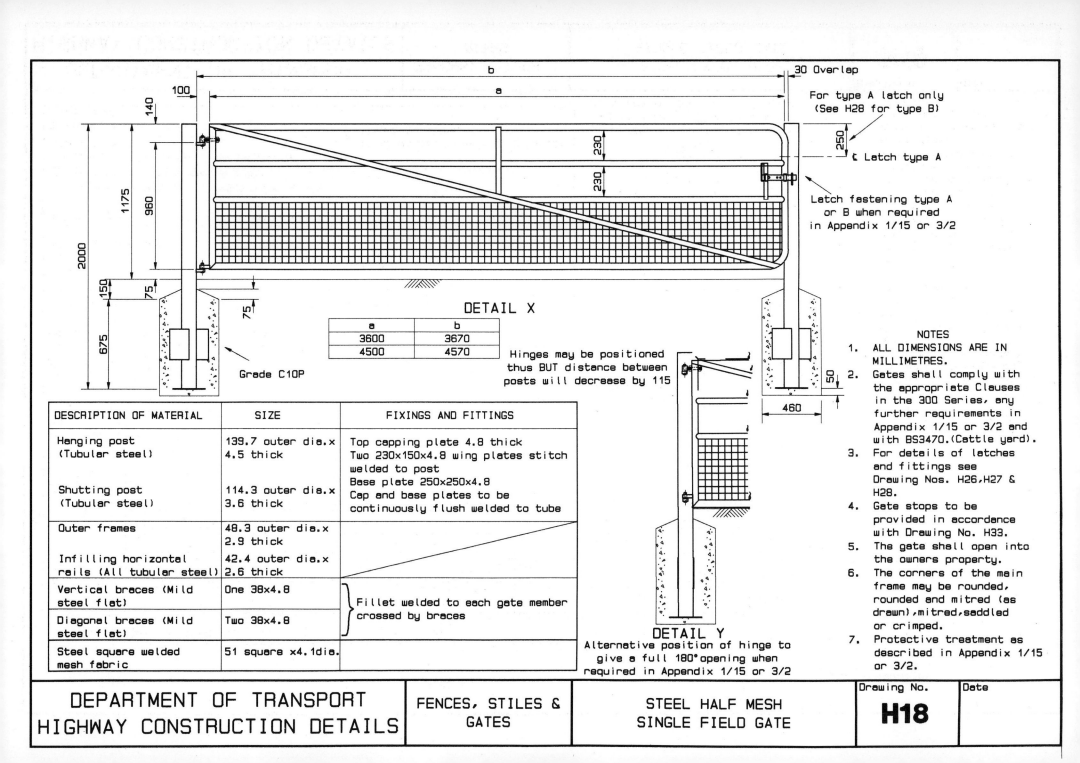

DETAIL X

a	b
3600	3670
4500	4570

Hinges may be positioned thus BUT distance between posts will decrease by 115

b
a
100
30 Overlap

For type A latch only (See H28 for type B)

250

℄ Latch type A

Latch fastening type A or B when required in Appendix 1/15 or 3/2

140
1175
960
2000
150
75
675
75

Grade C10P

230
230

DETAIL Y
Alternative position of hinge to give a full 180° opening when required in Appendix 1/15 or 3/2

460
50

DESCRIPTION OF MATERIAL	SIZE	FIXINGS AND FITTINGS
Hanging post (Tubular steel)	139.7 outer dia.x 4.5 thick	Top capping plate 4.8 thick Two 230x150x4.8 wing plates stitch welded to post Base plate 250x250x4.8 Cap and base plates to be continuously flush welded to tube
Shutting post (Tubular steel)	114.3 outer dia.x 3.6 thick	
Outer frames	48.3 outer dia.x 2.9 thick	
Infilling horizontal rails (All tubular steel)	42.4 outer dia.x 2.6 thick	
Vertical braces (Mild steel flat)	One 38x4.8	Fillet welded to each gate member crossed by braces
Diagonal braces (Mild steel flat)	Two 38x4.8	
Steel square welded mesh fabric	51 square x4.1dia.	

NOTES

1. ALL DIMENSIONS ARE IN MILLIMETRES.
2. Gates shall comply with the appropriate Clauses in the 300 Series, any further requirements in Appendix 1/15 or 3/2 and with BS3470.(Cattle yard).
3. For details of latches and fittings see Drawing Nos. H26,H27 & H28.
4. Gate stops to be provided in accordance with Drawing No. H33.
5. The gate shall open into the owners property.
6. The corners of the main frame may be rounded, rounded and mitred (as drawn),mitred,saddled or crimped.
7. Protective treatment as described in Appendix 1/15 or 3/2.

DEPARTMENT OF TRANSPORT HIGHWAY CONSTRUCTION DETAILS	FENCES, STILES & GATES	STEEL HALF MESH SINGLE FIELD GATE	Drawing No. **H18**	Date

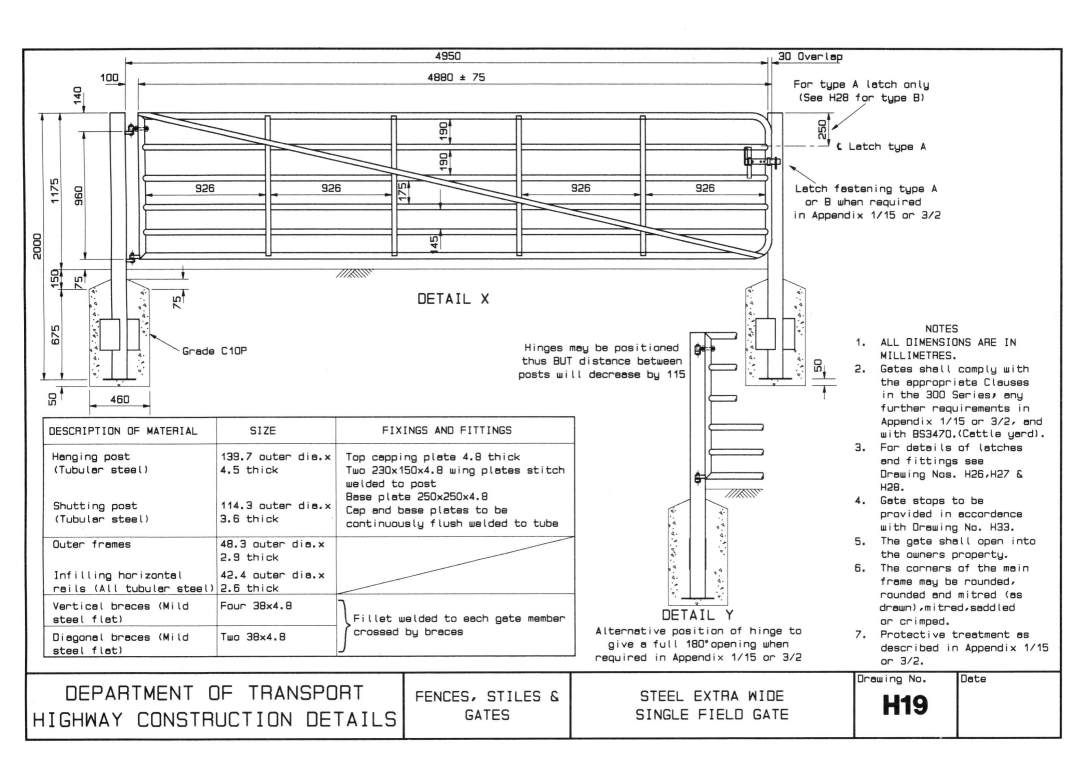

DETAIL X

Hinges may be positioned
thus BUT distance between
posts will decrease by 115

30 Overlap

For type A latch only
(See H28 for type B)

£ Latch type A

Latch fastening type A
or B when required
in Appendix 1/15 or 3/2

DESCRIPTION OF MATERIAL	SIZE	FIXINGS AND FITTINGS
Hanging post (Tubular steel)	139.7 outer dia.x 4.5 thick	Top capping plate 4.8 thick Two 230x150x4.8 wing plates stitch welded to post Base plate 250x250x4.8 Cap and base plates to be continuously flush welded to tube
Shutting post (Tubular steel)	114.3 outer dia.x 3.6 thick	
Outer frames	48.3 outer dia.x 2.9 thick	
Infilling horizontal rails (All tubular steel)	42.4 outer dia.x 2.6 thick	
Vertical braces (Mild steel flat)	Four 38x4.8	Fillet welded to each gate member crossed by braces
Diagonal braces (Mild steel flat)	Two 38x4.8	

DETAIL Y
Alternative position of hinge to
give a full 180° opening when
required in Appendix 1/15 or 3/2

NOTES
1. ALL DIMENSIONS ARE IN MILLIMETRES.
2. Gates shall comply with the appropriate Clauses in the 300 Series, any further requirements in Appendix 1/15 or 3/2, and with BS3470.(Cattle yard).
3. For details of latches and fittings see Drawing Nos. H26,H27 & H28.
4. Gate stops to be provided in accordance with Drawing No. H33.
5. The gate shall open into the owners property.
6. The corners of the main frame may be rounded, rounded and mitred (as drawn),mitred,saddled or crimped.
7. Protective treatment as described in Appendix 1/15 or 3/2.

Grade C10P

| DEPARTMENT OF TRANSPORT HIGHWAY CONSTRUCTION DETAILS | FENCES, STILES & GATES | STEEL EXTRA WIDE SINGLE FIELD GATE | Drawing No. **H19** | Date |

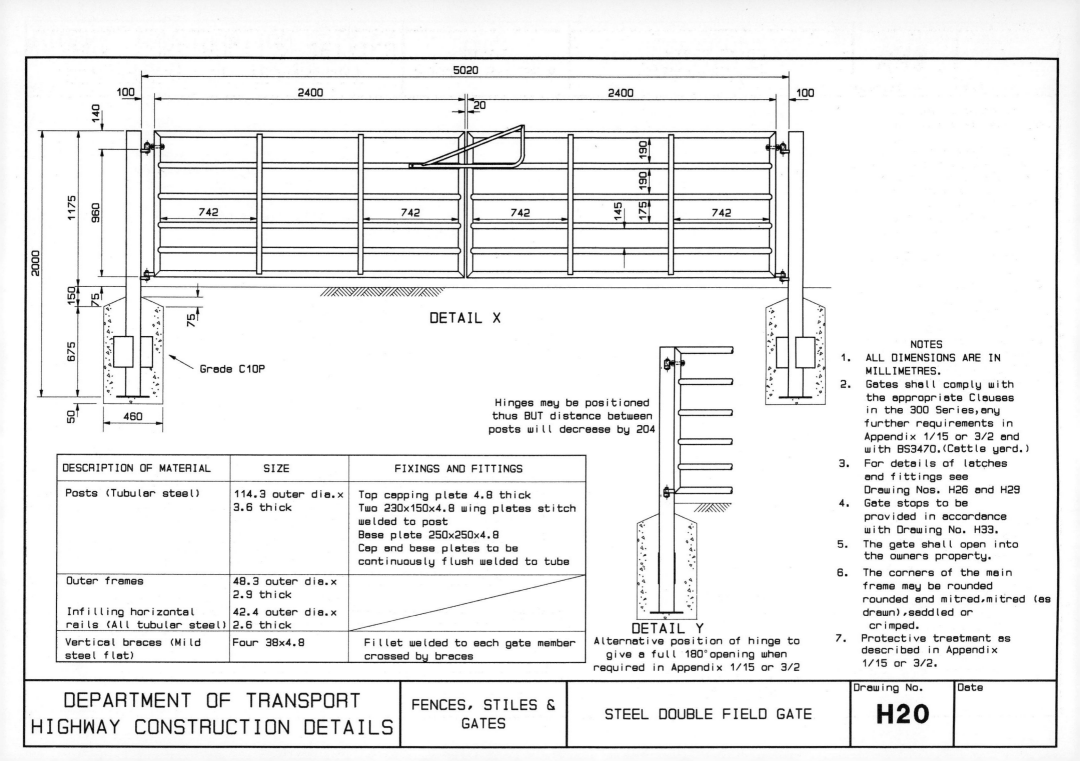

DETAIL X

Grade C10P

Hinges may be positioned
thus BUT distance between
posts will decrease by 204

DETAIL Y
Alternative position of hinge to
give a full 180° opening when
required in Appendix 1/15 or 3/2

DESCRIPTION OF MATERIAL	SIZE	FIXINGS AND FITTINGS
Posts (Tubular steel)	114.3 outer dia.x 3.6 thick	Top capping plate 4.8 thick Two 230x150x4.8 wing plates stitch welded to post Base plate 250x250x4.8 Cap and base plates to be continuously flush welded to tube
Outer frames	48.3 outer dia.x 2.9 thick	
Infilling horizontal rails (All tubular steel)	42.4 outer dia.x 2.6 thick	
Vertical braces (Mild steel flat)	Four 38x4.8	Fillet welded to each gate member crossed by braces

NOTES
1. ALL DIMENSIONS ARE IN MILLIMETRES.
2. Gates shall comply with the appropriate Clauses in the 300 Series, any further requirements in Appendix 1/15 or 3/2 and with BS3470.(Cattle yard.)
3. For details of latches and fittings see Drawing Nos. H26 and H29
4. Gate stops to be provided in accordance with Drawing No. H33.
5. The gate shall open into the owners property.
6. The corners of the main frame may be rounded rounded and mitred,mitred (as drawn),saddled or crimped.
7. Protective treatment as described in Appendix 1/15 or 3/2.

DEPARTMENT OF TRANSPORT HIGHWAY CONSTRUCTION DETAILS	FENCES, STILES & GATES	STEEL DOUBLE FIELD GATE	Drawing No. H20	Date

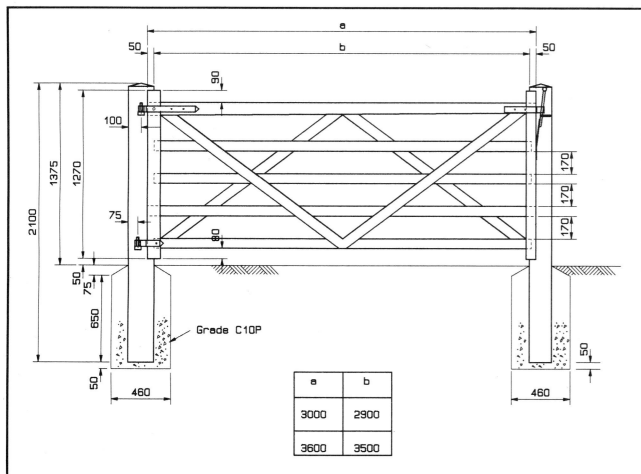

DESCRIPTION OF TIMBER MATERIALS	SIZE
Hanging post	200×200×2100 long
Shutting post	175×175×2100 long
Hanging stile	100X75 for 3m gate 125×75 for 3.6m gate
Shutting stile	75×75
Top rail	100x75 for 3m gate 125×75 for 3.6m gate both tapering to 75×75
Under rails	75×25
Braces housed in top rail	75×25

a	b
3000	2900
3600	3500

Grade C10P

NOTES

1. ALL DIMENSIONS ARE IN MILLIMETRES UNLESS OTHERWISE STATED.
2. Gates shall comply with the appropriate Clauses in the 300 Series, any further requirements in Appendix 1/15 or 3/2 and with BS3470.
3. All through tenons shall be pegged with 13 dia oak dowels.
4. For details of fittings for hanging and fastening see Drawing Nos. H30 and 31.
5. The gate shall be hung as shown for self closing with self latching stop post as shown on drawing No. H33.
6. The gate shall open into the owners property.

DEPARTMENT OF TRANSPORT HIGHWAY CONSTRUCTION DETAILS	FENCES, STILES & GATES	TIMBER SINGLE FIELD GATE	Drawing No. H21	Date

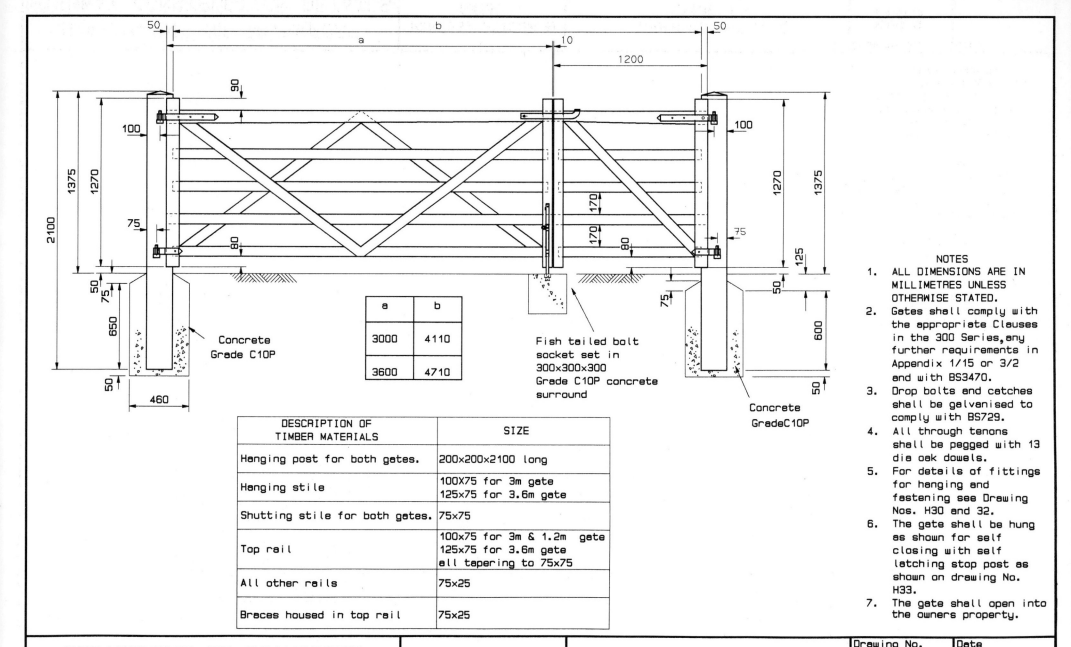

a	b
3000	4110
3600	4710

Concrete Grade C10P

Fish tailed bolt socket set in 300x300x300 Grade C10P concrete surround

Concrete GradeC10P

DESCRIPTION OF TIMBER MATERIALS	SIZE
Hanging post for both gates.	200x200x2100 long
Hanging stile	100X75 for 3m gate 125x75 for 3.6m gate
Shutting stile for both gates.	75x75
Top rail	100x75 for 3m & 1.2m gate 125x75 for 3.6m gate all tapering to 75x75
All other rails	75x25
Braces housed in top rail	75x25

NOTES
1. ALL DIMENSIONS ARE IN MILLIMETRES UNLESS OTHERWISE STATED.
2. Gates shall comply with the appropriate Clauses in the 300 Series, any further requirements in Appendix 1/15 or 3/2 and with BS3470.
3. Drop bolts and catches shall be galvanised to comply with BS729.
4. All through tenons shall be pegged with 13 dia oak dowels.
5. For details of fittings for hanging and fastening see Drawing Nos. H30 and 32.
6. The gate shall be hung as shown for self closing with self latching stop post as shown on drawing No. H33.
7. The gate shall open into the owners property.

DEPARTMENT OF TRANSPORT HIGHWAY CONSTRUCTION DETAILS	FENCES, STILES & GATES	TIMBER DOUBLE FIELD GATE	Drawing No. H22	Date

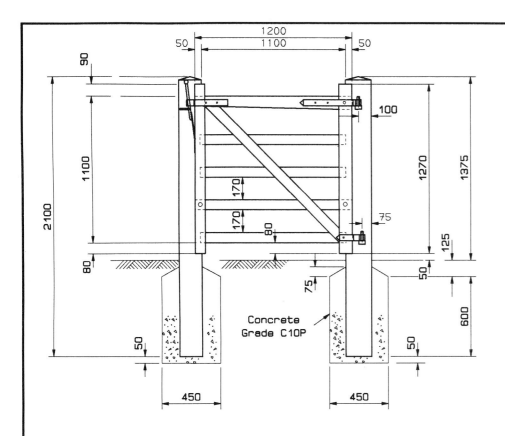

DESCRIPTION OF TIMBER MATERIALS	SIZE
Hanging post	200x200x2100 long
Shutting post	175x175x2100 long
Hanging stile	100x75
Shutting stile	75x75
Top rail	100x75 tapering to 75x75
Under rails	75x25
Brace housed in top rail	75x25

Concrete Grade C10P

NOTES
1. ALL DIMENSIONS ARE IN MILLIMETRES UNLESS OTHERWISE STATED.
2. Gates shall comply with the appropriate Clauses in the 300 Series, any further requirements in Appendix 1/15 or 3/2 and the appropriate Clauses in both BS3470 and BS5709.
3. All through tenons shall be pegged with 13 dia oak dowels.
4. For details of fittings for hanging and fastening see Drawing Nos. H30 and 31.
5. The gate shall open into the owners property.

DEPARTMENT OF TRANSPORT HIGHWAY CONSTRUCTION DETAILS	FENCES, STILES & GATES	TIMBER WICKET GATE TYPE 1	Drawing No. **H23**	Date

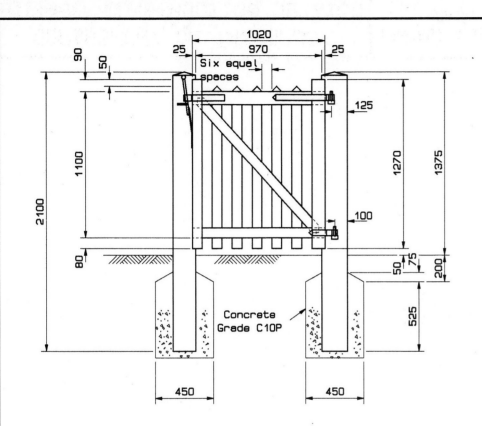

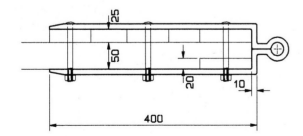

Concrete Grade C10P

Detail of joint between top & bottom rails and hanging stiles.

DESCRIPTION OF TIMBER MATERIALS	SIZE
Hanging post	200x200x2100 long
Shutting post	175x175x2100 long
Hanging stile	100x75
Shutting stile	75x75
Top rail	100x50
Bottom rail	75x50
Brace housed in both rails	75x25
Pales with pointed tops secured to each rail and the braces by two galvanised 63x10 s.w.g. nails dovetail driven.	75x25x1220 long

NOTES

1. ALL DIMENSIONS ARE IN MILLIMETRES UNLESS OTHERWISE STATED.
2. Gates shall comply with the appropriate Clauses in the 300 Series, any further requirements in Appendix 1/15 or 3/2 and the appropriate Clauses in both BS3470 and BS5709.
3. All tenons shall be pegged with 13 dia oak dowels.
4. For details of fittings for hanging and fastening see Drawing Nos. H30 and 31.
5. The gate shall open into the owners property.

DEPARTMENT OF TRANSPORT HIGHWAY CONSTRUCTION DETAILS	FENCES, STILES & GATES	TIMBER WICKET GATE TYPE 2	Drawing No. H24	Date

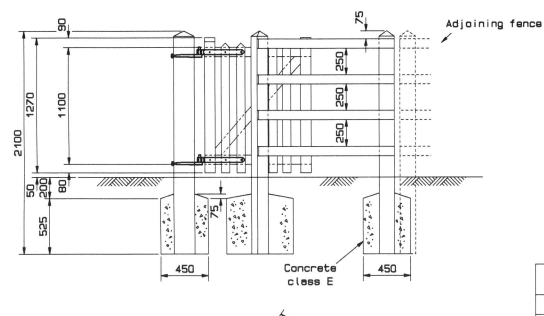

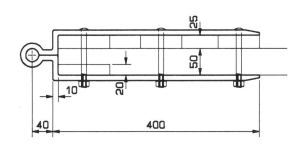

Adjoining fence

Detail of joint between
top & bottom rails
and hanging stile

Concrete
class E

DESCRIPTION OF TIMBER MATERIALS	SIZE
Wing posts	125x100x2100 long
Apex posts	150x150x2100 long
Fence rails cut to length and housed in the apex post	87x38x1600 long

NOTES

1. ALL DIMENSIONS ARE IN MILLIMETRES UNLESS OTHERWISE STATED.
2. Gates shall comply with the appropriate Clauses in the 300 Series, any further requirements in Appendix 1/15 or 3/2 and the appropriate Clauses in BS5709.
3. Gate itself shall be Wicket gate Type 2 (Drawing No. H24).
4. All nails shall be galvanised.
5. All tenons shall be pegged with 13 dia oak dowels.

DEPARTMENT OF TRANSPORT HIGHWAY CONSTRUCTION DETAILS	FENCES, STILES & GATE	TIMBER KISSING GATE	Drawing No. H25	Date

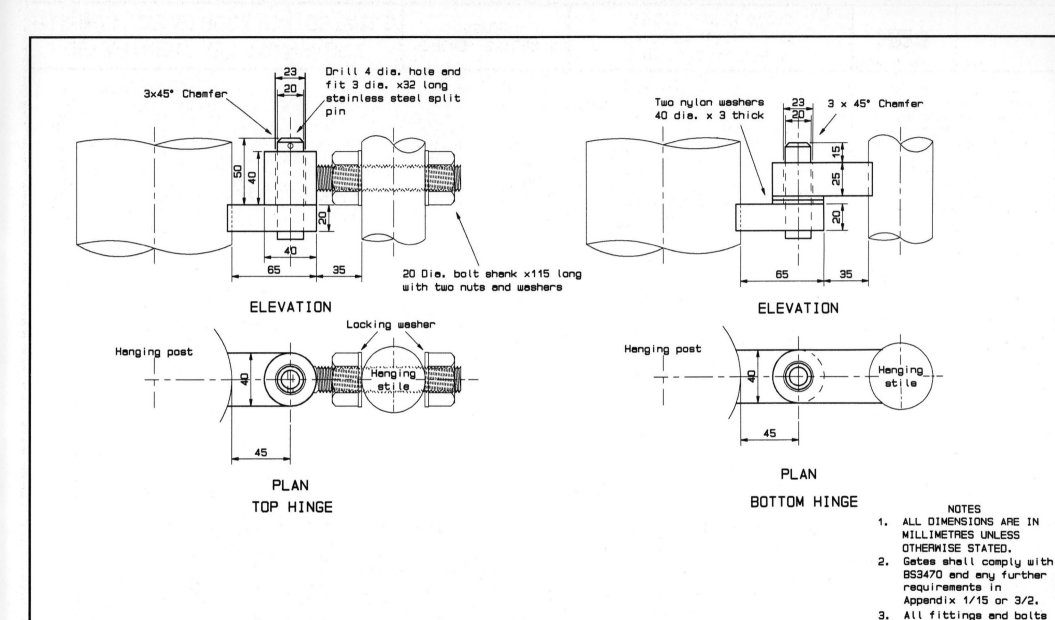

ELEVATION

3x45° Chamfer

23
20

Drill 4 dia. hole and
fit 3 dia. x32 long
stainless steel split
pin

50
40
20
40
65
35

20 Dia. bolt shank x115 long
with two nuts and washers

PLAN
TOP HINGE

Hanging post

Locking washer

40

Hanging
stile

45

ELEVATION

Two nylon washers
40 dia. x 3 thick

23
20

3 x 45° Chamfer

15
25
20
65
35

PLAN
BOTTOM HINGE

Hanging post

40

Hanging
stile

45

NOTES

1. ALL DIMENSIONS ARE IN
   MILLIMETRES UNLESS
   OTHERWISE STATED.
2. Gates shall comply with
   BS3470 and any further
   requirements in
   Appendix 1/15 or 3/2.
3. All fittings and bolts
   shall be galvanised
   mild steel.

| DEPARTMENT OF TRANSPORT HIGHWAY CONSTRUCTION DETAILS | FENCES, STILES & GATES | HINGES FOR STEEL FIELD GATES | Drawing No. **H26** | Date |

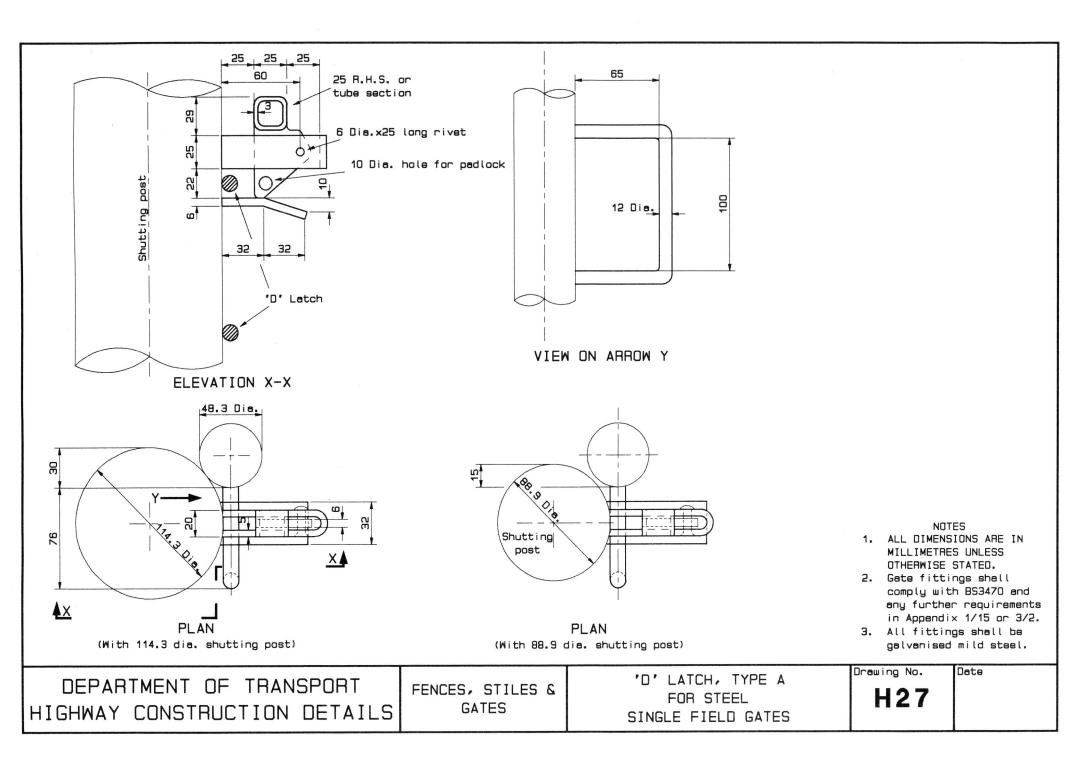

ELEVATION X-X

25 R.H.S. or tube section

6 Dia.x25 long rivet

10 Dia. hole for padlock

'D' Latch

VIEW ON ARROW Y

12 Dia.

PLAN
(With 114.3 dia. shutting post)

PLAN
(With 88.9 dia. shutting post)

Shutting post

NOTES
1. ALL DIMENSIONS ARE IN MILLIMETRES UNLESS OTHERWISE STATED.
2. Gate fittings shall comply with BS3470 and any further requirements in Appendix 1/15 or 3/2.
3. All fittings shall be galvanised mild steel.

| DEPARTMENT OF TRANSPORT HIGHWAY CONSTRUCTION DETAILS | FENCES, STILES & GATES | 'D' LATCH, TYPE A FOR STEEL SINGLE FIELD GATES | Drawing No. **H27** | Date |

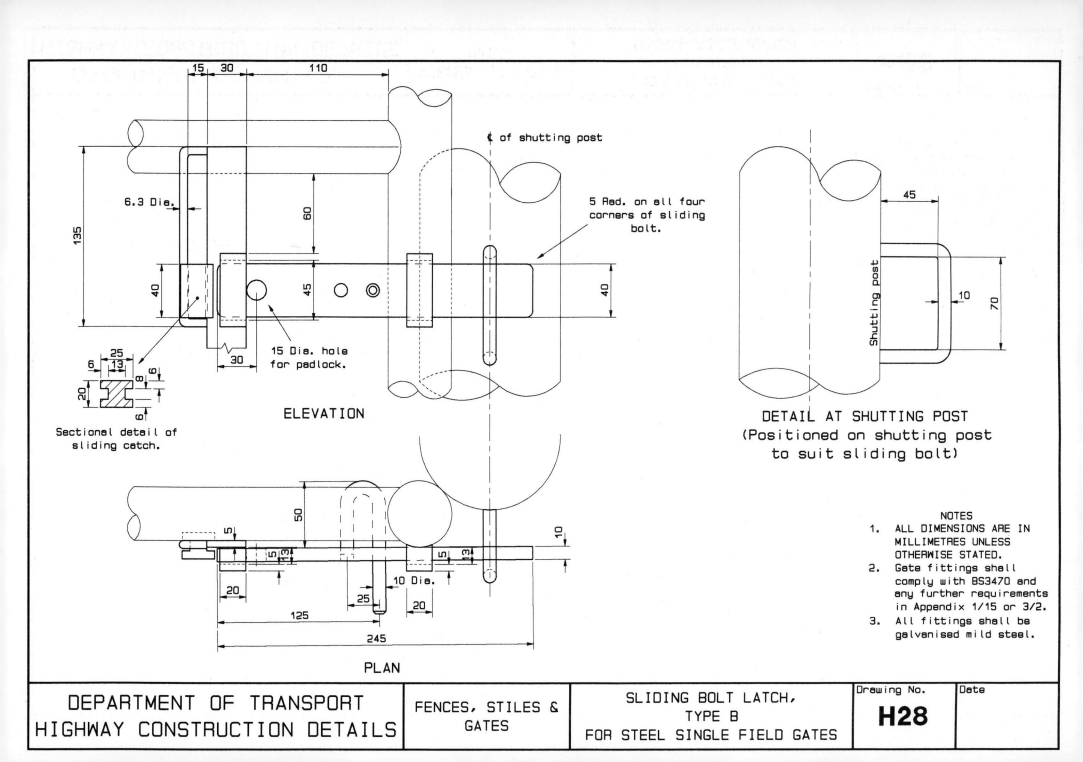

¢ of shutting post

6.3 Dia.

5 Rad. on all four corners of sliding bolt.

15 Dia. hole for padlock.

ELEVATION

Sectional detail of sliding catch.

DETAIL AT SHUTTING POST
(Positioned on shutting post
to suit sliding bolt)

Shutting post

10 Dia.

PLAN

NOTES
1. ALL DIMENSIONS ARE IN
   MILLIMETRES UNLESS
   OTHERWISE STATED.
2. Gate fittings shall
   comply with BS3470 and
   any further requirements
   in Appendix 1/15 or 3/2.
3. All fittings shall be
   galvanised mild steel.

| DEPARTMENT OF TRANSPORT HIGHWAY CONSTRUCTION DETAILS | FENCES, STILES & GATES | SLIDING BOLT LATCH, TYPE B FOR STEEL SINGLE FIELD GATES | Drawing No. **H28** | Date |

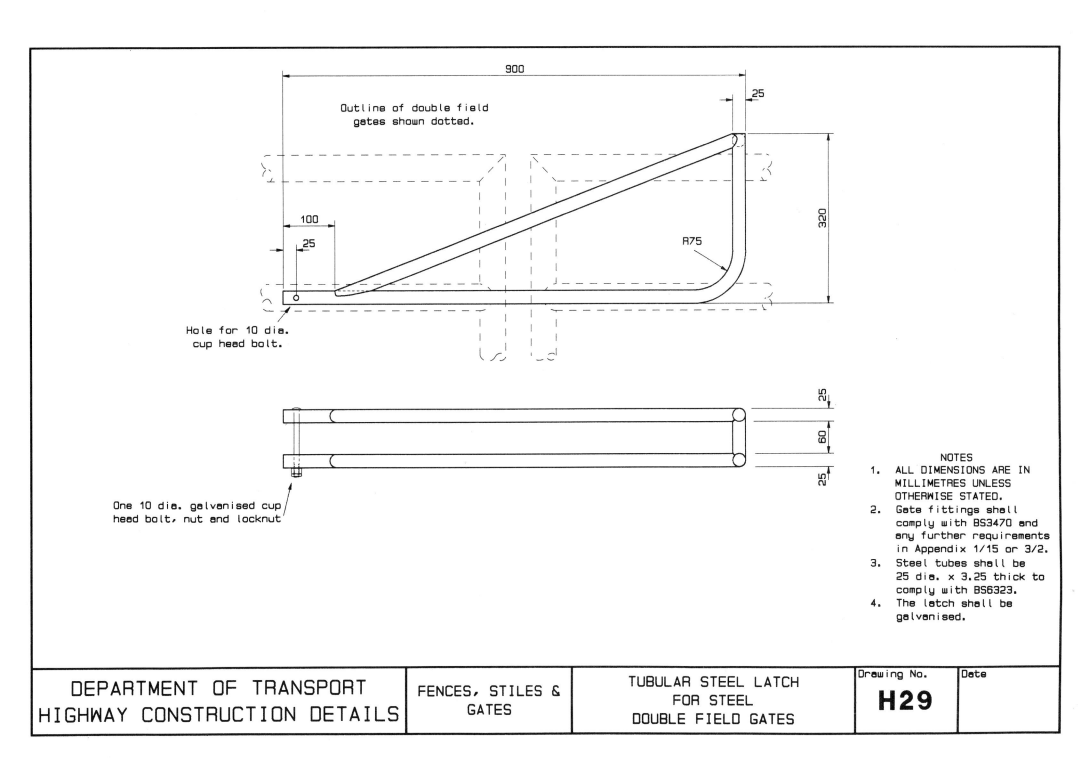

900

25

Outline of double field
gates shown dotted.

320

100

25

R75

Hole for 10 dia.
cup head bolt.

25

60

25

One 10 dia. galvanised cup
head bolt, nut and locknut

NOTES
1. ALL DIMENSIONS ARE IN
    MILLIMETRES UNLESS
    OTHERWISE STATED.
2. Gate fittings shall
    comply with BS3470 and
    any further requirements
    in Appendix 1/15 or 3/2.
3. Steel tubes shall be
    25 dia. × 3.25 thick to
    comply with BS6323.
4. The latch shall be
    galvanised.

| DEPARTMENT OF TRANSPORT HIGHWAY CONSTRUCTION DETAILS | FENCES, STILES & GATES | TUBULAR STEEL LATCH FOR STEEL DOUBLE FIELD GATES | Drawing No. H29 | Date |

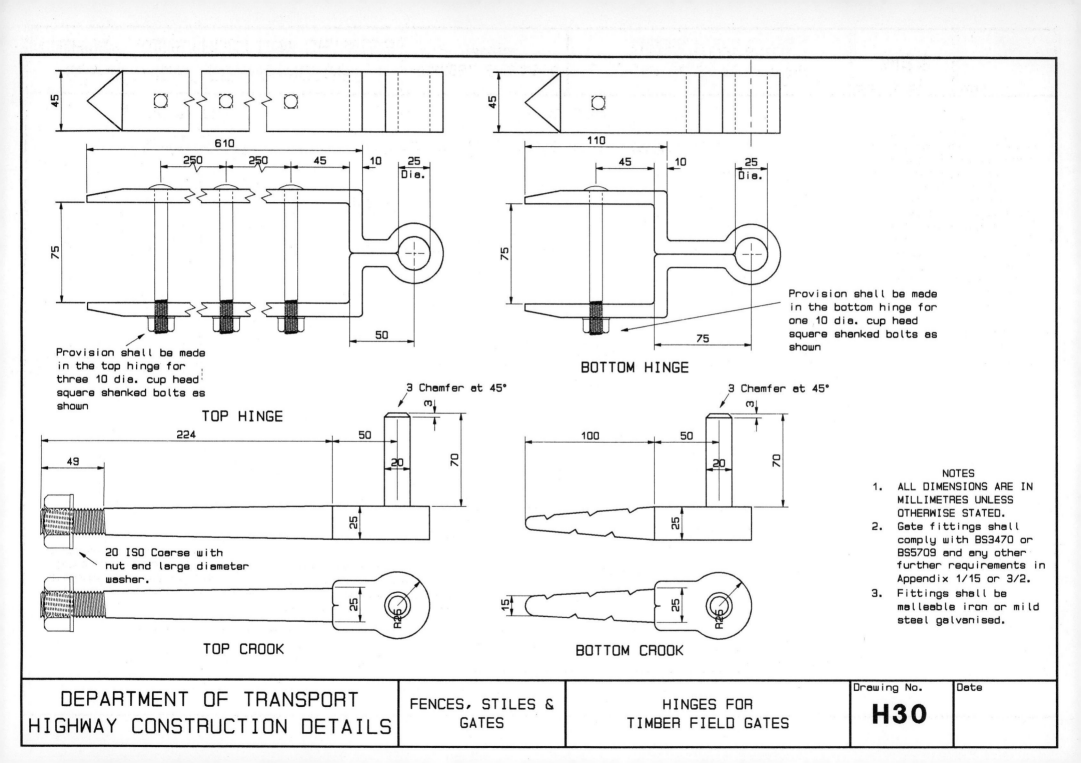

45

610

250   250   45   10   25 Dia.

75

50

Provision shall be made
in the top hinge for
three 10 dia. cup head
square shanked bolts as
shown

TOP HINGE

45

110

45   10   25 Dia.

75

75

Provision shall be made
in the bottom hinge for
one 10 dia. cup head
square shanked bolts as
shown

BOTTOM HINGE

3 Chamfer at 45°

224   50   3   70

49   20

25

20 ISO Coarse with
nut and large diameter
washer.

25   R25

TOP CROOK

3 Chamfer at 45°

100   50   3   70

20

25

15   25   R25

BOTTOM CROOK

NOTES
1. ALL DIMENSIONS ARE IN
    MILLIMETRES UNLESS
    OTHERWISE STATED.
2. Gate fittings shall
    comply with BS3470 or
    BS5709 and any other
    further requirements in
    Appendix 1/15 or 3/2.
3. Fittings shall be
    malleable iron or mild
    steel galvanised.

| DEPARTMENT OF TRANSPORT HIGHWAY CONSTRUCTION DETAILS | FENCES, STILES & GATES | HINGES FOR TIMBER FIELD GATES | Drawing No. **H30** | Date |

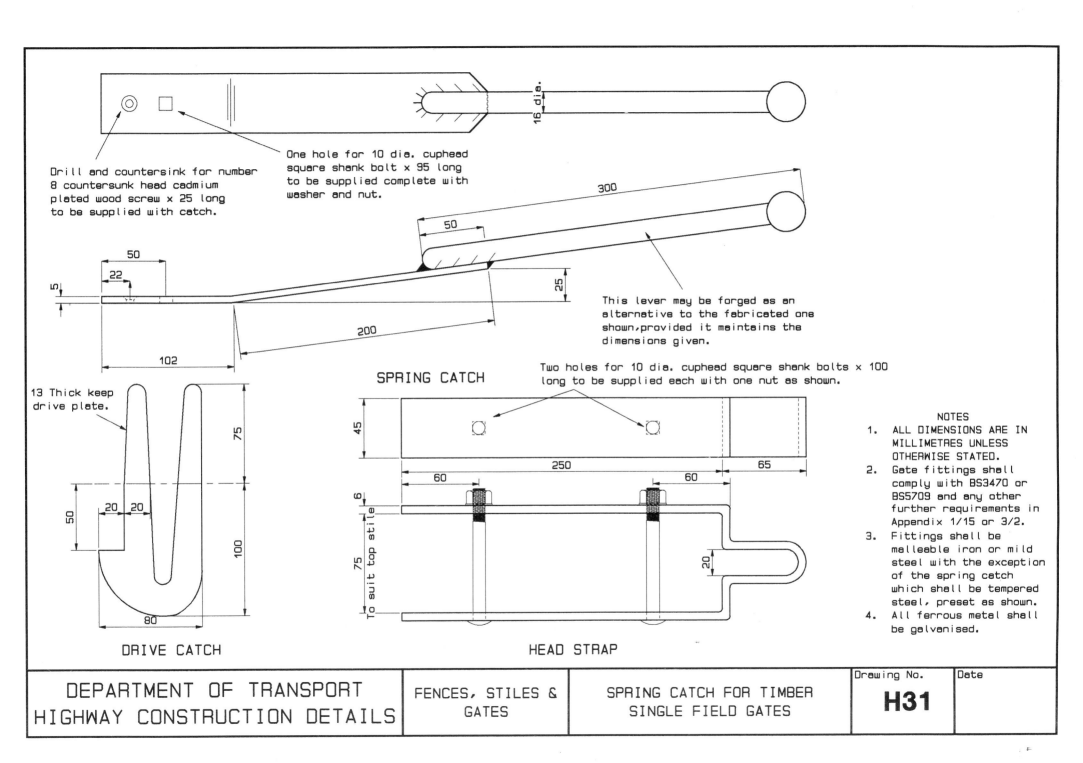

16 dia.

Drill and countersink for number 8 countersunk head cadmium plated wood screw x 25 long to be supplied with catch.

One hole for 10 dia. cuphead square shank bolt x 95 long to be supplied complete with washer and nut.

300

50

50

22

5

25

200

102

This lever may be forged as an alternative to the fabricated one shown, provided it maintains the dimensions given.

SPRING CATCH

Two holes for 10 dia. cuphead square shank bolts x 100 long to be supplied each with one nut as shown.

13 Thick keep drive plate.

75

45

250

65

60

60

50

6

20   20

100

75   To suit top stile

20

80

DRIVE CATCH

HEAD STRAP

NOTES
1. ALL DIMENSIONS ARE IN MILLIMETRES UNLESS OTHERWISE STATED.
2. Gate fittings shall comply with BS3470 or BS5709 and any other further requirements in Appendix 1/15 or 3/2.
3. Fittings shall be malleable iron or mild steel with the exception of the spring catch which shall be tempered steel, preset as shown.
4. All ferrous metal shall be galvanised.

DEPARTMENT OF TRANSPORT HIGHWAY CONSTRUCTION DETAILS	FENCES, STILES & GATES	SPRING CATCH FOR TIMBER SINGLE FIELD GATES	Drawing No. **H31**	Date

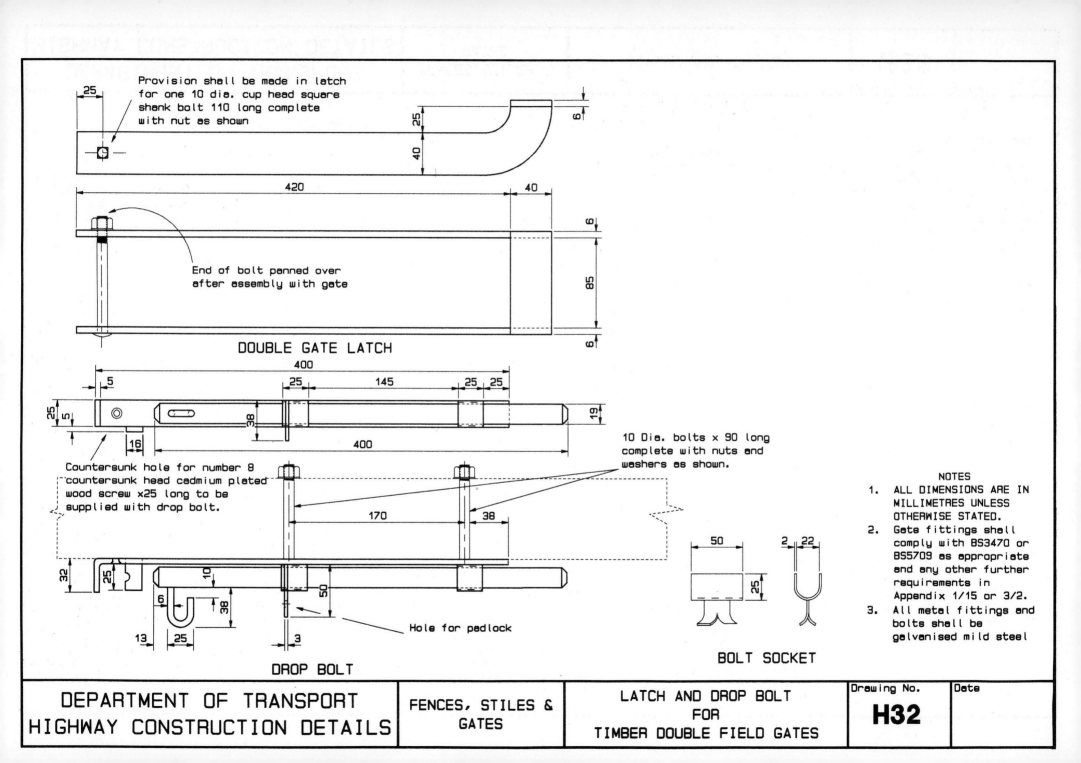

Provision shall be made in latch for one 10 dia. cup head square shank bolt 110 long complete with nut as shown

End of bolt panned over after assembly with gate

DOUBLE GATE LATCH

Countersunk hole for number 8 countersunk head cadmium plated wood screw x25 long to be supplied with drop bolt.

10 Dia. bolts x 90 long complete with nuts and washers as shown.

Hole for padlock

DROP BOLT

BOLT SOCKET

NOTES
1. ALL DIMENSIONS ARE IN MILLIMETRES UNLESS OTHERWISE STATED.
2. Gate fittings shall comply with BS3470 or BS5709 as appropriate and any other further requirements in Appendix 1/15 or 3/2.
3. All metal fittings and bolts shall be galvanised mild steel

| DEPARTMENT OF TRANSPORT HIGHWAY CONSTRUCTION DETAILS | FENCES, STILES & GATES | LATCH AND DROP BOLT FOR TIMBER DOUBLE FIELD GATES | Drawing No. H32 | Date |

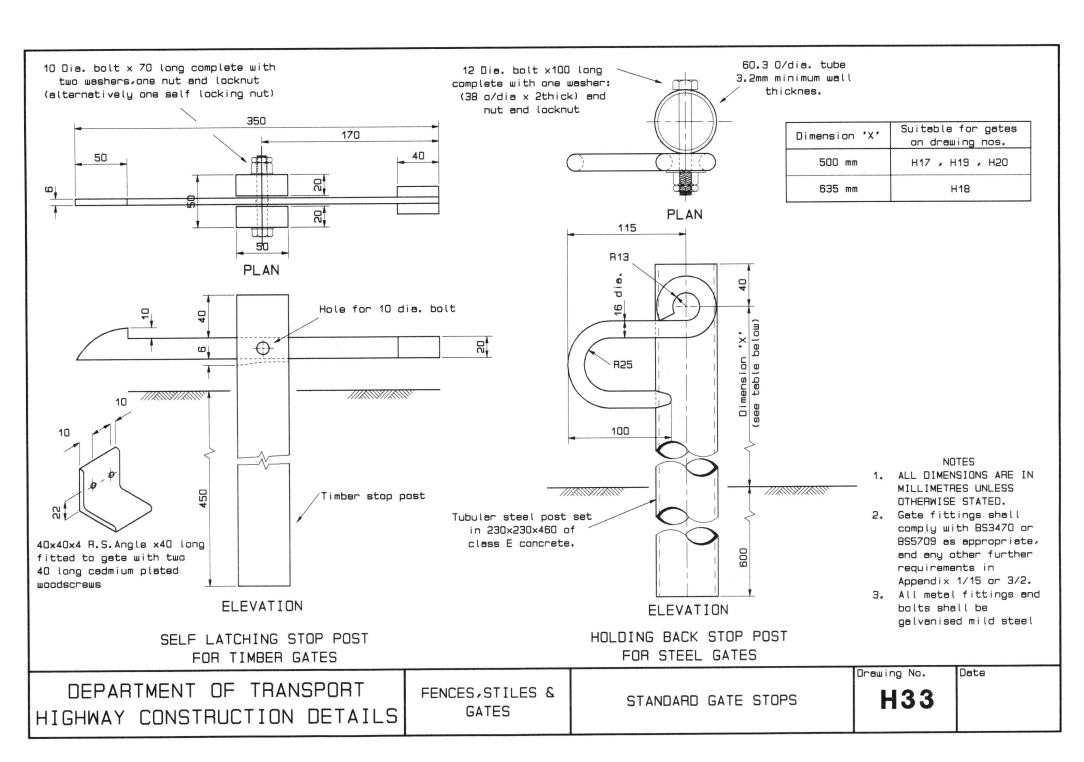

10 Dia. bolt x 70 long complete with
two washers, one nut and locknut
(alternatively one self locking nut)

350
170
50
40
6
20
50
20
50

PLAN

12 Dia. bolt x100 long
complete with one washer:
(38 o/dia x 2thick) and
nut and locknut

60.3 O/dia. tube
3.2mm minimum wall
thicknes.

PLAN

Dimension 'X'	Suitable for gates on drawing nos.
500 mm	H17 , H19 , H20
635 mm	H18

10
40
6
Hole for 10 dia. bolt
20

10
10
22
40x40x4 R.S.Angle x40 long
fitted to gate with two
40 long cadmium plated
woodscrews

450

Timber stop post

ELEVATION

SELF LATCHING STOP POST
FOR TIMBER GATES

115
R13
16 dia.
R25
100
40
Dimension 'X'
(see table below)

Tubular steel post set
in 230x230x460 of
class E concrete.

600

ELEVATION

HOLDING BACK STOP POST
FOR STEEL GATES

NOTES
1. ALL DIMENSIONS ARE IN
   MILLIMETRES UNLESS
   OTHERWISE STATED.
2. Gate fittings shall
   comply with BS3470 or
   BS5709 as appropriate,
   and any other further
   requirements in
   Appendix 1/15 or 3/2.
3. All metal fittings and
   bolts shall be
   galvanised mild steel

DEPARTMENT OF TRANSPORT HIGHWAY CONSTRUCTION DETAILS	FENCES, STILES & GATES	STANDARD GATE STOPS	Drawing No. **H33**	Date

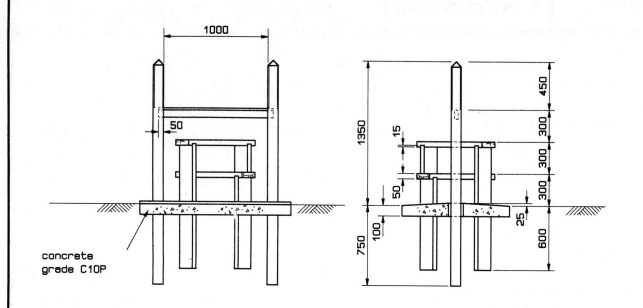

1000

50

1350

750

450

300

300

300

15

50

25

100

600

concrete
grade C10P

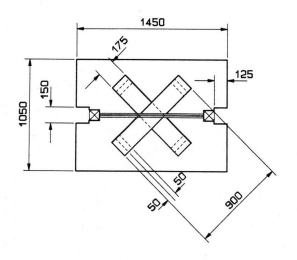

1450

175

125

150

1050

50

50

900

DESCRIPTION OF TIMBER MATERIALS	SECTION SIZE
Posts	100x100
Crosshead wrought. Top edge double chamfered	87x38 minimum
Steps	175x50
Supports Secured by two 100 long x 4 galvanised round wire nails skew driven	175x50

NOTES

1. ALL DIMENSIONS ARE IN MILLIMETRES UNLESS OTHERWISE STATED.

2. All timber shall be in accordance with the appropriate Clauses in the 300 Series and any other requirements in Appendix 1/15 and 3/2 and BS5709.

3. All steelwork shall be galvanised to comply with B.S. 729.

4. Stile posts shall be set in line of fence.

| DEPARTMENT OF TRANSPORT HIGHWAY CONSTRUCTION DETAILS | FENCES, STILES & GATES | TIMBER STILE - TYPE 1 | Drawing No. H34 | Date |

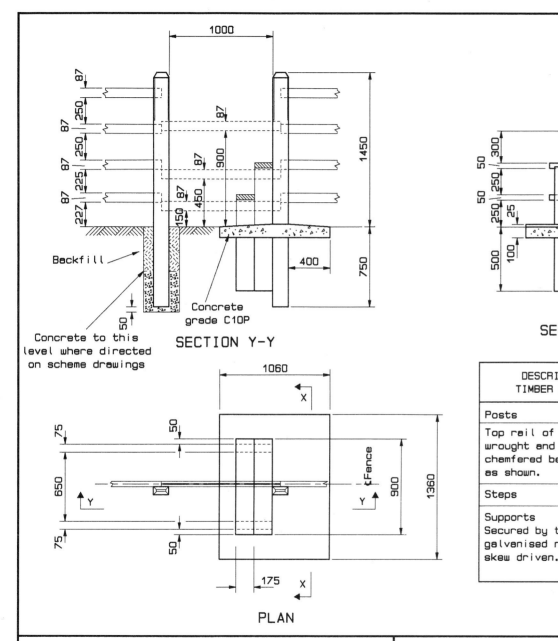

Backfill

Concrete
grade C10P

SECTION Y-Y

Concrete to this
level where directed
on scheme drawings

PLAN

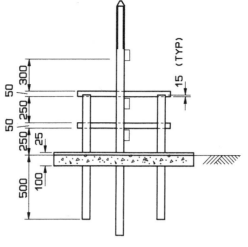

SECTION X-X

DESCRIPTION OF TIMBER MATERIALS	SECTION SIZES
Posts	100×100
Top rail of fence shall be wrought and top edge double chamfered between the posts as shown.	87×38 (min)
Steps	175×150
Supports Secured by two 100 long x 4 galvanised round wire nails skew driven.	150×75

NOTES
1. ALL DIMENSIONS ARE IN MILLIMETRES.
2. All timber shall be in accordance with the appropriate clauses in the 300 Series and any further requirements in Appendix 3/2 or 1/15 and BS5709.
3. All steelwork shall be galvanised to comply with B.S.729.

DEPARTMENT OF TRANSPORT HIGHWAY CONSTRUCTION DETAILS	FENCES, STILES & GATES	TIMBER STILE - TYPE 2	Drawing No. **H35**	Date

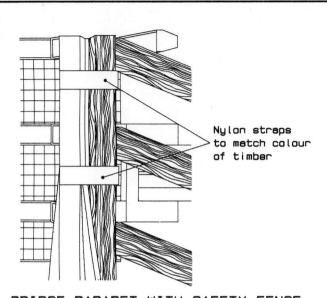

Nylon straps
to match colour
of timber

BRIDGE PARAPET WITH SAFETY FENCE
AND TIMBER POST AND RAIL FENCE

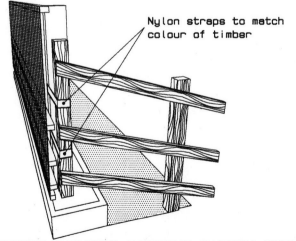

Nylon straps to match
colour of timber

BRIDGE PARAPET WITHOUT SAFETY FENCE
TO TIMBER POST AND RAIL FENCE

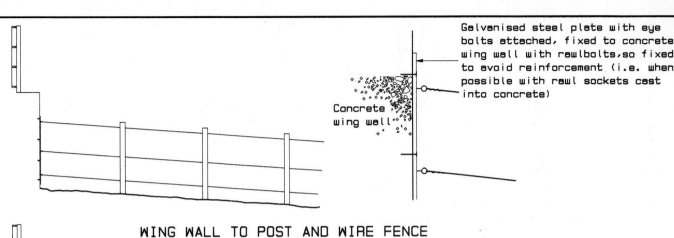

Galvanised steel plate with eye
bolts attached, fixed to concrete
wing wall with rawlbolts, so fixed
to avoid reinforcement (i.e. when
possible with rawl sockets cast
into concrete)

Concrete
wing wall

WING WALL TO POST AND WIRE FENCE

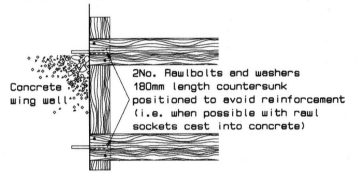

Concrete
wing wall

2No. Rawlbolts and washers
180mm length countersunk
positioned to avoid reinforcement
(i.e. when possible with rawl
sockets cast into concrete)

WING WALL TO POST AND RAIL FENCE

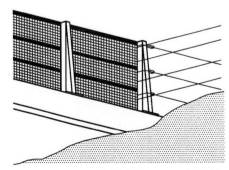

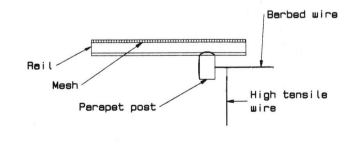

Barbed wire

Rail

Mesh

Parapet post

High tensile
wire

BRIDGE PARAPET TO POST AND WIRE FENCE

DEPARTMENT OF TRANSPORT HIGHWAY CONSTRUCTION DETAILS	FENCES, STILES & GATES	DIAGRAMMATIC METHODS OF ATTACHING FENCING TO STRUCTURES	Drawing No. **H36**	Date

Series I—
Underground Cable Ducts

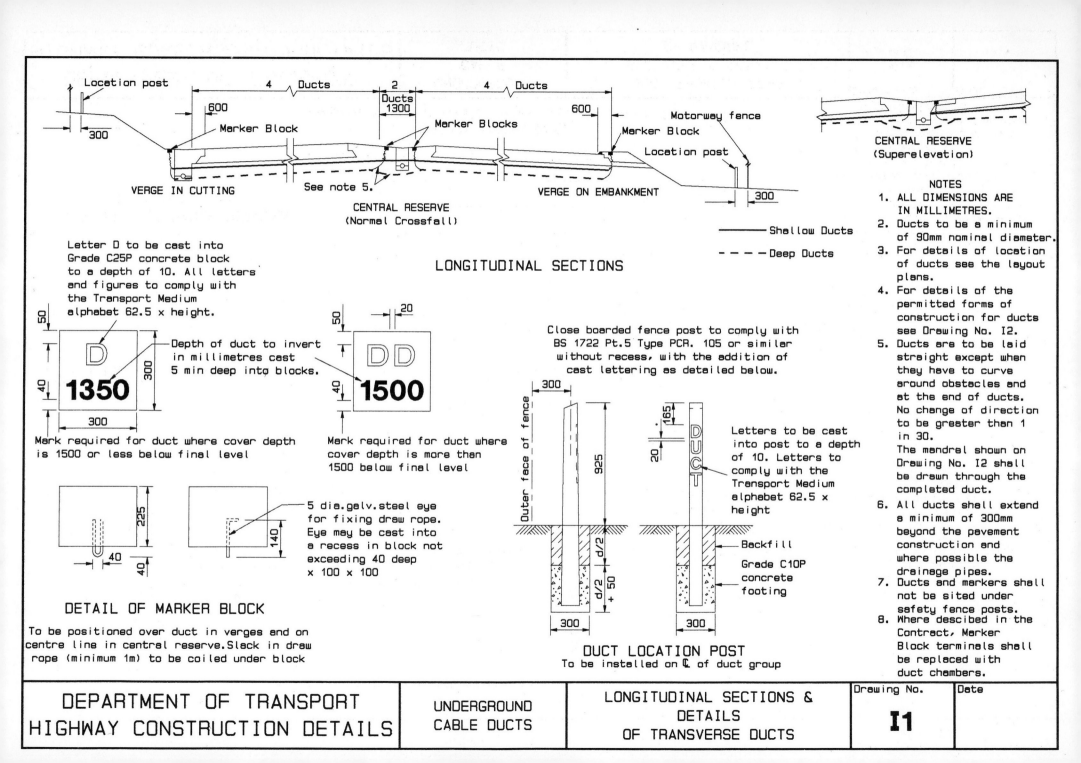

LONGITUDINAL SECTIONS

Location post

4 Ducts | 2 Ducts 1300 | 4 Ducts

600

300

Marker Block

VERGE IN CUTTING

See note 5.

CENTRAL RESERVE
(Normal Crossfall)

Marker Blocks

Motorway fence

600

Marker Block

Location post

300

VERGE ON EMBANKMENT

CENTRAL RESERVE
(Superelevation)

———— Shallow Ducts

– – – – Deep Ducts

Letter D to be cast into
Grade C25P concrete block
to a depth of 10. All letters
and figures to comply with
the Transport Medium
alphabet 62.5 x height.

50

D

1350

300

40

300

Mark required for duct where cover depth
is 1500 or less below final level

50 | 20

DD

1500

40

Depth of duct to invert
in millimetres cast
5 min deep into blocks.

Mark required for duct where
cover depth is more than
1500 below final level

225

40

40

5 dia.galv.steel eye
for fixing draw rope.
Eye may be cast into
a recess in block not
exceeding 40 deep
x 100 x 100

140

DETAIL OF MARKER BLOCK

To be positioned over duct in verges and on
centre line in central reserve. Slack in draw
rope (minimum 1m) to be coiled under block

Close boarded fence post to comply with
BS 1722 Pt.5 Type PCR. 105 or similar
without recess, with the addition of
cast lettering as detailed below.

300

Outer face of fence

925

300

d/2

d/2 + 50

165

20

DUCT

Letters to be cast
into post to a depth
of 10. Letters to
comply with the
Transport Medium
alphabet 62.5 x
height

Backfill

Grade C10P
concrete
footing

300

DUCT LOCATION POST
To be installed on ℄ of duct group

NOTES

1. ALL DIMENSIONS ARE
   IN MILLIMETRES.
2. Ducts to be a minimum
   of 90mm nominal diameter.
3. For details of location
   of ducts see the layout
   plans.
4. For details of the
   permitted forms of
   construction for ducts
   see Drawing No. I2.
5. Ducts are to be laid
   straight except when
   they have to curve
   around obstacles and
   at the end of ducts.
   No change of direction
   to be greater than 1
   in 30.
   The mandrel shown on
   Drawing No. I2 shall
   be drawn through the
   completed duct.
6. All ducts shall extend
   a minimum of 300mm
   beyond the pavement
   construction and
   where possible the
   drainage pipes.
7. Ducts and markers shall
   not be sited under
   safety fence posts.
8. Where descibed in the
   Contract, Marker
   Block terminals shall
   be replaced with
   duct chambers.

| DEPARTMENT OF TRANSPORT HIGHWAY CONSTRUCTION DETAILS | UNDERGROUND CABLE DUCTS | LONGITUDINAL SECTIONS & DETAILS OF TRANSVERSE DUCTS | Drawing No. I1 | Date |

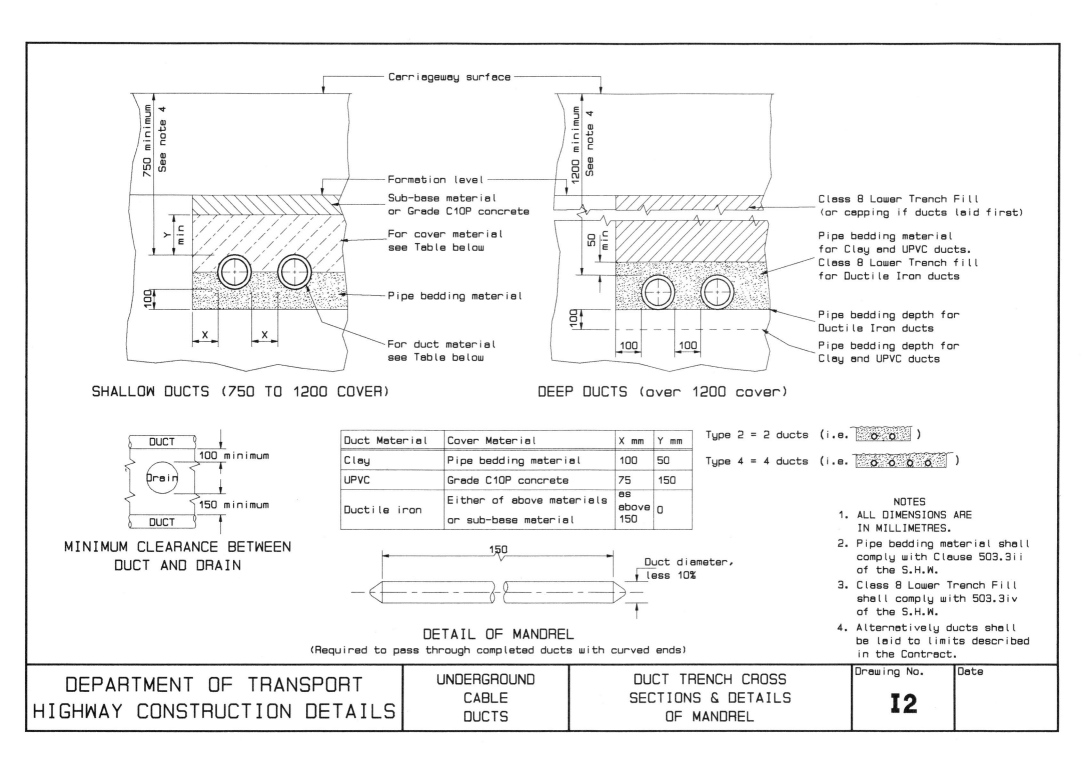

Carriageway surface

SHALLOW DUCTS (750 TO 1200 COVER)

750 minimum
See note 4

Formation level

Sub-base material
or Grade C10P concrete

Y min

For cover material
see Table below

100

Pipe bedding material

X   X

For duct material
see Table below

DEEP DUCTS (over 1200 cover)

1200 minimum
See note 4

50 min

Class 8 Lower Trench Fill
(or capping if ducts laid first)

Pipe bedding material
for Clay and UPVC ducts.
Class 8 Lower Trench fill
for Ductile Iron ducts

100

100   100

Pipe bedding depth for
Ductile Iron ducts

Pipe bedding depth for
Clay and UPVC ducts

DUCT
100 minimum
Drain
150 minimum
DUCT

**MINIMUM CLEARANCE BETWEEN
DUCT AND DRAIN**

Duct Material	Cover Material	X mm	Y mm
Clay	Pipe bedding material	100	50
UPVC	Grade C10P concrete	75	150
Ductile iron	Either of above materials or sub-base material	as above 150	0

Type 2 = 2 ducts (i.e. ⬤⬤)

Type 4 = 4 ducts (i.e. ⬤⬤⬤⬤)

NOTES
1. ALL DIMENSIONS ARE
   IN MILLIMETRES.
2. Pipe bedding material shall
   comply with Clause 503.3ii
   of the S.H.W.
3. Class 8 Lower Trench Fill
   shall comply with 503.3iv
   of the S.H.W.
4. Alternatively ducts shall
   be laid to limits described
   in the Contract.

150

Duct diameter,
less 10%

DETAIL OF MANDREL
(Required to pass through completed ducts with curved ends)

DEPARTMENT OF TRANSPORT HIGHWAY CONSTRUCTION DETAILS	UNDERGROUND CABLE DUCTS	DUCT TRENCH CROSS SECTIONS & DETAILS OF MANDREL	Drawing No. **I2**	Date

Series J — Flexible Composite Carriageway

J1 Example layouts for longitudinal construction joints in cement bound road bases

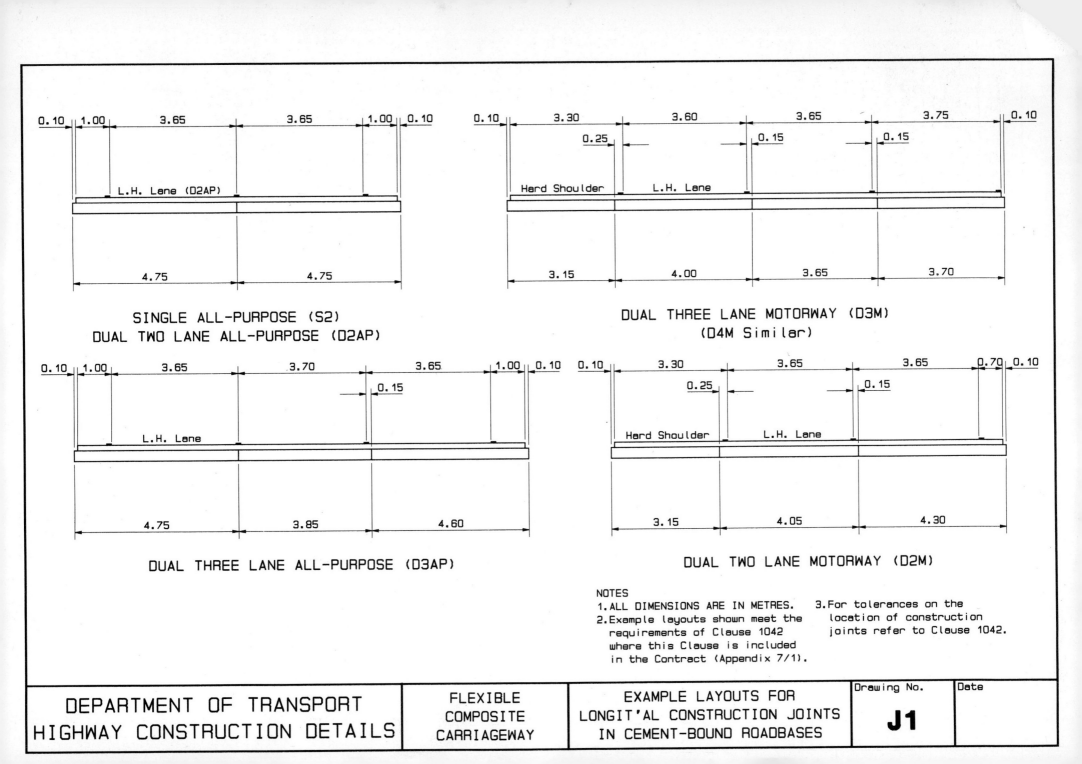

SINGLE ALL-PURPOSE (S2)
DUAL TWO LANE ALL-PURPOSE (D2AP)

DUAL THREE LANE MOTORWAY (D3M)
(D4M Similar)

DUAL THREE LANE ALL-PURPOSE (D3AP)

DUAL TWO LANE MOTORWAY (D2M)

NOTES
1. ALL DIMENSIONS ARE IN METRES.
2. Example layouts shown meet the requirements of Clause 1042 where this Clause is included in the Contract (Appendix 7/1).
3. For tolerances on the location of construction joints refer to Clause 1042.

| DEPARTMENT OF TRANSPORT HIGHWAY CONSTRUCTION DETAILS | FLEXIBLE COMPOSITE CARRIAGEWAY | EXAMPLE LAYOUTS FOR LONGIT'AL CONSTRUCTION JOINTS IN CEMENT-BOUND ROADBASES | Drawing No. **J1** | Date |